Cleaning Our Environment The Chemical Basis For Action

A *Report* by the Subcommittee on Environmental Improvement, Committtee on Chemistry and Public
Affairs, American Chemical
Society WASHINGTON, D.C.
1969

Published September 1969
Price: $2.75

Order from American Chemical Society, Special Issues Sales,
1155 Sixteenth St., N.W., Washington, D.C. 20036

Library of Congress Catalog Card 74-96123

Contents

Foreword

This report grew out of conversations initiated late in 1965 by the American Chemical Society's then-new Committee on Chemistry and Public Affairs (Prof. Charles C. Price, Chairman) with the Society's Division of Water, Air, and Waste Chemistry and its *ad hoc* Committee on Air Pollution. The Committee on Chemistry and Public Affairs saw in environmental improvement an area in which it might perform the kind of specific public service that was its proposed mission. This view was stimulated, in November 1965, by the publication of "Restoring the Quality of Our Environment," the report of the environmental pollution panel of the President's Science Advisory Committee.

The American Chemical Society already was active in matters of the environment, largely through the scientific meeting papers and activities of its Division of Water, Air, and Waste Chemistry. A further step came early in 1966, when the Society, with the support of the Division, decided to launch the monthly publication, *Environmental Science and Technology*. The first issue appeared in January 1967.

Since the divisional programs and the new journal provide services largely for the expert, it appeared desirable to produce a report aimed primarily at the involved and educated layman. To oversee the project, the Committee on Chemistry and Public Affairs appointed four of its members as a subcommittee on environmental improvement (Dr. Lloyd M. Cooke, Chairman). The Division of Water, Air, and Waste Chemistry recruited the task force of experts that worked directly on the project.

In addition to those members of the American Chemical Society who were intimately involved with the preparation of this report, a number of other authorities, both members and nonmembers of the Society, were kind enough to provide comment and information; the authors have drawn also on the writings of many others. To all of these people, the ACS Committee on Chemistry and Public Affairs wishes to express its gratitude for their very considerable help.

Franklin A. Long

ACS Committee on Chemistry and Public Affairs

Preface

We have had two goals in preparing this report. First, we have set down an objective account of the current status of the science and technology of environmental improvement: what is known and how it is being used; what must be learned and how it might be used. Second, we have analyzed the information thus assembled and have recommended a number of measures that, if adopted, should help to accelerate the sound development and use of that science and technology.

We have focused strongly on chemistry, chemical engineering, and the related disciplines. By so doing, we hope to expand the chemical awareness and the flow of chemical know-how which are essential to any long-term rational approach to understanding and controlling our environment.

We did not set out to inform the experts, the men and women who must deal daily and directly with the challenging problems of managing the environment. If we refresh the expert, so much the better, but we hope primarily to buttress the technical awareness of legislators, administrators, and others who must deal with environmental problems at one or more steps removed from direct involvement with the pertinent science and technology. We hope also to attract the interest of those scientists and engineers not now involved in such problems who may have useful ideas and work to contribute to their solution.

We have stressed the fact that a strong vein of chemistry runs throughout environmental science and technology. We have stressed that fact without fear of being accused of displaying excessive self-interest. We have tried to stress it without obscuring or appearing to obscure the undeniable complementary fact that solving the technical problems of environmental management will require the best efforts of scientists and engineers from many disciplines. The American Chemical Society speaks with special concern to the world of chemistry, however, and we believe that environmental problems do provide at the very least a fit intellectual match for the talents of those chemical scientists and engineers who wish to work at the worthy mission of making a cleaner world.

Lloyd M. Cooke

Dr. E. P. Lichtenstein
Professor of Entomology
Department of Entomology
University of Wisconsin

Dr. D. J. Lisk
Professor of Entomology
New York State College of Agriculture
Department of Entomology
Cornell University

Dr. Louis Lykken
Specialist
Division of Entomology
College of Agricultural Sciences
University of California, Berkeley

Dr. Robert L. Rudd
Professor of Zoology
Department of Zoology
University of California, Davis

Dr. W. M. Upholt
Executive Secretary
Federal Committee on Pest Control
Washington, D. C.

Dr. M. R. Zavon
Clinical Professor of Industrial
  Medicine
College of Medicine
Department of Environmental Health
University of Cincinnati

Other Contributors

*Analytical and
Instrumentation*

Dr. David Hume
Professor of Chemistry
Department of Chemistry
Massachusetts Institute of Technology

Mrs. Foymae Kelso West
Chief, Analytical Chemistry
Environmental Chemistry
Gulf South Research Institute

Dr. Philip W. West
Boyd Professor of Chemistry
Department of Chemistry
Louisiana State University

Biological Aspects

Dr. Robert Ball
Professor of Zoology and Research
Department of Fisheries and Wildlife
Michigan State University

Dr. Daniel Nelson
Limnologist
Oak Ridge National Laboratory

Dr. Charles Renn
Professor of Sanitary Engineering
School of Engineering
The Johns Hopkins University

Subcommittee consultant

Dr. Melvin J. Josephs, Managing Editor,
Environmental Science & Technology
(now Managing Editor, *Chemical &
Engineering News*)

Staff

Managing Editor: K. M. Reese
Production Editor: Irene G. Kiefer
Design: Joseph Jacobs

Summary and Recommendations

1

Summary and Recommendations

INTRODUCTION

The 73 Recommendations distilled from the content of this document and summarized here are designed both to exploit and to upgrade man's knowledge of his environment and of how to control it, particularly from a chemical point of view. That knowledge already is extensive. The science and technology of environmental control, despite many deficiencies, have advanced to a point at which this country can take enormous strides, now, toward a cleaner environment. The crucial requirement is that sufficient energy and support be devoted to the task.

In the past few years, the nation has taken many of the legal and administrative measures required to clean up its environment. What is required now is a period of concerted attention to implementation of those measures. Existing science must be developed into usable technology; new and existing technology must be brought to bear on a wide scale on environmental problems. In short, the nation's effort to improve its environment should be concentrated, for the present, on the use of existing science and technology.

Emphasis on existing knowledge, however, should not be allowed to obscure the fact that extensive fundamental research is required to elevate man's understanding of the environmental system, in all its myriad aspects, to a more nearly adequate level than exists today. The need is clear in ecology, in analytical chemistry, in the effects of pollutants, and in a number of other areas. Such research must be started now, if it is to provide the fundamental knowledge required for the new technology that will be needed in the not-too-distant future. It is critical, however, that this research be focused sharply on those areas where it will be truly effective. To provide such a focus is the intent of the Recommendations in this report that call for further research effort.

No one can doubt that cleaning up our air and earth and water demands the best efforts of many people from a variety of disciplines. The environment is a global system of almost infinite complexity. Any attempt to manage and control that system, moreover, must involve not only the pertinent science and technology, but the law, sociology, politics, and economics as well. This document concerns itself little with the management and nonscientific aspects of environmental control; others have examined them ably and at length (5,7,8). Nonscientific matters do, however, warrant attention here to the extent required to leaven the scientific and technological discussion with reasonable perspective.

In any such discussion nowadays the hand of the Federal Government is ubiquitous, both implicitly and explicitly, and this is so for several reasons. To begin with, the environment is impure in large measure because society demands the benefits of technology, and the practice of technology often generates pollutants. The individual acts against pollution, if he acts at all, in accordance with his own self-interest. This is fully as true of the man in the street as it is of the legal person called the corporation or of any government agency. People may rail at companies for making detergents that contain the algal nutrient, phosphorus, but how many families have switched from synthetic detergents to soap for that reason? Companies may rail at the actions of pollution control officials, but how many companies have acted to abate pollution without some inducement in addition to the simple desire not to pollute, be it improved public relations, the possibility of profit, or threat of legal action? Self-interest is, of course, old to the affairs of men, and society deals with it generally, in the larger good, by striking a balance called the law. In matters of the environment, the range of self-interests to be served is national in scope, and the basic law has thus come to be federal law.

The environmental system, furthermore, is by nature thoroughly geopolitical. Air and water contaminants do not respect political boundaries. People drive their cars across state lines. Companies may manufacture in more than one jurisdiction; they may compete with companies who manufacture in one or more different jurisdictions. A given source of pollutants may be quite a different problem in a big city than in a rural area. Local laws and regulations must reflect local problems, but they must also be grounded in basic legislation that applies equitably and effectively to all jurisdictions. Such legislation can be created best at the federal level.

It should be noted also that air and water contaminants respect international political boundaries no more than they do state and local boundaries. The long-lived pesticide DDT has been detected in wildlife in Antarctica, far from the unknown point at which it must have been applied. The global concentration of carbon dioxide is changing, and the concentration of fine particles appears to be changing. Both could affect climate. A need exists ultimately, in fact, to consider international arrangements on environmental control. Reasonable stepping-stones include programs such as the International Biological Program (3) and the United Nations conference on the human environment planned for 1972.

The federal involvement extends beyond environmental control legislation. It includes the performance or support of certain types of research and development, environmental surveillance and other types of data collection, and construction aid for pollution abatement facilities. Such projects generally encompass work that the profit-making corporation is not, by nature, designed to undertake on its own, and that state and local governments cannot afford.

In the long run, the cost of pollution and its control will be borne by the citizen, in taxes and in the prices he pays for the products of technology. Cost, moreover, is probably the most powerful constraint that the nation must deal with in the near-term future. One can readily visualize costs in the range of hundreds of millions of dollars annually for controlling pollution by the automotive internal combustion engine alone. On that score, society in the U.S. has made a value judgment. It has elected to pay, and is paying, for control systems that will gradually reduce pollution by auto-

4

mobiles during the next half dozen years or so. A parallel value judgment underlies the establishment and implementation of water quality criteria now going forward across the nation. In the area of solid wastes, on the other hand, municipalities have been largely reluctant to pay for the level of incinerator technology that the manufacturers can surely provide if the market demands it. Similar instances are not difficult to find. It is always possible that scientists and engineers will learn to recycle or dispose of wastes at a profit, but that does not seem likely to happen soon on a broad basis.

If not fiscal profit, what is to be gained by investing huge sums in environmental control? Better health is to be gained. It is true that the relationships between human health and specific concentrations of specific pollutants are often tenuous today, and these relationships must be studied systematically at a fundamental level. It is equally true, however, that our population will increase, that our urban areas will expand, and that our ability to contaminate the environment will flourish in like measure. It is difficult to detect any promise of positive effects on health in this pattern of growth if it proceeds without environmental controls.

In addition to health, the money spent to manage the environment buys cleaner laundry in the back yard, longer life for the paint on houses, less corrosion and breakdown of electrical and other equipment. It buys cleaner lakes and rivers for recreation. It buys relief from annoyance: a speck of ash in one's eye, unpleasant odors, yellowed foliage in the springtime. It buys nature as it ought to be, although it must be recognized that a modern industrial civilization and a pristine environment cannot coexist.

Nature or, more broadly, the environment and the associated phenomena constitute what has come to be called a system, and it is fashionable to speak of systems analysis as an almost magical route to the solution of many problems. Systems analysis can be indeed a powerful and necessary tool. It is vital to recognize, however, that the environmental system is made up of a bewildering number of subsystems that often are only distantly interdependent.

The pollution problems of an electric power plant burning fuel oil are different from those of a plant burning high-sulfur coal, which in turn are different from those of a plant burning low-sulfur coal. The nutrient whose availability governs the proliferation of algae in one lake may be different from the governing nutrient in another lake. Environmental problems, in short, are rarely amenable to sweeping solutions; the benefits of even major breakthroughs in research are more likely than not to be limited to discrete subsystems of the overall system.

Several problem areas emerge as explicit themes in this report. One such theme is the primitive condition of our fundamental knowledge of how living things are affected by long-term, low-level exposure to pollutants.

Partly related to this theme is a second, the even more primitive condition of our knowledge of the effects of pollutants on the ecology, that is, on the aggregate of living things as they exist together in nature. The relationship of contaminants to the ecology is very nearly a total mystery, and scientists are just beginning to study ecosystems on the multidisciplinary basis that is clearly required.

A third theme is the analytical chemical methods that are used to monitor, control, and study the environment and related phenomena. Those methods generally are not as good as they ought to be. The technology that is used to monitor air pollutants, for example, is largely 10 to 20 years old. In contrast, scientists working with pesticides and radioactive substances recognized early the need for new and more discriminating methods and have made remarkable progress in analytical chemistry in the past three decades. Similar progress is required today in many other areas of environmental science and technology where analytical methods too often remain deficient.

Among other problems in the field is the fact that the nomenclature is far from standardized. For this reason, and in the interest of broader understanding, the authors have minimized the use of specialized language. Of the special terms that do perforce appear, the most common are "contaminant" and "pollutant" and the corresponding verbs and adjectives.

The tendency in the field is to regard as a "contaminant" anything added to the environment that causes a deviation from the mean geochemical composition, the average composition that a particular phase of the environment would have in the absence of human activity. Thus contaminants are introduced by many natural phenomena—forest fires, volcanic eruptions, collapsing river banks—as well as by nearly all human activities. A contaminant is considered a "pollutant" only if it can adversely affect something that man values and is present in high enough concentration to do so. These definitions cause a certain amount of confusion. Water vapor, for example, is scarcely considered a contaminant, but if it is added to the atmosphere by a large cooling tower in sufficient amount to befog a busy highway it is clearly a pollutant.

Furthermore, the classification of a substance as contaminant or pollutant changes with time. If the substance is to be formally classified as a pollutant, its effects must be perceived. Man's perception once was nearly limited to soiling of houses and laundry by soot. Scientists look now for subtle effects on the human lifespan, and they are beginning to look for even broader effects, such as modification of regional and even global climate. In the final analysis, all contaminants may well prove to be pollutants as well. By dictionary definition, the two words are in any case synonymous and are used interchangeably in this report.

Other special terms employed herein include "source," "sink," and "receptor." "Source" is the source of a pollutant substance, such as a volcano or agricultural runoff and drainage. "Sink" is the long-term, but not necessarily permanent, repository of a substance. The seas, for example, are a major sink for carbon dioxide, but they also release carbon dioxide to the air. "Receptor" is a living or nonliving object on which a pollutant exerts its effect. Electrical equipment corroded by nitrogen oxides in the air is a receptor.

Although this report is scientifically and technologically far-ranging, it is not perfectly comprehensive. Topics that are not covered include thermal pollution (1,2,4), pollution by radioactive materials, and pollution by aircraft engine exhaust (6). The omission of such topics reflects the authors' arbitrary selection of a reasonable cutoff point, not the view that the problems involved are necessarily well under control.

Literature Cited:

1. "Considerations Affecting Steam Power Plant Site Selection," a report sponsored by the Energy Policy Staff, Office of Science and Technology, Executive Office of the President, Washington, D. C., 1969, Chapter V.
2. Davidson, B., Bradshaw, R. W., "Thermal Pollution of Water Systems," *Environ. Sci. Technol.* **1**, 618 (1967).
3. "IBP," *Environ. Sci. Technol.* **2**, 411 (1968).
4. "Industrial Waste Guide to Thermal Pollution," U. S. Department of the Interior, Federal Water Pollution Control Administration, Pacific Northwest Water Laboratory, Corvallis, Ore., September 1968.
5. "Managing the Environment," Report of the Subcommittee on Science, Research, and Development to the Committee on Science and Astronautics, U. S. House of Representatives, Government Printing Office, Washington, D. C., 1968.
6. "Nature and Control of Aircraft Engine Exhaust Emissions," Report of the Secretary of Health, Education, and Welfare to the United States Congress pursuant to Public Law 90-148, the Air Quality Act of 1967, December 1968.
7. "Restoring the Quality of Our Environment," Report of the Environmental Pollution Panel, President's Science Advisory Committee, Government Printing Office, Washington, D. C., 1965.
8. "Waste Management and Control," a Report to the Federal Council for Science and Technology by the Committee on Pollution, National Academy of Sciences-National Research Council Publication 1400, National Academy of Sciences-National Research Council, Washington, D. C., 1966.

RECOMMENDATIONS

The summary of content and Recommendations that follows includes 58 of the 73 Recommendations made in the four main sections of this report. The 15 Recommendations of less immediate import, as well as those summarized here, appear on the pages indicated, following the full supporting discussion.

The Air Environment

Flow, Dispersion, Degradation (Recommendations A1-A5, page 45)

Although considerable research has been done on the chemical and physical mechanisms of flow, dispersion, and degradation of substances in air, the knowledge of such mechanisms remains in large measure fragmentary. Knowledge of the sources and sinks of air contaminants is equally fragmentary. Contaminants spend variable periods of time between source and sink. Little is known of the factors that affect this time or that effect chemical and physical changes in contaminants along the way. The average time that contaminants spend enroute is not even known. For only one gas, carbon dioxide, are the data sufficient to demonstrate whether the gas's global concentration is changing.

Recommendation A1: *Systematic measurement should be undertaken for a number of relatively long-lived substances in the general atmosphere, in-*

cluding carbon monoxide, nitrous oxide, methane, carbon dioxide, and sulfur hexafluoride. The general turbidity of the atmosphere should be measured systematically on as wide a basis as possible, and more effort should be devoted to determining the nature of the aerosols that cause such turbidity.

Recommendation A3: *Research should be continued and selectively expanded on atmospheric reactions of many kinds. Such work should extend to measurements in the field in order to help relate the results of laboratory and smog-chamber work to what actually happens in the urban and regional atmospheres.*

The ability to predict the flow of pollutants through urban and regional atmospheres, and the effects of pollutants on air quality at points away from their sources, is still a developing science. The use of unique tracers, monitoring systems, mathematical models, and computers is far enough advanced to provide guidance in air pollution control and research, but full understanding of fundamental processes has yet to be achieved.

Recommendation A5: *Study of urban diffusion processes should be continued and selectively expanded, including coordinated use of long-lived tracers and work on optimum deployment and use of air monitoring instruments.*

Motor Vehicles (Recommendations A6-A12, page 58)

Emission control systems required on 1968 and later models of gasoline-powered vehicles, and the related research and development programs now under way in the Federal Government and private industry, represent significant steps in the control of automotive pollution. Continued surveillance of vehicles in normal use is required to determine the degree of control that actually has been achieved. Mandatory periodic inspection and maintenance of emission control systems is required to insure their performance, but available procedures and equipment are not well suited to routine periodic inspection.

Recommendation A6: *Development of procedures and equipment by government and industry for periodic inspection of emission control systems in normal use should be stimulated to move ahead at the best possible rate.*

Recommendation A7: *The development of improved instrumentation for measuring automotive emissions should be supported by all interests to a degree that will assure rapid progress in the ability to assess emissions in terms of both their amount and their reactivity in the atmosphere.*

The 1970 and 1971 federal standards for automotive emissions of hydrocarbons and carbon monoxide can be met with available technology. Any further reductions in allowable emissions, particularly if reduction of nitrogen oxides emissions were required, would necessitate more complex systems. The development of certain possible solutions to emission control problems is hampered by the presence of lead in gasoline.

Recommendation A8: *Federal emission standards more stringent than those to take effect in 1970 should be developed and promulgated at an early date so that auto makers will have sufficient time to develop the necessary control systems. Such standards should be designed to counteract the effects of the rising population of motor vehicles until at least 1980, and should include standards for nitrogen oxides.*

Recommendation A9: *The effects of the lead compounds in gasoline on possible control systems of the future should be assessed carefully in terms of the emission levels that might be achieved with and without lead, or with reduced amounts of lead, and in terms of the associated costs to the industries involved and to the consumer. Economic studies should include the relationship of lead to projected emission control systems, to the gasoline and lead additive manufacturing industries, and to the design and performance of the internal combustion engine itself.*

Advanced propulsion systems such as gas turbines, steam engines, and electric power are unlikely to have a significant impact on automotive pollution for at least another decade. Of the three, electric power is the least advanced technologically for use in mass-produced vehicles of satisfactory performance for the U.S. market. Work on public transportation systems that the public would find acceptable in the future is at an appallingly low level.

Recommendation A10: *The Federal Government should press its assessment of advanced, low-polluting power systems, including steam and electric power, to provide the basis for sound industrial research and development on such systems.*

Recommendation A12: *More attention should be given to the development of acceptable means of public transportation.*

Industrial Facilities (Recommendations A13-A15, page 63)

Improvements have been made and are being made in air pollution control in industry, but the general situation is growing worse because of instances of failure to apply existing control technology, growth of industry, and lack of economic technology in some cases.

In the absence of federally-established air quality criteria, and the consequent air quality standards, industry often finds it impractical to select and apply the necessary control methods. As of early 1969, the Federal Government had established criteria only for sulfur oxides and particles, although work is in progress on criteria for other air contaminants.

Recommendation A13: *The promulgation of air quality criteria by the Federal Government should be supported in a manner that will allow it to proceed with all possible speed.*

Effective and economic control equipment for many industrial emissions is available and is being used widely. Design of such equipment is frequently empirical, and a more fundamental understanding of the physical

9

and chemical phenomena involved could produce benefits in performance.
Recommendation A14: *The development of new and improved control technology and equipment for industrial emissions must be stimulated, particularly for types of industries for which economic means of control do not now exist. Low-cost equipment for small industries is particularly essential.*

The Recommendations for utility power plants, which follow, are also pertinent to industrial power generation.

Utility Power Plants (Recommendations A16-A21, page 73)
Abatement of sulfur oxides emissions from utility power plants nationwide has not yet started to a significant degree, except in a few large metropolitan areas that are requiring that low-sulfur fuel be used. Abatement will require the use of a variety of methods: low-sulfur fuels, stack-gas cleaning, and the tall stack.

Recommendation A16: *Translation of federal air quality criteria for sulfur oxides and particles into air quality standards should proceed rapidly so as to speed widespread application of the available means of controlling these emissions.*

Recommendation A17: *Existing research to define the overall effectiveness of the tall stack in meeting air quality standards should consider the effects of mass emissions of pollutants not only on local, ground-level concentrations, but on the local and regional air masses and on ground-level concentrations outside the local area.*

Recommendation A18: *Investigations of techniques for desulfurizing fuels must be carried to the point where economic evaluation is possible. Particularly desirable would be early definition of the amounts and locations of coals that can be cleaned economically of significant amounts of pyritic sulfur. The development of economical coal cleaning processes is a responsibility of the coal industry, and more comprehensive studies should be made than have been made in the past. Further research appears to be required on hydrodesulfurization catalysts that are not deactivated by the heavy metals in residual fuel oils.*

Recommendation A19: *The development of first-generation processes for removing sulfur oxides from utility stack gases should be supported and stimulated so as to achieve early commercialization, particularly in order to offer a control option for existing power plants. Research and development on new and original methods of removing sulfur oxides from utility stacks should proceed rapidly to the point at which specific processes can be selected for advanced development.*

Technology is not available for achieving significant reduction of nitrogen oxides emissions by utility power plants nationwide. Reduction can be achieved in some plants by changes in design. Reduction has also been achieved by using natural gas as fuel, but gas does not consistently show an advantage in this respect.

Recommendation A20: *Current studies of nitrogen oxides emissions by stationary sources should define the economics and effectiveness of modifying existing power plants, where possible, or of using alternative fuels to reduce such emissions.*

Space Heating (Recommendations A22-A24, page 74)

The use of low-sulfur fuels and efficient combustion equipment for space heating can significantly abate urban emissions of sulfur oxides and particles. Contaminants cannot be removed practically from stack gases produced by space heating units except where energy is produced centrally in large units and distributed to the point of use.

Recommendation A22: *In its development of national fuels policies and inventories, the Federal Government should take proper account of the needs of present and developing urban areas for low-pollution fuels for space heating.*

Recommendation A24: *The economics of centralized production of heat for space heating should be re-evaluated. Such studies should consider the distribution of energy in the form of hot air, electricity, steam, or high-temperature water (400°F. and 274 pounds per square inch).*

Effects of Air Pollutants (Recommendations A25-A29, page 81)

Air pollution is clearly undesirable. Incidents have occurred of lethal accumulation of pollutants, and all pollutants are known to have catastrophic effects at sufficient concentrations. Typical urban concentrations are not acutely lethal, but it is difficult to argue that their lesser concentrations make them harmless.

Recommendation A25: *Epidemiological and laboratory studies of the effects of air pollution on humans, including model experiments on animals, should be carefully coordinated and selectively accelerated. Body burdens and environmental levels of potentially harmful metals should be monitored insofar as is feasible on a systematic and continuing basis.*

Knowledge of the effects of air pollutants on vegetation is represented largely by studies of acute damage to tissue. Information is limited on reduction of crop growth and productivity and on mechanisms of action.

The effects of air pollutants on many materials are reasonably well understood, but it is difficult if not impossible to attach an economic value to the damage, except in specific instances.

Recommendation A26: *Economic and scientific research on the effects of air pollutants on vegetation and materials should be maintained at a level in consonance with work on effects on humans.*

The relationship of air contaminants to the ecology at the current state of knowledge can only be surmised.

Recommendation A27: *A concerted research program on the ecological effects of air pollutants should be developed and carefully coordinated as a multidisciplinary effort.*

Analytical Chemistry and Instruments (Recommendations A30-A33, page 85)

The methods and equipment used in air monitoring systems today are providing useful data, but must be sharply improved. The methods and equipment used to monitor emissions continuously at the source, either in-stack or remotely, also require improvement. Progress is required, moreover, in standardization of analytical methods, both to establish their reproducibility in the hands of chemists in different laboratories and to help to optimize them.

Recommendation A30: *Development of simplified, less costly instrumentation for air monitoring should be accelerated markedly. Means should be found for stimulating industrial research and development in this area.*

Recommendation A31: *The development of better in-stack and remote source-monitoring instrumentation for pollutants is essential and should be accelerated. Federal stimulation may be necessary to achieve adequately rapid innovation and dissemination.*

Recommendation A32: *Standardization of analytical methods and instruments should also be accelerated. Such standardization should include criteria for acceptable methods of sampling and storage as well as for the analytical methods themselves and for the interpretation and use of the resulting data. A program should be considered for certification of air-monitoring instruments on the basis of federally-established standards of performance.*

The Water Environment

Flow, Dispersion, Degradation (Recommendations W1-W6, page 105)

Knowledge of the specific chemical compounds in waste streams and in natural waters is generally inadequate to support quantitative understanding of the flow, dispersion, and degradation of water pollutants. Data on the magnitude of waste streams from all significant sources are also far from adequate.

Recommendation W1: *Regional inventories, on a selective trial basis, should be made of pollutants from all sources that are known or expected to be important. An effort should be made to learn more of the specific chemical compounds, particularly organic compounds, that are present in both wastes and natural waters. Chemical and biological research on natural waters, polluted or not, should be emphasized.*

General descriptions of the remarkably complex behavior of natural populations of microorganisms in natural water environments are unlikely to emerge. Research on the role of microorganisms in pollutant transport, including biological degradation, must include knowledge of specific chemical compounds and measurement of their degradation products. More and more, the collective chemical parameters now in common use will prove inadequate for understanding the behavior of complex natural systems.

Recommendation W2: *Fundamental research should be expanded on the action of natural mixed populations of bacteria and other organisms on* *specific compounds. Such research will require the development of analytical methods for identifying and quantifying specific compounds produced by biological degradation.*

Data on the size distribution and chemical, physical, and biological properties of particles in waste waters and natural waters are much too sparse to allow useful assessments of the role played by particles in pollutant transport.

Recommendation W3: *Comprehensive investigations of naturally-occurring and pollutant particles in water should be undertaken to determine such characteristics as size, charge, composition, and adsorptive properties. Expanded knowledge of particles would be important in studies of sedimentation, erosion, and certain waste treatment processes, as well as in work on transport.*

Intelligent management of the water environment in the long run must rely in part on the use of mathematical descriptions of natural water systems subject to pollution, but the chemical-biological complexity of those systems continues to defy attempts to describe them mathematically. Good progress has been made in describing the physical processes of convection and dispersion, and the main uncertainties now in describing pollutant transport mathematically appear to lie in the degradation processes. A more specific problem is the lack of knowledge of the molecular nature of substances as they exist in water.

Recommendation W4: *Research on improved mathematical descriptions of natural water systems subject to pollution should be strongly supported. The chemical-biological complexity of those systems requires that such research be highly interdisciplinary, involving scientists from disciplines such as chemistry, chemical engineering, civil engineering, biology, and ecology. Sheer complexity may ultimately limit the generality of the mathematical descriptions that can be developed, but it is essential to find a proper balance between the difficulty of understanding natural water systems and the need to describe them mathematically.*

Knowledge of pollutant transport in soil and ground water is growing more important because of the trend toward recharging ground waters with treated waste waters. Gaps remain, however, in the fundamental understanding of how the soil functions as a filter and biological medium and, more particularly, in the ability to exploit the available fundamental knowledge of the soil system.

Recommendation W5: *Systematic studies should be encouraged on the flow and reactions of forms of phosphorus and nitrogen, and various organic substances, in soil and ground water.*

Municipal waste water treatment (Recommendations W7-W9, page 122)

Conventional primary-secondary treatment of municipal waste waters is cheap and effective, to a point, and there is at present no adequate substitute for it. However, the performance of conventional treatment plants has been measured and controlled traditionally in terms of collective parameters, such as biochemical oxygen demand. These collective measurements do not produce the specific data, such as the fate of specific organic compounds in the treatment process, that are required to develop meaningful general interpretations of the biochemical and biological aspects of conventional processes. Thus reliance on collective parameters, though useful in process control, has resulted in a severe shortage of the specific data required, particularly at the operating level, to work toward optimizing conventional processes.

Recommendation W7: *Biochemists and biologists should become more involved in research on sewage treatment, primarily to seek radical innovations, based on fundamental understanding of microbiological processes. Emphasis should be laid on the use of adequate chemical tools to develop data that will allow the biochemical and biological aspects of treatment processes to be interpreted more meaningfully and that can be used in process optimization.*

Handling and disposing of the sludges from conventional processes is the leading technological problem in waste water treatment today. New and more efficient methods are required. The use of synthetic polymers to improve flocculation and sedimentation of sludges and to condition them for dewatering is very promising, but knowledge of the fundamental process parameters falls short of what is needed to exploit polymers fully for these purposes.

Recommendation W8: *Research should be expanded on new methods of handling waste water treatment sludges and on the fundamental process parameters involved in using synthetic polymers and polyelectrolytes and other novel surface-active chemicals to improve flocculation, sedimentation, and conditioning of such sludges. Comprehensive data should be developed on the economics and technology of complementary and/or alternative means of sludge disposal, such as incineration, use as fertilizer or soil conditioner, underground disposal, and pipeline transportation.*

Advanced waste treatment (Recommendations W10-W12, page 138)

A number of advanced waste water treatment processes are in development, several are at the pilot plant stage, and one full-scale demonstration plant is now operating that integrates several such processes into a single water reclamation system. Comprehensive operating and economic data at the commercial level are not yet available for most advanced waste treatment processes.

Recommendation W10: *Chemical and biological characterizations should be made of advanced treatment systems operating at the large pilot-plant or demonstration-plant level, including the identification of specific chemical compounds, studies of the effects of chlorine or other oxidants on organic residues, and other necessary investigations. Such studies should be comprehensive research and development efforts, not simply demon-*

strations that the systems operate properly in terms of the traditional parameters.

Industrial Facilities (Recommendations W13-W14, page 141)

Much of the conventional treatment technology for municipal waste waters applies also to industrial waste waters, and a trend appears to be developing toward more joint use of treatment facilities by industry and municipalities. Industrial waste water treatment is certain to become more extensive because of the general move toward providing the equivalent of secondary treatment. Increased use of joint facilities might ease the overall economic burden of such treatment, as reflected ultimately in the prices of products and services.

Data on the specific substances contained in industrial waste waters do not appear to be adequate to support rational assessments of their pollutant potential or the development of regional inventories of important or potentially important pollutants.

Recommendation W13: *Information should be gathered and made widely available on the technology of joint municipal-industrial treatment of waste waters for the guidance of companies and municipalities who wish to consider such an approach. This task should be managed at the federal level.*

Recommendation W14: *Inventories should be made, on a selective trial basis, of the specific substances in industrial waste waters that are important or potentially important pollutants. This task should be managed at the federal level.*

Nonmunicipal, nonindustrial water pollution (Recommendations W15-W16, page 146)

Known sources of water pollution other than conventional municipal and industrial sources are not always identified or well delineated, and control technology is often weak or nonexistent.

Agriculture is a major source of potential water pollutants and presents difficult problems in developing both basic data and means of control. Perhaps the greatest source of pollution by agriculture is soil transport in runoff due largely to failure to apply soil conservation practices. This results in transport of pesticides on soil particles to streams, development of high suspended solids and turbidity, and high sedimentation rates in lakes and reservoirs. The inefficient use associated with the rapid rate of increase in use of fertilizers is becoming alarming in some parts of the country.

Recommendation W15: *Basic research should be encouraged on economic means of treating and disposing of animal wastes in agriculture.*

Recommendation W16: *Basic data should be gathered systematically to delineate the relative importance of the various agricultural and rural sources of compounds of nitrogen and phosphorus in surface waters and ground waters.*

Effects of Water Pollution (Recommendations W17-W21, page 151)

The main concern over the effects of water pollutants on human health at present lies in the effects of long-term, low-level exposure. Relative to this kind of exposure, very little is known of the possible effects on human health of the variety of largely unidentified chemical compounds that enter sources of water supply.

Recommendation W17: *Research should be strongly encouraged on the effects of known water pollutants in long-term, low-level exposure. Both laboratory and epidemiological work will be required.*

Studies of the behavior of viruses in existing water reuse systems and their movement in soil and ground waters have been remarkably few. It is difficult to evaluate the soundness of certain water reuse schemes without knowing more of the potential for viral disease.

Recommendation W18: *Studies should be maintained on enteric viruses and their movement in soil and ground water.*

There is no significant epidemiological basis for the total coliform bacteria counts used today to establish standards for body-contact recreational waters.

Recommendation W19: *Correlations of bacterial indicator organisms with waterborne disease, particularly in recreational waters, should receive high priority.*

Not as much is known as should be known of specific compounds in waste treatment plant effluents. Accidents, negligence, and disasters do occur. Water treatment technology and normal treatment capacity are not necessarily adequate to cope with unknowns, sudden pollution loads, and man-made or natural disasters.

Recommendation W20: *Public water supply treatment methods should be upgraded through research on removal and destruction of potentially harmful substances not removed by waste treatment practices, or bypassed with insufficient dilution during plant outage periods or in times of disaster such as power failures.*

Knowledge of the fundamental processes involved in eutrophication is well below the level that will be required to develop sound, long-range control measures. The current emphasis on removal of phosphorus from waste waters should be tempered by the realization that the effectiveness of the measure may not be known for some years.

Recommendation W21: *Investigations should be pursued of the fundamental chemical and biological parameters of eutrophication and its effects. Development of effective and economic long-term controls will depend on considerably improved knowledge of factors such as mass balances for significant nutrients; the forms in which those nutrients exist in water; natural population dynamics; potentially limiting nutrients in specific situations; and algal, bacterial, and plant physiology in general.*

Analytical Chemistry and Instruments (Recommendations W22-W23, page 153)

Research on eutrophication, potentially toxic pollutants, tastes and odors, and other aspects of water pollution would be eased by the development of improved analytical methods and procedures for low levels of phosphorus, nitrogen, trace metals, and trace organic compounds.

Recommendation W22: *Emphasis should be placed on the development of analytical methods for specific organic pollutants at all concentrations and in all waste sources and receiving waters, including estuaries and the oceans. Similar effort should be devoted to developing methods for low levels of phosphorus, nitrogen, and other nutrients that are involved in eutrophication.*

The evaluation and standardization of analytical chemical methods has not kept pace with the need engendered by progress in water pollution research and control. Evaluation should include sampling methods and changes in composition during transport and storage.

Recommendation W23: *Analytical methods for gathering basic data, monitoring, research, and treatment control should be actively and continuously upgraded by systematic evaluation and standardization.*

Solid Wastes

Municipal Refuse (Recommendations S1-S4, page 180)

The technology is available to sharply upgrade the handling and disposal of municipal refuse in the U.S., but it is being applied only to a very limited extent.

Recommendation S1: *The appropriate federal, state, and local government agencies should press their efforts to define the nature and magnitude of the solid wastes problem both now and in the future. Education, research, and demonstration, and local and regional planning for solid wastes management, utilization, and disposal are all necessary for progress in this neglected area.*

Sanitary landfill and incineration, when properly designed and operated to prevent ground water and air pollution, have both been demonstrated to be effective, nuisance-free means of disposal from which positive values can be obtained in the form of reclaimed land and waste heat. Composting has succeeded economically in only a few instances, but it has yet to be put on the kind of scientific basis that will allow its general potential to be assessed definitively.

Recommendation S2: *The use of known peripheral science and technology in developing improved methods for sanitary landfill and incineration should be encouraged and supported. Efforts to develop a more scientific basis for composting should also be supported, particularly in the area of the biochemistry and related aspects of the degradation process, so that the potential of the method, which appears to date to be quite limited, can be assessed more definitively.*

Junked Automobiles (Recommendation S5, page 182)

Disposal of discarded vehicles appears to be largely a problem of applying technology to produce a marketable scrap at a cost that can be borne by scrap processors. Important factors are the costs of transportation, of the required processing equipment, and of air pollution control equipment.

Recommendation S5: *Efforts by private industry to improve the economics of the auto scrap processing industry should be stimulated. The development of scrapping methods that would permit the use of less costly equipment, and of radically new scrapping methods, should be pursued at all levels. The development of new means of utilizing junked vehicles should also be encouraged and supported, with emphasis on methods of recycling the metals.*

Industrial Solid Wastes (Recommendations S6-S7, page 185)

Large amounts of the materials of production are recycled both in-plant and as secondary materials and thus never become true solid wastes.

Recommendation S6: *Efforts to improve the economics of recycle of solid materials by the secondary materials industry should be encouraged. A distinction should be maintained between solid materials that are recycled and those that are true solid wastes.*

A time may be approaching when industry will find it economical to burn more of its own solid wastes than to dispose of them in on-site landfill or to hire outside contractors to remove them.

Recommendation S7: *Studies should be made of the chemical and physical nature and the volume of industrial solid wastes, insofar as proprietary problems allow, in order to support the conception and design of equipment, including incinerators, for disposing of them economically.*

Mining and Processing Wastes (Recommendation S8, page 187)

Mining and processing wastes are accumulating steadily. Often they represent a loss of resources and create esthetic and other problems. Minerals are being recovered where it is economic to do so, and some mining and processing wastes can be used as aggregate or for other structural purposes.

Recommendation S8: *Research and development on processes for recovering various minerals from mining and processing wastes should be maintained at an adequate level against the day when changing economics warrant the recovery of such minerals. Work on other means of utilizing or disposing of these wastes should also be maintained at a steady level.*

Effects of Solid Wastes (Recommendation S9, page 188)

A well-defined relationship between solid wastes and human health has not been demonstrated under the conditions that prevail in the U.S., although it is possible to conclude that, for some diseases, a relationship exists. The more obvious effects of solid wastes include the esthetics problem and pollution of air and water by improper means of disposal.

Recommendation S9: *The effort to upgrade solid wastes management, util-*

ization, and disposal should be justified on the basis of esthetic values and control of air and water pollution.

Pesticides in the Environment

Pesticide Residues in Soil, Water, and Air (Recommendations P1-P3, page 217)

More detailed information is available on pesticide residues in the environment than for most other contaminants. This is due primarily to the excellence of analytical methods for the determination of minute amounts of pesticides.

Most pesticides are biodegradable and, therefore, do not persist in the environment. Their effects are thus limited to the areas of application and are of relatively short duration. No undesirable long-term side effects are known to be caused by use of these biodegradable materials.

Residues of some persistent pesticides, mainly the chlorinated hydrocarbon insecticides, are very widespread in the environment. The most widespread of these compounds is DDT. In addition, arsenic and some herbicides have been found to persist in some soils.

Available data show that most crops grown on pesticide-contaminated soils absorb only very small amounts of the soil contaminant. In most cases the residues resulting from soil contamination are far below the tolerances established for human food and, therefore, are below the concentrations which would be harmful to humans. Occasionally, illegal residues may occur if the pesticide with which the soil is contaminated is not registered for use on the crop being grown.

Available evidence indicates that residues present in soils in most cases are not harmful either to the crop or to the soil microflora.

In the United States, most surface waters and their attendant sediments contain chlorinated hydrocarbon insecticides, particularly DDT and its degradation products, as well as some herbicides such as 2,4-D. The concentrations in water itself are in the range of parts per billion or less.

Little is known about pesticide residues in air outside the immediate vicinity of application.

Recommendation P1: *Pesticide monitoring programs on all phases of the environment should be continued. In the case of air (and wildlife) the present programs should be extended.*

Recommendation P2: *For purposes of chemical analysis, research should be pursued on the development of more adequate methods for the separation of minute amounts of pesticides from water and air.*

Recommendation P3: *Research should be expanded on the toxicity of pesticides when they are inhaled as opposed to dermal exposure or oral intake.*

Minimizing Contamination of the Environment with Pesticides (Recommendations P4-P6, page 224)

Optimum methods of pest control will involve careful integration of

19

chemical, biological, and cultural techniques. Such things as better application methods, improved formulations, effects of pesticides on insect parasites and predators, studies of population dynamics, and eradication of pests will all help to decrease contamination of the environment with pesticides. Only in this way can the objective of economic control of pests on crops and animals be obtained with minimal environmental and ecological impact.

Recommendation P4: *An extensive educational program at all government levels is required to teach all pesticide users the optimum methods of pest control.*

Recommendation P5: *Research on biological and cultural methods of pest control should be continued.*

Recommendation P6: *Persistent pesticides should only be used in minimal amounts and under conditions where they have been shown not to cause widespread contamination of the environment. Where possible, highly-persistent materials should be replaced by rapidly degradable materials.*

Pesticides and Wildlife (Recommendation P7, page 230)

Wildlife species in most parts of the United States carry appreciable loads of chlorinated hydrocarbon pesticides. The principal hazard of persistent pesticides in the environment is their concentration in the food chain with consequent harmful effects on fish and wildlife. Residues have accumulated in the food chain to a marked degree in a number of well documented cases. These have caused death or debility of some nontarget species and have, in some cases, depressed reproduction. However, when one considers the widespread use of pesticides over the past 15 to 20 years, the problems of this sort which have been encountered have been relatively few.

Recommendation P7: *More research should be conducted on the relationship between environmental pesticide contaminants and wildlife. This research, though based on chemistry and biology, should be done in an ecological context.*

Pesticides and Human Health (Recommendation P8, page 236)

Humans in the United States and elsewhere carry a body burden of 10 to 20 ppm of chlorinated hydrocarbon pesticides and their conversion products. By far the greatest part of this residue is DDT and its degradation products. There is no evidence that long-term, low-level exposure to residues of pesticides such as occurs in the diet or environment in the United States has any undesirable effect on human health.

Recommendation P8: *Additional research is required on the impact of long-term, low-level exposure to pesticides on humans and other forms of life. In this connection, study is also required of the dose-response relationship of pesticide chemicals suspected of being carcinogens.*

Section **1**

The Air Environment

Contents

The Air Environment
INTRODUCTION

It is not easy today to find a topic more likely than air pollution to generate vigorous debate and sometimes violent argument. This is true among the legislators who make the laws, among the businessmen and taxpayers who bear the costs, and among the scientists and engineers who seek out and apply the basic chemical and physical principles. Such debate is often a sign of serious gaps in the scientific and technological knowledge that is required to support rational management of the air environment. But the areas of ignorance are paralleled by the respectable body of existing science and technology that is being used to abate air pollution (95, 96, 97), albeit not yet to anywhere near the extent that will be required.

This body of knowledge has been worked out in the teeth of formidable scientific odds. Contaminants in the air must often be detected and measured at concentrations in the range of parts per million (ppm) or less by volume or micrograms (millionths of a gram) per cubic meter ($\mu g/m^3$) by weight. The physical, chemical, and physiological behavior of contaminants at these very low concentrations must be investigated. The analytical chemistry involved in such studies is only one of a number of challenging and crucial scientific problems.

Despite the scientific difficulties, a legal and administrative framework has begun to emerge in this country in the past few years that, if vigorously implemented and supported by the necessary knowledge, should make it possible to begin to manage the air environment intelligently. This framework doubtless is not the last word, and the action for which it calls is only just beginning to get under way. Plainly the time is not ripe for complacency, if indeed such a time ever arrives, in man's effort to preserve the quality of the air. The success of that effort, moreover, rests now and will rest in the future on man's grasp of the science and technology of four broad and interrelated areas:

- The flow and dispersion of air contaminants and their degradation or conversion to other chemical and physical forms in the local, regional, and global atmospheres.
- The means of avoiding the generation of air pollutants or of abating pollution if it cannot be avoided.
- The effects of air pollutants on plant and animal life and on inanimate objects and materials.
- The means of detecting and measuring air pollutants and their effects.

BACKGROUND

The atmosphere is a dynamic system. It steadily absorbs a range of solids, liquids, and gases from both natural and man-made sources. These substances may travel through the air, disperse, and react among themselves and with other substances, both chemically and physically. Eventually, whether or not in their original form, they may reach a sink, such as the ocean, or a receptor, such as a man. Some, such as helium, escape from the earth's atmosphere. Others, such as carbon dioxide, may enter the atmosphere faster than they return to their sinks and thus gradually accumulate in the air.

Clean, dry air contains 78.09% nitrogen, by volume, and 20.94% oxygen (Table 1). The remaining 0.97% of the gaseous constituents of dry air includes small amounts of carbon dioxide, helium, argon, krypton, and xenon, as well as very small amounts of other inorganic and organic gases whose concentrations may differ with time and place. Water vapor is normally present in air in concentrations of 1 to 3%. The air also contains aerosols, dispersed solid or liquid particles. They may range in size from clusters of a few molecules to diameters of a few tens of microns (a micron is one thousandth of a millimeter).

The local air mass and its contents are part of the regional and global atmospheres and ultimately must be treated as such. Contaminants generated locally often leave the local atmosphere. Very little is known of the fate of many such substances, but they may have important geochemical or geophysical effects. Two examples are carbon dioxide and fine particles. Both are produced in large amounts by man, and both may be affecting the temperature of the earth by their behavior in the global atmosphere.

Table 1

Composition of clean, dry air near sea level

COMPONENT	% by volume	CONTENT ppm	COMPONENT	% by volume	CONTENT ppm
Nitrogen	78.09%	780,900 ppm	Hydrogen	.00005%	0.5 ppm
Oxygen	20.94	209,400	Methane	.00015	1.5
Argon	.93	9,300	Nitrogen		
Carbon			dioxide	.0000001	0.001
dioxide	.0318	318	Ozone	.000002	0.02
Neon	.0018	18	Sulfur		
Helium	.00052	5.2	dioxide	.00000002	.0002
Krypton	.0001	1	Carbon		
Xenon	.000008	0.08	mon-		
Nitrous			oxide	.00001	0.1
oxide	.000025	0.25	Ammonia	.000001	.01

NOTE: The concentrations of some of these gases may differ with time and place, and the data for some are open to question. Single values for concentrations, instead of ranges of concentrations, are given above to indicate order of magnitude, not specific and universally accepted concentrations.

SOURCE: "Air Chemistry and Radioactivity," Junge, C. E., Academic Press, New York, 1963, p. 3.
"Air Pollution," Vol. I, 2nd ed. Stern, A. C., Ed., Academic Press, New York, N.Y., 1968, p. 27.
"Sources, Abundance, and Fate of Gaseous Atmospheric Pollutants," Robinson, E., Robbins, R. C., Prepared for American Petroleum Institute by Stanford Research Institute, Menlo Park, Calif., 1968.

Table 2

National air pollutant emissions, millions of tons per year, 1965

	Totals	% of Totals	Carbon monoxide	Sulfur oxides	Hydro-carbons	Nitrogen oxides	Particles
Automobiles	86	60%	66	1	12	6	1
Industry	23	17%	2	9	4	2	6
Electric power plants	20	14%	1	12	1	3	3
Space heating	8	6%	2	3	1	1	1
Refuse disposal	5	3%	1	1	1	1	1
Totals	**142 million**		**72 million**	**26 million**	**19 million**	**13 million**	**12 million**

SOURCE: "The Sources of Air Pollution and Their Control," Public Health Service Publication No. 1548, Government Printing Office, Washington, D.C., 1966

In the U.S., the five most common primary air pollutants in tons emitted annually nationwide are carbon monoxide, sulfur oxides, hydrocarbons, nitrogen oxides, and particles (Table 2). Their major sources are automobiles, industry, electric power plants, space heating, and refuse disposal. These and other sources, in addition, emit a range of other pollutants peculiar to the types of activities involved.

Rankings of the amounts and sources of pollutants are estimates based on such factors as the national consumption of fuels in combustion, the leading pollutant-producing process. Rankings in order of weight emitted, moreover, do not parallel rankings in order of effects produced. Some primary pollutants are more reactive chemically than others. Some may interreact with other substances in the air to yield secondary pollutants that exert relatively large effects at relatively low concentrations. (Carbon dioxide, a product of combustion, is an air contaminant by the definition given on page 6 of this report, and its emissions far exceed those of the five major pollutants listed above. It is omitted from Table 2 because it is not considered a contaminant that can be controlled, except by replacing the combustion process with another source of energy, such as nuclear power.)

Few data exist on the precise concentrations of pollutants that were present in air before the early 1950's, when intensive air monitoring began in this country. Carbon dioxide, carbon monoxide, and sulfur dioxide were measured in the U.S. and Europe as long ago as the 1920's and in some instances earlier (21, 126, 129). Such analyses were few and far between, however, and generally of questionable accuracy. Since the early 1950's considerable data on the concentrations of major air pollutants in urban areas in the U.S. have been gathered by state and local monitoring agencies and by the National Air Surveillance Network of the National Air Pollution Control Administration (NAPCA) in the Department of Health, Education, and Welfare (HEW). The levels of concentrations involved are shown in Tables 3 and 4 (pages 26, 28).

Table 3

Summary of concentrations of particles and two gases in U.S. in 1964 and 1965

BI-WEEKLY SAMPLING STATIONS

Urban Stations	Number of stations	Concentrations in μg/m³ unless noted Arithmetic average [a]	Maximum
Particles	291	105	1254
Fractions: [c]			
Benzene-soluble organics	218	6.8	[b]
Nitrates	96	2.6	39.7
Sulfates	96	10.6	101.2
Ammonium	56	1.3	75.5
Antimony	35	0.001	0.160
Arsenic	133	0.02	[b]
Beryllium	100	<0.0005	0.010
Bismuth	35	<0.0005	0.064
Cadmium	35	0.002	0.420
Chromium	103	0.015	0.330
Cobalt	35	<0.0005	0.060
Copper	103	0.09	10.00
Iron	104	1.58	22.00
Lead	104	0.79	8.60
Manganese	103	0.10	9.98
Molybdenum	35	<0.005	0.78
Nickel	103	0.034	0.460
Tin	85	0.02	0.50
Titanium	104	0.04	1.10
Vanadium	99	0.050	2.200
Zinc	99	0.67	58.00
Sulfur dioxide	36	69 (0.024 ppm)	1201 (0.420 ppm)
Nitrogen dioxide	31	105 (0.051 ppm)	408 (0.198 ppm)
Nonurban Stations			
Particles	32	37	312
Fractions:			
Benzene-soluble organics	28	1.2	[b]
Arsenic	24	<0.005	0.02

[a] Arithmetic averages are presented to permit comparable expression of averages derived from quarterly composite samples; as such they are not directly comparable to geometric means calculated for previous years' data. The geometric mean for all urban stations during 1964-65 was 90 μg/m³, for the nonurban stations, 28 μg/m³.

[b] No individual sample analyses performed.

[c] The "fractions" of particles reported here derive from imprecise measurements. The particles are collected on glass fiber filters, which contain differing amounts of the very substances being measured. For example, sodium, potassium, silicon, aluminum, and chloride would be expected to comprise substantial fractions of airborne particles, but cannot be measured because they are major ingredients of the glass in the fiber filters.

SOURCE: "Air Quality Data from the National Air Sampling Networks and Contributing State and Local Networks, 1964-1965," U.S. Department of Health, Education, and Welfare, 1966.

26

The federal legislative framework for managing the air environment is based on the Clean Air Act of 1963, as amended, most recently by the Air Quality Act of 1967. Under this legislation, the Secretary of HEW has established eight atmospheric areas in the 48 contiguous states and five outside the contiguous states. The areas are based on long-term meteorological factors that affect the transport and diffusion of air pollutants. NAPCA is working to establish in those areas some 57 air quality control regions that will be the basis for regional air pollution control programs. The 57 proposed regions would cover more than 70% of the U.S. urban population (Fig. 1, page 30). They will be defined on the basis of such factors as meteorology, location and amount of pollutant emissions, social and governmental aspects, and patterns of urban growth. As of March 1969, air quality control regions had been designated in the metropolitan areas of New York City, Philadelphia, Chicago, Denver, Los Angeles, and Washington, D. C.

HEW must also publish air quality criteria for specific pollutants as well as information on the cost and effectiveness of control systems and techniques that can be used to abate those pollutants. On the basis of these criteria, the states will develop air quality standards and plans for implementing them; these standards and plans will then be applied in the air quality control regions.

Documents on air quality criteria and control technology for sulfur oxides and particulate matter were published in January 1969 (3, 4, 25, 26). Work is under way on photochemical oxidants, carbon monoxide, atmospheric fluorides, nitrogen oxides, and hydrocarbons. The development of criteria is being considered for other pollutants, including beryllium, hydrogen sulfide, odors, lead, certain other heavy metals, asbestos, possible organic carcinogens, aldehydes, ethylene, pesticides, and rocket fuel components and their combustion products.

FLOW, DISPERSION, DEGRADATION

Efficient management of the air environment in the long run must depend on thorough knowledge of how contaminants flow, disperse, and are degraded or converted into other physical and chemical forms as they move from source to sink or receptor. Such knowledge is particularly needed today on a local and regional basis, and ultimately it will be needed on a global basis. The mechanisms of flow, dispersion, and degradation are not well understood, and it is not possible at the current level of knowledge to state with reasonable precision the lifetime of any contaminant in air. For only one gas, carbon dioxide, are enough data available to demonstrate that the gas's global concentration is changing. Nevertheless, a fragmentary picture at least has begun to take shape in the past decade or so for some substances (61, 101, 121).

Sulfur dioxide

Sulfur dioxide is one of several forms in which sulfur exists in air. The others include hydrogen sulfide, sulfuric acid, and sulfate salts. Of

27

Table 4

Summary of concentrations of six gases from continuous air monitoring stations in U.S., 1962-65

| | ARITHMETIC AVERAGE, ppm | | | |
	1962	1963	1964	1965
Carbon monoxide				
Chicago	a	8.2	12.1	17.1
Cincinnati	a	7.0	6.1	4.0
Denver				7.2
Philadelphia	a	a	7.1	8.1
San Francisco	a	5.4	5.2	
St. Louis			6.3	6.5
Washington	5.3	7.0	5.6	3.7
Nitric oxide				
Chicago	0.104	0.097	0.100	0.096
Cincinnati	0.031	0.032	0.038	0.031
Denver				0.033
Philadelphia	0.040	0.046	0.045	0.048
San Francisco	0.055	0.087	0.089	
St. Louis			0.036	0.026
Washington	0.029	0.038	0.033	0.033
Nitrogen dioxide				
Chicago	0.043	0.041	0.046	0.043
Cincinnati	0.030	0.030	0.032	0.035
Denver				0.036
Philadelphia	0.039	0.038	0.038	0.036
San Francisco	0.033	0.049	0.056	
St. Louis			0.033	0.026
Washington	0.030	0.034	0.036	0.034

the molecules of sulfur dioxide in the air at any given time, close to 80% are emitted as hydrogen sulfide, which is later converted to sulfur dioxide, and roughly 20% are emitted as sulfur dioxide. Estimates of worldwide emissions of sulfur dioxide emitted as sulfur dioxide, both man-made and natural, suggest that more than 80% of it, or 16% of the total in the air at any given time, comes from combustion of fuels that contain sulfur. The smelting of nonferrous metals and petroleum refining account for most of the rest. The only apparent natural source of sulfur dioxide is volcanic gases, whose contribution, though believed to be small, is not known with any accuracy.

It is not yet possible to construct a detailed scheme for the fate of sulfur dioxide in the air, but the initial step is oxidation to sulfur trioxide. The latter gas dissolves in water droplets to form sulfuric acid, which may react further to form sulfate salts, such as ammonium sul-

	ARITHMETIC AVERAGE, ppm			
	1962	1963	1964	1965
Sulfur dioxide				
Chicago	0.108	0.150	0.175	0.130
Cincinnati	0.033	0.025	0.038	0.030
Denver				0.021
Philadelphia	0.088	0.069	0.082	0.085
San Francisco	a	0.009	0.017	
St. Louis			0.064	0.047
Washington	0.055	0.046	0.048	0.046
Total hydrocarbons				
Chicago	3.3	3.2	3.0	2.7
Cincinnati	3.2	3.4	3.0	2.8
Denver				2.5
Philadelphia	2.7	2.5	2.2	2.2
San Francisco	2.3	2.6	2.8	
St. Louis			3.1	2.9
Washington	a	2.8	3.0	2.1
Total oxidants				
Chicago	Oxidant data for 1962–		0.030	0.026
Cincinnati	63 not included be-		0.028	0.033
Denver	cause of SO_2 interfer-			0.033
Philadelphia	ence with analytical		0.026	0.026
San Francisco	method.		0.019	
St. Louis			0.031	0.031
Washington			0.030	0.028

a Average not calculated because of insufficient or poorly distributed data.

SOURCE: "Air Quality Data from the National Air Sampling Networks and Contributing State and Local Networks, 1964-1965," U.S. Department of Health, Education, and Welfare, 1966.

fate. The primary oxidation process may take several different routes and can proceed rapidly in polluted atmospheres. In air that contains nitrogen dioxide and certain hydrocarbons, sulfur dioxide is oxidized in a photochemical (light-stimulated) reaction process that produces aerosols containing sulfuric acid. Also, sulfur dioxide can be oxidized in water droplets that contain ammonia, the end product being ammonium sulfate aerosol. Oxidation in water droplets can be catalyzed (speeded) by the ions of metals such as iron and manganese.

Both the sulfuric acid and sulfate salts thus formed exist in air as aerosols. They are removed by precipitation and, to a lesser extent, by gravitational settling. A given volume of sulfur dioxide that enters the air will be removed by these mechanisms, as acid or salt, in a time estimated at five days to two weeks.

A large part of the sulfur in the global atmosphere is emitted as

Figure 1

Atmospheric areas and air quality control regions in the 48 contiguous states

The first step in controlling air pollution on a regional basis was the designation of atmospheric areas. The lines on the map show the boundaries of the eight atmospheric areas designated by the Department of Health, Education, and Welfare in the contiguous U.S.; five additional areas have been designated outside the contiguous U.S. Designation of areas is based on long-term meteorological factors that affect transport and diffusion of air pollutants. The next step was to designate air quality control regions. The dots on the map show the regions scheduled for designation in the contiguous U.S. Altogether there will be 57 regions, covering more than 70% of the nation's urban population. Air quality control regions are designated on the basis of such factors as meteorology, location and amounts of pollutant emissions, social and governmental aspects, and patterns of urban growth.

SOURCE: Department of Health, Education, and Welfare.

hydrogen sulfide produced naturally by decaying organic matter on land and in the oceans and by volcanoes. Hydrogen sulfide is also emitted by some industrial operations. The available data are sketchy for both natural and man-made sources, but estimates of the environmental sulfur cycle suggest that the industrial contribution of hydrogen sulfide is not significant on a global basis. Hydrogen sulfide, like sulfur dioxide, is oxidized in the air and converted eventually to sulfur, sulfur dioxide, sulfuric acid, and sulfate salts. Sources and sinks for sulfur compounds also include the emission of sulfate salts by sea spray, and the direct absorption of sulfur dioxide by the oceans and by plant life (Fig. 2).

On a local or regional basis, the mechanisms that remove sulfur compounds from the air may produce significant effects. In the early 1960's, the concentration of sulfur compounds in air over Europe began to rise, as did the acidity of precipitation. Both phenomena are attributed to increased use of sulfur-containing fuels. Rain and snow absorb sulfur compounds in the air and, as a result, become more acid, a change that is reflected by lowered pH. (pH is a measure of the acidity or alkalinity of a solution. On the pH scale, a value of 7.0 is generally considered to be neutral, values below 7.0 are increasingly acidic, and values above 7.0 are increasingly alkaline.) In 1958 in Europe, precipitation was showing values of less than pH 5.0 only in limited areas over the Netherlands. By 1962, the area where values of less than pH 5.0 could be found had extended over central Europe, and values of less than pH 4.0 could be found over the Netherlands. In 1966, the area where precipitation of pH 4.5 could be found had reached central Sweden.

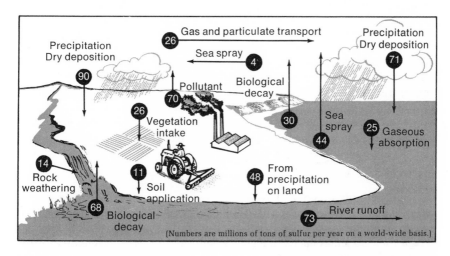

Figure 2

The environmental sulfur cycle

Sulfur circulates globally between land, sea, and air in amounts estimated to be as shown. Sulfur dioxide is one of several forms in which sulfur exists in air. The others include hydrogen sulfide, sulfuric acid, and sulfate salts. A large part of the sulfur in the global atmosphere is emitted originally as hydrogen sulfide, much of it coming from natural sources. Much of the hydrogen sulfide emitted is converted later to sulfur dioxide and is the source of close to 80% of the sulfur dioxide molecules present in air at any given time. Cycles similar to the one shown here can be constructed for other elements, such as nitrogen and carbon.

SOURCE: Robinson, E., Robbins, R. C., "Where Does It All Go?", *Stanford Research Institute Journal*, December 1968, p. 4.

Some precipitation goes into surface waters, which could account at least in part for the fact that the pH of Lake Vanern in Sweden fell from about 7.3 at the beginning of 1965 to about 6.8 by mid-1967. The pH of the Morrumsan River fell from about 6.8 to 6.2 in the same period. These trends correspond with the trend to lower pH in precipitation. Declining pH is a threat to aquatic life, since most organisms cannot live at less than pH 4.0, and some fish, such as salmon, are wiped out at pH 5.5. It is true that the pH of surface waters can be affected significantly by factors other than precipitation. In lakes, pH varies with seasonal variations in temperature and biological activity. In both lakes and rivers the extent to which precipitation can change the pH significantly is affected by the mineral composition of the receiving waters. Nonetheless, sulfur compounds in the air must be regarded as a possible contributing factor, at least near highly populated and industrialized areas.

The global importance of man-made emissions of sulfur compounds to the air is essentially unknown, although such emissions are estimated roughly to account for about a third of the sulfur that enters the atmosphere annually. The existing data are not definitive enough to show whether sulfur compounds are accumulating in the atmosphere. A layer of sulfate particles exists worldwide in the stratosphere, but its mechanisms of formation, its effects, and its relationship to man-made emissions are not clear. There are indications of a net increase, globally, in the concentration of fine particles in the air, and compounds of sulfur could be a contributor to such an increase. The concentration of particles in the air can affect mean global temperature. Thus, in the long run, man-made emissions of sulfur compounds cannot be excluded as a factor in geochemical and geophysical phenomena.

Particles

Particles, both liquid and solid, are enormously complex and are perhaps the most widespread of all the substances that are usually considered pollutants (3). They spring from a range of sources. Particles larger than 10 microns in diameter come mainly from mechanical processes such as erosion, grinding, and spraying. Those between 1 and 10 microns are more numerous in the atmosphere and generally include the largest weight fraction of particles. They stem from mechanical processes and also include industrial dusts, ash, and the like. Particles in the size range between 0.1 and 1 micron tend to contain more of the products of condensation than do larger particles. Ammonium sulfate and the products of combustion begin to predominate, along with aerosols formed by photochemical reactions in the air. Very little is known of the chemical nature of particles in the size range below 0.1 micron. Over cities, however, their concentration characteristically is higher than the natural level, and the difference seems to be due largely to combustion.

Particles of all kinds and sizes share a number of physical properties. They grow by condensation, adsorb and absorb vapors and gases, coagulate or disperse, and absorb and scatter light. It is not possible to generalize on the chemical behavior of particles because they are so diverse and because so little is known of them. Studying the chemistry of particles that weigh on the order of trillionths of a gram is extremely difficult. Particles in the air must interreact chemically, especially in the size range below 0.1 micron, where they collide relatively frequently with each other, but particle-particle reactions have been studied very little. Chemical reactions between a particle and a gas have been studied somewhat more, but still to a very limited extent.

An important question in gas-particle reactions in the air is the role of water vapor. For practical purposes the question has been answered for only one system, the reaction between gaseous ammonia and sulfuric acid mist to form the salt, ammonium sulfate. At high humidity, the rate of reaction is controlled by the rate at which ammonia in the air can diffuse to the sulfuric acid droplets, where it reacts. At low humidity, the rate of reaction is controlled by the rate at which ammonium sulfate formed in the reaction diffuses away from the surface and into the acid droplets, thus exposing more surface for reaction with ammonia. Besides explaining the effect of water vapor on a specific gas-particle reaction, this work shows clearly how the reaction is affected by the accumulation of its products at the gas-particle interface. The latter effect, moreover, should apply generally in the absorption of airborne substances in droplets.

Gravitational settling is the main mechanism by which particles are removed ultimately from the air, but there are intervening mechanisms that vary with the size of the particle. Particles that are less than 0.1 micron in diameter move randomly in air, collide often with other particles, and thus grow rapidly by coagulation. Particles in this size range would soon vanish from the air were they not replenished constantly by condensation processes. Particles in the next larger size range, 0.1 to 1.0 micron, probably are also removed from the air primarily by coagulation. They grow more slowly than the smaller particles, however, because they are somewhat less numerous, move less rapidly in air, and thus collide less often with other particles. At diameters larger than 1 micron, particles begin to develop appreciable settling velocities, and above 10 microns they begin to settle relatively rapidly, although particles as large as 10 microns can be kept airborne by turbulence for extended periods.

Particles may be removed from the air by impinging on buildings, trees, and other objects. Rain also removes them, but the effect is negligible at particle diameters of less than 2 microns. Particles much smaller than 2 microns can occur in rain water if they originate in clouds, since cloud droplets are more effective than rain drops in collecting small particles.

The processes that remove particles from the air, combined with the steady generation of small particles by condensation and of large particles by mechanical processes, tend to cause particulate matter to maintain a relatively constant size distribution in air (40). This distribution covers a range of diameters of about 0.001 micron to a few tens of microns. Particles in the range of 0.1 to 10 microns account for most of the mass and a large fraction of the numbers of those present.

Particles generated in an urban atmosphere normally remain airborne for only a few days, although, depending on their size, they may remain airborne for several weeks. Gravitational settling prevents larger particles, such as fly ash and soil, from traveling very far from their sources. The lifetime of a particle in air is a strong function of the height at which it is introduced, however, and large or intense sources, such as big metropolitan areas, erupting volcanoes, nuclear explosions, and forest fires, can produce particles that travel internationally.

Measurements of the concentration of airborne particles at remote points are scanty, but there are indications that the global level is rising. These indications include measurements of both atmospheric turbidity (75) and the electrical conductivity of the air (48), which decreases as the concentration of fine particles increases. Particles in the air scatter incoming sunlight, reducing the amount that reaches the earth and thus tending to lower the temperature of the earth. The mean global temperature has been falling in recent years, and some attribute the fact to rising concentrations of airborne particles caused by volcanic eruptions and the activities of man. Other factors can also affect mean global temperature, but the fact remains that particulate matter generated by man could be contributing to important geophysical phenomena.

Carbon monoxide

Carbon monoxide appears to be almost exclusively a man-made pollutant. The only significant source known is combustion processes in which carbon is oxidized partially to carbon monoxide instead of fully to carbon dioxide. The automobile is estimated to contribute more than 80% of carbon monoxide emissions globally, with smaller amounts coming from other combustion processes. Very small amounts of carbon monoxide are produced by photochemical reactions of hydrocarbons in polluted atmospheres. Plant and animal life may also emit carbon monoxide. Plants have been known to produce the gas under some kinds of stress, and some marine organisms (siphonophores) can emit large numbers of gas bubbles that contain up to 80% carbon monoxide.

The behavior of carbon monoxide at the local level is governed in part by the fact that it is chemically inert. It apparently reacts with no other constituent of urban air to a significant degree. A reaction has been postulated, but not demonstrated, with the hydroxyl radical, which contains one atom each of oxygen and hydrogen. It has been postulated also that carbon monoxide might be oxidized at ground level on surfaces that catalyze the reaction.

Carbon monoxide has been monitored for some years in urban areas, and NAPCA data show a three-year (1964-66) average of 7.3 ppm for off-street sites in five major cities. The minimum yearly average was 6.7 ppm, and the maximum was 7.9 ppm. Instantaneous concentrations of 100 ppm and higher have been found, particularly near heavy auto traffic in restricted areas where the gas may not dissipate readily. The correlation of carbon monoxide concentration with auto traffic is shown by a study made in New York City in 1967 (58). At one in-street site, the level exceeded 15 ppm consistently from 9 A.M. to 7 P.M., but dropped to 1 or 2 ppm between 1 A.M. and 2 A.M. Since no significant chemical reactions are known for the gas, it must disperse into the surrounding urban air and escape eventually to the general atmosphere.

Data on the background concentration of carbon monoxide in air are still very limited. Solar spectra were the only guide until the past few years, which have seen the development of an instrument designed to measure carbon monoxide continuously at the levels found at remote points (98). The measurements made since then, while not exhaustive, indicate a maximum global level in the range of 0.1 ppm. Calculations based on this concentration show that a given amount of carbon monoxide that enters the air will disappear in around three years.

Comparison of the data from solar spectra and direct analyses does not suggest that carbon monoxide is accumulating in the atmosphere, at least over the past 15 years, although the data are not comprehensive enough to bar the possibility of a slow but accelerating increase. Even assuming such an increase, however, much of the large amount of the gas that is being emitted must be returning to one or more major sinks. None has yet been identified, but present theories include chemical reactions, perhaps with hydroxyl radicals, absorption and retention by plant life on land, and absorption and oxidation by biological processes in the ocean. Chemical intuition suggests that the most likely sink for carbon monoxide is conversion to carbon dioxide, but such conversion has not yet been demonstrated either to happen or not to happen.

Nitrogen oxides

Of the eight possible oxides of nitrogen, only three are known to be important constituents of the atmosphere. Of the three—nitrous oxide, nitric oxide, and nitrogen dioxide—the most plentiful in the atmosphere is nitrous oxide. It is relatively inert, is not known to be man-made, and has a global concentration of about 0.25 ppm. Nitric oxide lately has been detected in nonurban air in Panama. The data are too sketchy to support an estimate of average concentration, but this was the first indication that nitric oxide might be a trace constituent of the air. Data on the concentration of nitrogen dioxide at remote points are fragmentary, but the gas appears to have a concentration in the range of a few parts per billion or less.

Some man-made nitrogen oxides are emitted by chemical processes, but the major source is combustion processes. Combustion converts nitrogen from the air chiefly to nitric oxide, which in urban air is oxidized slowly by oxygen, and quite rapidly by ozone, to nitrogen dioxide. Man-made sources cannot account for all of the nitrogen dioxide that evidently enters the air on a global basis or even for a major part of it. Biological processes that take place in soil are one possible major contributor, and lightning is another, but the question of source remains basically unanswered.

Nitrogen dioxide is a strong absorber of ultraviolet light from the sun and is the trigger for the photochemical reactions that produce smog * in polluted air. The gas can also combine with water vapor to form nitric acid. The acid in turn can react with ammonia or particles in the air to form nitrate salts, such as ammonium nitrate. Not all of the nitrogen oxides that react photochemically can be accounted for on a mass basis. However, all of the nitrogen dioxide that does not react photochemically ultimately becomes nitrate salt aerosol, largely in the particle size fraction larger than 1 micron or so, which settles from the air or is removed by rain. A given amount of the gas in urban air, if it does not react photochemically, will be removed from the air in about three days.

On a global basis, nitric oxide and nitrogen dioxide are only two of a number of compounds that take part in the nitrogen cycle. Nitrogen gas itself makes up about 80% of the earth's atmosphere by volume, and compounds of nitrogen are essential to plant and animal growth. Organic nitrogen compounds break down to yield the nitrogen compound, ammonia, and possibly some of the nitrogen oxides. On the whole, however, the global nitrogen cycle is not well understood, although of the total amount of nitrogen compounds in the global atmosphere, the amount contributed by man is relatively insignificant.

Hydrocarbons

Man produces only an estimated 15% of total global emissions of hydrocarbons to the air, but he is the leader in urban areas, where these compounds of carbon and hydrogen exert their chief pollutant effect by taking part in the chemical reactions that cause photochemical smog. Man-made sources of hydrocarbons include incineration, evaporation of industrial solvents, and combustion of coal and wood, but the leading contributor is the processing and use of petroleum. In this processing-use chain, gasoline is the major source of hydrocarbon emissions. The emissions come both from evaporation and the internal combustion engine, which exhausts unburned (unoxidized) and partially burned hydrocarbons. Natural sources include forests and vegetation, which emit large amounts of hydrocarbons of the terpene class, and bacterial decomposition of organic matter, which produces very large amounts of methane.

Photochemical smog was first recognized as a serious air pollution problem in Los Angeles County, Calif., in the late 1940's. The research that gradually explained its causes was a milestone in the study of the chemistry of polluted air. Los Angeles has a very large population of automobiles, which are a significant source of hydrocarbons (and nitrogen oxides) in the air. The city enjoys regular sunshine, which provides the

---

* "Smog" is a word coined several decades ago, from "smoke" and "fog", to describe the characteristic, highly polluted fogs of London. For no obvious reason it was appropriated, and is used widely, to describe the photochemically generated pollution haze first identified in Los Angeles. Ironically, if either smoke or fog is present in quantity, this variety of smog cannot occur.

Table 5

Summary of maximum hourly oxidant levels for eight U.S. cities, 1964-65, from continuous air monitoring stations

City	Year	Days of Valid Data	Days having maximum hourly oxidant equal to or greater than indicated concentration					
			0.15 ppm		0.10 ppm		0.05 ppm	
			No.	%	No.	%	No.	%
Chicago	1964	254	0	0	15	6	149	59
	1965	275	0	0	9	3	120	44
Cincinnati	64	303	5	1.5	36	12	137	45
	65	310	5	1.5	19	6	182	59
Denver	65	285	14	5	51	18	226	79
Los Angeles	64	349	83	24	149	42	221	63
	65	365	121	33	185	51	275	75
Philadelphia	64	289	9	3	37	13	124	43
	65	266	4	1.5	23	9	109	41
St. Louis	64	253	6	2.5	26	10	156	62
	65	329	8	2.5	33	10	206	63
San Francisco	64	298	1	.5	13	4	72	24
Washington	64	293	4	1	40	14	163	56
	65	284	3	1	25	9	150	53

SOURCE: "Air Quality Data from the National Air Sampling Networks and Contributing State and Local Networks, 1964-1965," U.S. Department of Health, Education, and Welfare, 1966.

ultraviolet light that initiates the photochemical reaction. And the local meteorology favors the formation of smog: Diffusion and dispersion of pollutants are limited horizontally by low winds and surrounding mountains and vertically by the inversion that lies over the area some 320 days of the year.

Although Los Angeles remains the predominant locale for photochemical smog, the phenomenon has been detected in most major metropolitan areas in recent years. It is characterized by a relatively high level of oxidants,* chiefly ozone. An average oxidant level of 0.15 ppm or more for one hour is considered evidence of serious photochemical smog. On this basis, Los Angeles experienced smog on about 29% of the 714 days in 1964 and 1965 for which valid air analysis data were available. For seven other cities in the same period the maximum was 5% (Table 5).

The role played by hydrocarbons in the complex series of chemical reactions that cause photochemical smog (7, 49) depends on their reactivity. Some, such as those of the olefin class, tend to be quite reactive;

---

* "Oxidant" is a general term meaning substances, such as oxygen and ozone, which oxidize other substances. In air pollution usage, "oxidant" usually means a compound which oxidizes a particular chemical reagent used to measure it (generally potassium iodide).

Table 6

Simplified reaction scheme for photochemical smog [a]

NO_2 Nitrogen dioxide	+	Light	→	NO Nitric oxide	+	O Atomic oxygen
O	+	O_2 Molecular oxygen	→	O_3 Ozone		
O_3	+	NO	→	NO_2	+	O_2
O	+	Hc Hydrocarbon	→	HcO• Radical		
HcO•	+	O_2	→	HcO_3• Radical		
HcO_3•	+	Hc	→	Aldehydes, ketones, etc.		
HcO_3•	+	NO	→	HcO_2• Radical	+	NO_2
HcO_3•	+	O_2	→	O_3	+	HcO_2•
HcO_x• Radical	+	NO_2	→	Peroxyacyl nitrates		

[a] This reaction scheme is intended to be illustrative, not definitive. Research is still in progress on the detailed chemistry of the smog-forming process.

others, such as benzene, tend to be only slightly reactive; methane, emitted in substantial quantities in auto exhaust, is practically nonreactive. A few tenths of a part per million of nitrogen oxides and less than 1 ppm of reactive hydrocarbons suffice to initiate the process.

In broad outline (Table 6), the process begins when nitrogen dioxide absorbs ultraviolet light from the sun and is broken down to nitric oxide and atomic oxygen. (Oxygen in the air is normally in the molecular form, two atoms bound together.) Atomic oxygen reacts with molecular oxygen to form ozone, which reacts in turn with nitric oxide to form nitrogen dioxide and molecular oxygen. Atomic oxygen also reacts with reactive hydrocarbons to form chemical species called radicals. These radicals take part in a series of reactions involving the formation of more radicals, which react with molecular oxygen, hydrocarbons, and nitric oxide. Nitrogen dioxide is regenerated, the nitric oxide eventually disappears, and ozone begins to accumulate and react with hydrocarbons. Secondary pollutants are formed, including formaldehyde and other aldehydes, ketones, and peroxyacyl nitrates (PAN). When sulfur dioxide is present, aerosols also are formed, and there is evidence that hydrocarbons containing six carbon atoms or more will take part in aerosol formation when sulfur dioxide is not present.

Many features of this overall scheme remain obscure. The specific nature and behavior of the radicals that act as intermediates are far from clear. The initial ratio of hydrocarbons to nitrogen oxides has been found experimentally to affect the intensity of some effects of photochemical smog. On this basis, many scientists have concluded that very large reductions in the concentration of nitrogen oxides would be required to reduce the effects of the process significantly (82). Others disagree (50, 51).

The ultimate fate of the substances involved in the smog-forming process is another question mark. Of the nitrogen that enters the process in nitrogen oxides, some appears to end up in particles as organic nitrogen, some as nitrate, and some probably reverts to elemental nitrogen by reactions still unknown. However, a successful mass balance on nitrogen in a synthetic smog chamber has yet to be achieved. Nor can all of the aromatic and paraffinic classes of hydrocarbons that enter the smog-forming process be accounted for.

For other than urban areas, the data on hydrocarbon concentrations are quite limited, except for methane. The gas's background concentration is about 1.5 ppm (32), but it is not certain whether the global concentration of methane is changing. Although the gas is produced in automobile exhaust and by other combustion processes, the major source globally is bacterial decomposition of organic matter. The main sink for methane appears to be the troposphere, the lowest layer of the atmosphere, which extends about 11 kilometers up from the earth's surface. The mechanism of destruction of methane is not known, although electrical discharges have been suggested as one important mechanism. Some bacteria consume methane in water, but whether they can do so at the concentration found in the atmosphere is an open question.

Carbon dioxide

Carbon dioxide is not commonly regarded as an air pollutant, although man generates an enormous amount of it in combustion processes using fossil fuels such as coal, oil, and natural gas. Carbon dioxide is a normal constituent of the air, where it takes part in no significant chemical reactions with other substances in the air. However, its global concentration is rising above the natural level by an amount that could increase global temperature enough to affect climate markedly. Carbon dioxide is not the only factor that could alter mean global temperature, nor even the only one that can be affected by the activities of man. Man-made particles in air could act to reduce the temperature. Carbon dioxide is, however, the substance that has been studied most thoroughly in terms of possible geophysical effects.

Estimates of annual emissions of man-made carbon dioxide in the U.S. show an 18-fold increase between 1890 and 2000 (102). Electric power plants and internal combustion engines are leading sources. The rate of increase of man-made emissions of carbon dioxide in the rest of the world is expected to at least equal that of the U.S. in the same period. Natural sources of carbon dioxide are not believed to be contributing significantly to the increase in global concentration, although bacterial oxidation of soil humus and the peat in bogs has been suggested as a possible major source (29).

The huge man-made emissions of carbon dioxide have been entering the air faster than the gas's natural cycle can adjust to them. This cycle can be broken into several parts involving progressively longer periods of time.

The exchange of carbon dioxide between the air and plant and animal life is one part of the natural cycle of carbon, the basis of all organic compounds. Carbon is essential to plant and animal life in the form of proteins, fats, carbohydrates, and other compounds. Animals acquire carbon-containing compounds in their foods. Plants acquire carbon by assimilating carbon dioxide from the air or from water that contains it in solution. Both animals and plants exhale carbon dioxide produced by their metabolic processes, which can be viewed as biochemical combustion. (Plants produce oxygen as well.) The gas is also produced by bacterial oxidation of dead plant and animal material. Carbon dioxide moves through this biochemical cycle relatively rapidly and with little net effect on the global concentration of the gas in air.

Another part of the overall natural cycle involves the oceans, which are a huge sink for carbon dioxide. The exchange takes place in two steps: between the air and the top 50 to 100 meters of water; and between the top layer of water and the water beneath. The exchange of carbon dioxide between the top layer of water and the air depends strongly on such factors as the acidity, salinity, and temperature of the water. In some areas, especially in the tropics, the seas release the gas to the air instead of the other way around. The net global effect is that the air and the top layer of sea water take perhaps five years to adjust themselves to equilibrium concentrations of carbon dioxide following a massive new injection of the gas into the air. The upper and lower layers of sea water exchange carbon dioxide in several chemical forms, but this process may take up to 1500 years to adjust to a fresh injection of carbon dioxide into the air.

Still another process involves the limestone (calcium carbonate) in the ocean sediments. Fresh carbon dioxide added to the water makes it more acid, and it reacts with the limestone to take up more carbon dioxide in the form of bicarbonate ion. This process may take 10,000 years or more to adjust to an injection of carbon dioxide into the atmosphere.

The most time-consuming part of the carbon dioxide cycle is the weathering of silicate rocks by carbon dioxide in the air. This process produces limestone and dolomite (calcium magnesium carbonate). The net effect of the process over geologic time is to take carbon dioxide from the air and put it into marine limestone.

Man has stepped into this cycle by burning fossil fuels, and so releasing carbon dioxide to the air, in far less time than the fuels took to form from organic materials in the sediments. If the oceans were perfectly mixed at all times, a fresh injection of carbon dioxide into the air would distribute itself about five sixths in the water and about one sixth in the air. The available data show that in fact the distribution is about half and half. The reason is believed to be the relatively slow mixing of the oceans, as exemplified by the relatively slow movement of carbon dioxide from the upper layer of the seas into the water beneath.

Carbon dioxide's effect on global temperature, the "greenhouse effect," is due to the ability of the gas to absorb the relatively long wave-length infrared radiation (heat energy) emitted by the earth and radiate it back to earth. Energy from the sun arrives as short wave-length radiation that passes through the carbon dioxide in the air. If energy is arriving from the sun at a constant rate, an increase in the level of carbon dioxide in the air will decrease the amount of heat re-emitted by the earth. Less heat will escape to outer space, and mean global temperature will rise. If carbon dioxide content increases 10%, the temperature will rise an estimated 0.5° C.

Mean global temperature can also be affected by water vapor in the air, which exerts a greenhouse effect of its own. Changes in the intensity of the radiation from the sun is another factor. Still another is the turbidity of the atmosphere. Solid and liquid aerosols tend to scatter incoming sunlight at all wave lengths, thus decreasing the amount of heat that reaches the earth from outer space. Calculations show that a 25% increase in turbidity would counteract a 100% increase in carbon dioxide concentration. All of these factors may have been at play in the changes that have taken place in mean global temperature in the past 80 to 100 years, and several schools of thought exist among scientists as to the relative importance of each (19).

It is generally agreed that the 10-year mean global temperature rose about 0.4° C. between 1880 and 1940 and then reversed itself, falling nearly 0.2° C. by 1967. The carbon dioxide concentration in the atmosphere, meanwhile, is believed to have risen from 296 ppm in 1900 to 318 ppm today, or about 7.4%. The most accurate set of measurements shows an increase of 1.36% between 1958 and 1963 (15).

Whether the amount of water vapor in the air has changed markedly in the past few decades is unknown. Sunspot activity has been increasing since about 1900. This might mean that the intensity of the radiation from the sun has risen slightly in that period, but the point is not yet subject to proof. The turbidity of the atmosphere does appear to have been increasing, although the data are not as conclusive as they might be, particularly for remote areas.

Increasing carbon dioxide concentration could explain the increase in mean global temperature up to about 1940, and increasing turbidity could explain the decrease in temperature since then. This line of reasoning may well be correct, but it does not take fully into account the relative importance of the other factors involved. To take them into account requires more accurate measurements than are now available of the intensity of the solar radiation that reaches the earth and the amount of it that is reflected and re-emitted by the earth. In theory the necessary data can be acquired by artificial satellites. Relating all of the data to changes in climate, however, probably will require that measurements be made for some years.

Lead

Lead aerosol is a common air contaminant in urban areas in the U.S. A considerable volume of research has been done on the health effects of lead at the concentrations at which it may occur in some industrial operations, but the metal generally has not been considered harmful at the levels at which it occurs in urban air. In the past few years, however, the results of one extensive research program have led to the contention that man's continuing use of lead has resulted in an environmental level far above that which would exist naturally, with consequent harmful effects on health (85, 86). It is argued that, whether or not the levels measured are of themselves dangerous to health, such an increase is likely to result in further concentration of lead in some food chains, leading ultimately to toxic doses for man or for some other important organism. This position is based on geochemical evidence, including analyses of sea water, sediments, and snow from remote areas, combined with theoretical calculations of the natural level of lead. The work indicates that the atmosphere of the Northern Hemisphere, for example, contains about 1000 times more lead than it would if man were not a contributor. Direct measurements of the preindustrial level of lead in the environment are not available, and the thesis that current levels of contamination are a threat to health remains controversial and the subject of continuing research.

Lead is a natural constituent of soil, water, vegetation, animal life, and air, although the levels of the natural concentrations are not certain. Significant sources of naturally-occurring lead in air would include silicate dusts from soils and particles from volcanoes. Man is the leading contributor, however, from such sources as manufacturing, use of pesticides, combustion of coal, incineration of refuse, and leaded gasoline. The available data indicate that combustion of leaded gasoline is the major source of airborne lead in urban areas (120).

Lead in the air can find its way into other phases of the environment. More than one year of rainfall data from 40-odd stations in the U.S. shows that the level of lead in rainfall in two major cities was roughly twice the maximum allowed in the U.S. Public Health Service standards for drinking water, which is 0.05 milligram per liter (mg/l). Mathematical analysis of the data shows a very high correlation (0.8) between lead concentration in the rainfall and sales of leaded gasoline in the counties where the rainfall collection stations were located (71).

In a major study of the lead in urban air in 1961-62, some 3400 samples were taken at 20 sites in Cincinnati, Philadelphia, and Los Angeles (127). Annual average concentrations of lead ranged from 1 to 3 $\mu g/m^3$. Mean concentrations of lead over relatively short periods in heavy traffic ranged from 14 $\mu g/m^3$ on Cincinnati streets, through about 25 $\mu g/m^3$ on Los Angeles freeways, to 44 $\mu g/m^3$ in a vehicular tunnel.

The concentrations found in this study were generally consistent with those found at comparable sites by the National Air Surveillance Network.

The lead exhausted by automobiles originates in the antiknock fluid in the gasoline. The fluid contains organic lead compounds (lead alkyls) and organic scavengers (ethylene dichloride and dibromide), whose function is to combine with the lead to form inorganic compounds that leave the engine in the exhaust gases. The main inorganic lead compounds exhausted are lead bromochloride and three species in which lead bromochloride is combined with ammonium chloride. Very small amounts of the lead alkyls in the gasoline escape to the air by evaporation. The Philadelphia-Cincinnati-Los Angeles study concluded that the concentrations of these organic lead compounds in air probably were well under 10% of the concentrations of the inorganic compounds.

Although lead aerosols have been analyzed for some years, the analyses normally have determined only the total concentration of lead in the samples. One of the rare studies of the size of the lead-bearing particles covered 59 samples from five cities in the East, Midwest, and Far West, and two samples from remote areas (99). Total concentrations in the urban areas were 1 to 5 $\mu g/m^3$ and in the remote areas a few tenths of a microgram per cubic meter.

The most significant finding of the study was that the size distribution of the particles was very similar in widely different environments across the U.S. Size distributions did not differ significantly in the urban and nonurban samples. The median diameter of the urban samples was 0.25 micron, and in half of the samples fell between 0.16 micron and 0.43 micron. The most likely reason for this uniformity was that the distribution is a very stable one that the lead compounds assume rapidly as they cool after being emitted in hot combustion or industrial effluents.

There is very little direct evidence of the composition and reactions of lead aerosols in air. One of the few series of studies that have been made involved analyses of aerosols from Hawaii; Fairbanks, Alaska; and Cambridge, Mass. (138). The results indicate that bromide, but not chloride, is selectively depleted in the aerosols, and that the extent of the depletion is about the same in Fairbanks and Cambridge. Natural marine aerosols collected over the Pacific Ocean show the same effect. In both cases the mechanism could be oxidation of bromide, but not the more stable chloride, followed by volatilization of bromine.

In another of the few studies made of the behavior of lead aerosols, rates of production of chlorine and bromine gas by photochemical decomposition of lead bromochloride in a carbon tetrachloride slurry were determined in the laboratory (89). The rates thus found were used along with certain assumptions to calculate the rates at which the two elements might be released on a sunny day in air containing 30 $\mu g/m^3$ of lead bromochloride, a value selected as representative of air near a heavily traveled freeway. The results show a release of 0.2 part per billion (ppb) by volume of bromine per hour and 0.1 ppb of chlorine. Whether this actually is what happens cannot be certain until the release of chlorine and bromine in air is measured directly. The fate of the chlorine and bromine produced by such a mechanism is not known, although both are oxidants.

It has also been suggested that airborne lead particles could combine with iodine vapor to form lead iodide particles that could seed clouds and thus modify climate (106).

Predicting the movement of pollutants

In order to manage the air environment well, it is necessary to be able to predict the movement of pollutants, particularly through urban and regional areas. The effects of specific emissions on the quality of the air at points away from the immediate vicinity of their sources must be known to resolve soundly such questions as the optimum degree of abatement for specific sources and the optimum location of air monitoring instruments. Pollutants diffuse through the air in a manner dictated not only by their chemical and physical nature, but by a number of other factors as well: meteorological conditions, topography, the height and number of buildings and other structures, and the storage and release of heat by such structures.

The number and complexity of the variables involved in predicting the movement of air contaminants requires the use of computers and mathematical models. This is still a developing science. A number of mathematical models have been devised that attempt to explain the behavior of emissions at the local level (83, 135). None of them does so accurately, although they can provide guidance in both air pollution control and research. Even for terrain as level as the grasslands of Nebraska, a precise fundamental explanation could not be developed for the travel and dispersion of a pollutant plume from a point source for a relatively short time with no major change in the weather (69).

One means of developing data for use in research on such models is to determine the sources and amounts of pollutant emissions in a city and measure the concentrations of the pollutants with a network of monitoring instruments in and around the city. This was done, for example, at Nashville, Tenn. (67, 117, 133). Such an approach can yield valuable information, but it has one inherent flaw. Any pollutant that is measured will be coming from many sources, and they will differ in rate of emission, altitude, temperature, and in other ways. It is thus impossible to use the data to trace the movement of individual parcels of air through the city.

One solution to this problem is to release at the point of interest a unique substance that can be detected at the very low concentrations it will have reached after traveling and dispersing downwind over a period of time. Zinc and cadmium sulfides and dyes of the uranine class (100) have been used in such studies, but each has disadvantages. Cadmium sulfide, for example, is toxic, which limits its use in heavily populated areas. The uranine dyes are assayed by fluorescence in water, and some natural substances fluoresce in the same spectral region, yielding a background level against which the tracer must be measured.

In the past few years, much better tracers have been found. One is sulfur hexafluoride; the others are the light chlorine- and fluorine-containing hydrocarbons called freons. These compounds are odorless, nontoxic, and practically indestructible in air. They can be measured in quantities as small as one millionth of a billionth of a gram (10^{-15} gram), using a combination of gas chromatography and the electron affinity detector (105). A few kilograms of such a tracer can still be detected at the concentration it will have reached after traveling and dispersing as far as 100 kilometers downwind from the point of release. NAPCA will be using one of these tracers, sulfur hexafluoride, to study the performance of tall stacks (800 to 1000 feet) in dispersing pollutant gases, particularly sulfur dioxide, in the atmosphere. Also to be used is a method involving the ratio of two isotopes of sulfur, S^{32} and S^{34}, in sulfur dioxide (73).

These new tracers are extraordinarily powerful tools. They could well contribute as much to the knowledge of small-scale air movements as radioactive tracer studies (64, 81) have contributed to knowledge of the global circulation of the stratosphere. Sulfur hexafluoride and the freons do present one problem, however. Since they are practically indestructible in the atmosphere, each successive experiment adds to the amount of tracer present. Thus the background levels conceivably could become high enough to interfere with further experimentation. Already there is a background of sulfur hexafluoride, probably as a result of its use as a cooling, insulating, and arc-quenching agent by the electric power industry. The level is still well below the concentrations used in tracer work, however.

Despite such progress as has been made, and projects now under way, much more research remains to be done on one of the truly difficult problems of air monitoring: precisely how many measurements must be made at what places and at what times in order adequately to characterize the transport of pollutants. A few studies have been made of the numbers and locations of sampling stations required to delineate, with various degrees of precision, the average distribution of such widespread pollutants as suspended dust and sulfur dioxide about the center of a major coal-burning city (113, 114, 115, 116). The less restricted case of any pollutant in any environment over any averaging period has not yet been seriously undertaken.

Recommendations: flow, dispersion, degradation

Recommendation A1: *Systematic measurement should be undertaken for a number of relatively long-lived substances in the general atmosphere, including carbon monoxide, nitrous oxide, methane, carbon dioxide, and sulfur hexafluoride. The general turbidity of the atmosphere should be measured systematically on as wide a basis as possible, and more effort should be devoted to determining the nature of the aerosols that cause such turbidity.*

Recommendation A2: *The effects of carbon dioxide, turbidity, and other factors on climate should be studied in a sustained coordinated program designed to delineate clearly, if possible, the pertinent variables and their relative importance. Satellite measurements are particularly important here, if measurement technology can be developed.*

Recommendation A3: *Research should be continued and selectively expanded on atmospheric reactions of many kinds. Such work should extend to measurements in the field in order to help relate the results of laboratory and smog-chamber work to what actually happens in the urban and regional atmospheres.*

Recommendation A4: *The rates at which specific important contaminants are removed from the air should be studied systematically on an item-by-item basis.*

Recommendation A5: *Study of urban diffusion processes should be continued and selectively expanded, including coordinated use of long-lived tracers and work on optimum deployment and use of air monitoring instruments.*

CONTROLLING AIR POLLUTION

Many technological and economic factors inevitably affect the selection of means of avoiding or controlling the emission of a pollutant, but the choice lies fundamentally among five alternatives:

- Select process inputs, such as fuels, that do not contain the pollutant or its precursors.
- Remove the pollutant or its precursors from the process inputs.
- Operate the process so as to minimize generation of the pollutant.
- Remove the pollutant from the process effluent.
- Replace the process with one that does not generate the pollutant.

A large fund of science and technology already is available to support the use of one or more of these alternatives. Combustion, the most common pollutant-generating process used by man, has been studied extensively (41, 70, 87). Combustion is the rapid combination of oxygen with other substances, notably with carbon, and the consequent release of energy. The chemistry of the combustion process is extremely complex and is still imperfectly understood.

Perfect combustion of a pure hydrocarbon fuel with the correct amount of pure oxygen yields only carbon dioxide and water. A combustion process is rarely perfect, however, and the reactants are rarely pure. Sulfur in the fuel is converted to sulfur oxides. The air that normally supplies the oxygen for combustion also supplies nitrogen, of which a very small amount reacts with oxygen to form nitrogen oxides. If less than the correct amount of oxygen is present, carbon monoxide and hydrogen will be among the products of combustion. Part of the fuel may escape oxidation wholly or partly. The extent of these phenomena depends on the device used to harness or contain the combustion process. Thus the device determines to a large extent the means that can be used to control whatever pollutants the process may generate.

46

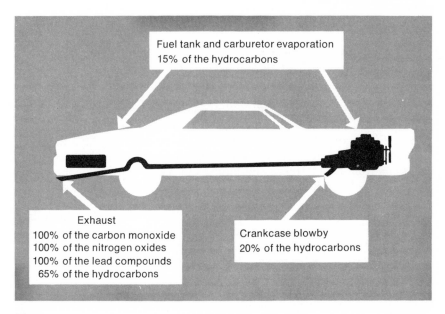

Fuel tank and carburetor evaporation
15% of the hydrocarbons

Exhaust
100% of the carbon monoxide
100% of the nitrogen oxides
100% of the lead compounds
65% of the hydrocarbons

Crankcase blowby
20% of the hydrocarbons

Figure 3

Patterns of emissions from an uncontrolled automobile

The pattern of automotive emissions shown here changes when controls are installed. On 1968 model cars, controls were installed nationwide for exhaust hydrocarbons and carbon monoxide and for crankcase blowby. Hydrocarbons evaporated from fuel tank and carburetor will come under control on 1971 model cars.

Motor vehicles: gasoline-powered

The 100 million gasoline-powered vehicles on the road in the U.S. today are a mobile source of a number of air pollutants: unburned and partially burned hydrocarbons, other organic compounds, carbon monoxide, nitrogen oxides, lead compounds, hydrogen, compounds of phosphorus and other elements that are contained in additives in fuels and lubricating oil. The amounts of these pollutants that an automobile emits depend on a number of factors, including the design and condition of the engine, the mode in which it is operating (idle, acceleration, etc.), and the composition of the fuel. Of the hydrocarbons emitted by a car with no controls, the exhaust gases account for roughly 65%, evaporation from the fuel tank and carburetor for roughly 15%, and blowby or crankcase emissions (gases that escape around the piston rings) for about 20%. Carbon monoxide, nitrogen oxides, and the lead compounds are emitted almost exclusively in the exhaust gases (Fig. 3).

Legislative control of automotive pollution began in California, where devices to control crankcase emissions were required on domestic cars of the 1961 model year. The automobile makers installed such equipment on all 1963 model cars sold in the U.S. Restrictions on exhaust emissions of hydrocarbons and carbon monoxide took effect in California with the 1966 model year, and the California standards for crankcase and exhaust emissions were adopted by the Federal Government for cars and light trucks of the 1968 model year (Table 7). Stiffer federal standards for exhaust emissions will take effect with the 1970 model year, and control of evaporative emissions is scheduled to take effect with the 1971 model year (24). The 1970 federal standards call in addition for 35% reduction of hydrocarbon exhaust emissions and 37% reduction of carbon monoxide emissions from heavy trucks and buses, and place controls on the visible smoke emitted by diesel-powered vehicles. Although the 1968 and 1970 federal standards do not limit nitrogen oxides emissions, California plans to do so starting with the 1971 model year for cars and light trucks. The standard will be 4.0 grams per vehicle mile for 1971, 3.0 grams for 1972-73, and 1.3 grams for 1974. The action is subject to the state's receiving a waiver from the Secretary of HEW, since the standards will be more stringent than the federal standards. The waiver was granted in 1969.

New vehicles and engines are certified to conform to the federal emission standards on the basis of accelerated tests of representative models by both the manufacturers and NAPCA. The standards apply to average emissions over the lifetime of the vehicle (100,000 miles), and the test procedures allow for gradual deterioration of the control systems with increasing mileage. Vehicle emissions are determined by running the car through the California test cycle, so called because it was first adopted by that state. In the test, which is designed to represent an average driving cycle, the car is driven through the cycle on a dynamometer, exhaust emissions are measured continuously, and composite values for emissions are calculated. The durability of the control systems is determined by driving some vehicles 50,000 miles with emissions tests being made at least every 4000 miles.

Hydrocarbon emissions are measured by a nondispersive infrared (NDIR) analyzer in terms of the six-carbon compound, hexane. This technique does not distinguish among specific hydrocarbons of differing photochemical reactivity, and the instrumentation itself responds better to the less reactive compounds than to the more reactive ones. Both the California cycle and the NDIR analyzer are regarded as adequate for the purpose today, but improved methods will be desirable in the future for both certification and routine inspection.

Better instrumental methods are available, such as flame ionization detection for measuring total hydrocarbons and gas chromatography for distinguishing among specific hydrocarbons. Such methods are used in research, but they have not yet been adapted to use in certification because of problems such as speed of response. There is no acceptable instrumental method for measuring hydrocarbon oxygenates, such as aldehydes, which occur in auto exhaust at very low levels, but are

Table 7

Federal standards for hydrocarbon and carbon monoxide emissions from cars and light trucks

	Emissions from typical uncontrolled car	Allowable emissions Model year	
		1968	1970
Exhaust			
Hydrocarbons	900 ppm	275 ppm [a] (3.2 grams per vehicle mile)	(180 ppm) [a] 2.2 grams per vehicle mile
Carbon monoxide	3.5%	1.5% [a] (33 grams per vehicle mile)	(1.0%) [a] 23 grams per vehicle mile
Crankcase blowby			
Hydrocarbons	20-25% of total hydrocarbons emitted	0	0
Evaporation from fuel tank and carburetor			
Hydrocarbons	15% of total hydrocarbons emitted	No standard	6 grams per test (equivalent to 90% control). Takes effect in 1971.

[a] Standards shown for 1968 are for engines of more than 140 cubic inches (about 2300 cubic centimeters) displacement. Allowable emissions increase with decreasing engine size to a maximum of 410 ppm hydrocarbons and 2.3% carbon monoxide for less than 50 cubic inches (about 820 cubic centimeters) displacement. The standards for 1970 do not change with engine size because they are on a mass basis, grams per vehicle mile, as opposed to the 1968 standards, which are on a volume basis, parts per million and per cent. Emission values in parentheses in columns for 1968 and 1970 are the volume or mass equivalent of the standard shown. Emissions are measured with nondispersive infrared analyzers.

SOURCE: "Control of Air Pollution from New Motor Vehicles and New Motor Vehicle Engines. Standards for Exhaust Emissions, Fuel Evaporative Emissions, and Smoke Emissions, Applicable to 1970 and Later Vehicles and Engines," *Fed. Regis.*, *33* (108), Part II, June 4, 1968.

"Progress in the Prevention and Control of Air Pollution. First Report of the Secretary of Health, Education, and Welfare to the United States Congress pursuant to Public Law 90-148, The Air Quality Act of 1967," Senate Document No. 92, 90th Congress, 2nd Session, June 28, 1968.

quite reactive. California will use the nondispersive infrared analyzer to measure nitrogen oxides emissions when the state's 1971 standards take effect. The device will be added to the NDIR instrument train used now to measure hydrocarbon and carbon monoxide emissions.

NAPCA is studying vehicles in normal use to determine how their emissions correlate with the results of the accelerated certification procedures. One such study, covering 300 passenger cars in five cities, showed that cars with controls were exhausting roughly half as much carbon monoxide and hydrocarbons as those without controls. Surveillance results support the expectation that emissions tend to increase with increasing mileage, although a study in California showed that the control systems used on 1967 cars there were much better in this respect than those used on 1966 models.

Continued surveillance is required to determine the long-term effectiveness of present control systems in actual use, but results to date suggest that substantial reductions of emissions have been achieved. On this basis, total national emissions should decline steadily as new vehicles gradually displace the older cars on the road. NAPCA expects the trend to start upward again in the mid-1970's, however, as the increasing number of vehicles in use begins to overcome the effects of the 1968 and 1970 federal emission standards. Control technology that exists now or is in development should be able to cope with the 1970 federal emission standards. To meet nitrogen oxides standards at the same time, as will be required for 1971 model vehicles in California, will be more difficult, and further reductions in hydrocarbons and carbon monoxide emissions also pose more complex problems (1, 10, 136).

One additional problem, which only time can solve, is the human one. Nearly all control devices so far devised decrease engine performance at least slightly. Hence some owners find it tempting to disconnect or otherwise disable the devices. Furthermore, the optimum adjustment of engines so equipped is different from that of past products, and many mechanics may resist learning new ways. As a result, they may either disable the devices so as to be able to return to the old ways of adjustment, or ignore them and misadjust the car. Finally, there is at least a persistent folklore that the devices are still unworkable in Alaska and the mountain West, since they make engines far harder to start in extremely cold weather. This may be a manifestation of the previous point, but there are clearly strong areas of resistance to control devices.

Control technology: hydrocarbons, carbon monoxide

Crankcase. Emission of hydrocarbons from the crankcase of automotive engines was largely eliminated by the positive crankcase ventilation (PCV) systems that were installed on new cars nationwide starting with the 1963 model year. These systems recycle crankcase ventilation air and blowby gases to the engine intake, instead of venting them to the atmosphere. The blowby gases are acidic, and poor engine oils are unable to absorb the acidic materials without sludging excessively. Sludge may plug the positive crankcase ventilation valve used in the blowby recycle system, thus rapidly increasing the rate of sludging. Engine oils with added polymeric dispersants and metallic detergents, which were already coming into use, proved adequate to prevent this sludging cycle.

Evaporation. For controlling evaporation of fuel from the carburetor and fuel system, as will be required by the 1970 California standards and the scheduled 1971 federal standards, systems are being developed that store fuel vapors in the crankcase, or in charcoal canisters that absorb hydrocarbons, for recycling to the engine. The main problem to be

50

solved with such storage systems is that carburetion is upset when the vapors are introduced to the engine.

Evaporative emissions might also be dealt with by changing the properties of gasoline, which could be done in two different ways. The first would be to reduce the volatility of the fuel, which would reduce emissions of both total hydrocarbons and total reactive hydrocarbons. The second type of change would be to replace the four- and five-carbon olefinic hydrocarbons in the fuel with the less-reactive four- and five-carbon paraffinic hydrocarbons. Such a change would not reduce total hydrocarbon emissions, but it would reduce reactive hydrocarbon emissions.

Mechanical methods will be used to control evaporative emissions on cars of the 1970 model year sold in California. Studies by the petroleum industry indicate that such methods will cost the consumer less in the long run than changing the properties of gasoline (22). These studies assume, however, that the mechanical devices will be 100% efficient and maintenance-free for 10 years, assumptions which remain to be confirmed. Fuel modification would have two advantages over mechanical devices. It would apply to all cars, not just new cars, and it would help to control evaporative emissions during the transfer operations between the refinery and the automobile fuel tank.

Exhaust. To meet the existing exhaust emission standards for hydrocarbons and carbon monoxide, the automobile manufacturers have used two basic methods. The first is to inject air into the exhaust manifold near the exhaust valves, where exhaust gas temperature is highest, thus inducing further oxidation of unoxidized or partially oxidized substances. In this approach, carburetion and spark timing are also adjusted to reduce the amounts of pollutants emitted. The second basic method is to design the cylinders and adjust the fuel-air ratio, spark timing, and other variables to reduce the amounts of hydrocarbons and carbon monoxide in the exhaust to the point where air injection is not required. Most 1968 model cars in the U.S. use the second basic method, with air injection being used mainly on vehicles with manual transmissions.

These methods should be capable of meeting the 1970 federal standards for hydrocarbon and carbon monoxide emissions, but to achieve even lower emissions would require more complex systems. Two devices that have been studied extensively for use in such systems are the exhaust manifold thermal reactor and the catalytic converter. Both are still in the development stage, but have been shown to be able to achieve very low emissions of hydrocarbons and carbon monoxide.

The exhaust manifold thermal reactor would replace the conventional exhaust manifold. Its basic principle is to allow the exhaust gases enough reaction time at high temperature to achieve a high degree of oxidation of hydrocarbons and carbon monoxide. This is done by using an insulated manifold of larger-than-normal volume, possibly with internal baffling to control the flow of exhaust gases, and by injecting air to provide the necessary oxidizing atmosphere. The exhaust manifold thermal reactor can be damaged by oxidation of metal surfaces and subsequent erosion of the oxide layer by exhaust-borne particles, such as those of lead compounds, which impinge at high velocity. Practical solutions to this problem are being sought along two lines: development of erosion resistant coatings; and redesign of the reactor core to minimize erosion. Overall, the main characteristics of the reactor that require further optimization are durability; adaptation of lower-cost materials, which must withstand up to 1700° F. at the core of the reactor; and some reduction in size, so that the device will fit under the hood. In one test, for 100,000 miles, an exhaust manifold thermal reactor held average emissions to 27 ppm hydrocarbons and 0.65% carbon monoxide, using the federal testing procedure (20).

The catalytic converter would also fit into the vehicle's exhaust system and promote the oxidation of hydrocarbons and carbon monoxide to carbon dioxide and water. Air would be injected to maintain the necessary oxidizing atmosphere. Catalysts are used widely in the chemical and petroleum industries, but catalyzing the required reactions in automotive exhaust presents problems of unusual difficulty. Industrial catalytic reactions normally take place at relatively constant temperature and flow rate and with relatively high and constant concentrations of reactants. In auto exhaust gas, temperature, flow rate, and composition can vary widely. The catalyst bed must warm up rapidly from a cold start and also be able to resist relatively high temperature for extended times. It must cope with gases, flowing at a relatively high rate, that contain relatively low concentrations of the contaminants to be oxidized. It must resist deactivation by compounds in the exhaust, notably compounds of lead.

Despite these problems, several companies built catalytic systems that were certified by California in 1964. To be certified the systems had to meet the state's 1966 standards, 275 ppm hydrocarbons and 1.5% carbon monoxide, averaged over 12,000 miles. These devices were never used, because the automobile makers elected to meet the standards more effectively by engine design and adjustment and air injection. Research and development on catalytic converters came practically to a halt in 1964. Today the pressure for ever lower limits on exhaust emissions is again prompting investigation of catalytic systems, which experimentally have achieved emissions as low as 50 ppm hydrocarbons and 0.5% carbon monoxide.

Development of the catalytic converter to date has not progressed far beyond the point reached in 1964, when the chief problems were catalyst life, mechanical durability, packaging, and cost. One cause of such problems is lead, which tends to coat the surface of the catalyst, where the reaction takes place, and reduce its effectiveness. The use of nonleaded gasoline would mean that less catalyst and a smaller converter could be used, which would ease the problems with space and warmup of the catalyst bed. Unleaded gasoline would not ease the problem of operating at high temperature, which also affects catalyst life, nor problems such as mechanical durability. Difficulties thus remain in the development of a catalytic converter that could meet even the 1968 or 1970 federal standards for hydrocarbons and carbon monoxide at reasonable cost and with reasonable lifetime.

The photochemical reactivity of exhaust hydrocarbon emissions can be reduced by changing the composition of the fuel. The relationship of fuel composition to exhaust composition is affected strongly, however, by chemical reactions in the combustion chamber. Reducing the content of reactive hydrocarbons, such as olefins, in gasoline appears to have only a marginal effect on the reactivity of the exhaust hydrocarbons. Rule 63, in Los Angeles County, Calif., is the only regulation in the U.S. designed to affect exhaust emissions by limiting the content of reactive hydrocarbons in gasoline.

The reactivity of exhaust hydrocarbon emissions can also be reduced by replacing gasoline altogether with fuels such as liquefied petroleum gas (LPG), which is now used to a limited extent in some kinds of vehicles. Hydrocarbons exhausted by an LPG-fueled engine may be only 10 to 20% as reactive as those from a gasoline-fueled engine. LPG is normally unleaded, and exhaust gases from LPG-fueled engines are sometimes treated catalytically to control hydrocarbons and carbon monoxide in confined areas. LPG presents a greater fire and explosion hazard than gasoline and thus requires more careful handling. Also, a major shift from gasoline to LPG would significantly disrupt current petroleum refining and fuel distribution practice. Experience with LPG-fueled vehicles shows that the fuel could be used, at least for public- and fleet-owned vehicles, but the more practical overall approach today appears to be to stick with gasoline and control the emissions.

Control technology: nitrogen oxides

Methods of markedly reducing emission of nitrogen oxides in automobile exhaust are still in the development stage, and no restriction now exists on such emissions. The limit that California plans to impose for the 1971 model year, 4 grams per vehicle mile, will require a reduction of roughly 25% in emissions. Nitrogen oxides in exhaust consist almost exclusively of nitric oxide, which forms in the cylinders when nitrogen and oxygen combine during the combustion process. The higher the peak combustion temperature, the more nitric oxide is formed. Certain adjustments in engine operation that are made to reduce the formation of hydrocarbons and carbon monoxide tend to increase the formation of nitric oxide, and others tend to decrease it. In the range of fuel-air mixtures normally used, for example, a lean and hotter-burning mixture tends to produce less hydrocarbons and carbon monoxide than a richer mixture, but it tends to produce more nitric oxide. On the other hand, retarded spark-timing, which decreases hydrocarbons and carbon monoxide, also decreases nitric oxide. Thus control of nitrogen oxides further complicates the series of tradeoffs that must be made to balance emission control against engine performance.

One means of controlling nitrogen oxides is to recycle part of the exhaust gas back into the engine, thus reducing peak combustion temperature and the amount of nitric oxide that forms. Prototypes of such systems, installed on vehicles equipped with the types of crankcase and exhaust hydrocarbon and carbon monoxide controls now used, have reduced nitrogen oxides emissions 80% without causing the exhaust to exceed the current limits of 275 ppm for hydrocarbons and 1.5% for carbon monoxide (28). On two cars that used air injection to control hydrocarbons and carbon monoxide, the total system achieved less than 190 ppm hydrocarbons, less than 1.3% carbon monoxide, and less than 280 ppm nitrogen oxides. When the exhaust gas recycle system is installed, other engine modifications must be made to maintain the driveability of the car and hold hydrocarbon and carbon monoxide emissions within limits. At this stage of development, the interaction of the operating variables in exhaust gas recycle systems is too delicately balanced for use on a mass production basis.

The use of a somewhat rich mixture, combined with the exhaust gas manifold reactor, has been proposed for reducing nitrogen oxides emissions. Nitrogen oxides formation would be reduced by the mixture adjustment. The higher amounts of hydrocarbons and carbon monoxide that result would be oxidized in the reactor, which does not itself affect nitrogen oxides. Another proposal is to combine such a system with an exhaust gas recycle system to achieve further reduction in nitrogen oxides emissions.

The catalytic converter has been studied for reducing emissions of nitrogen oxides, but its feasibility has yet to be demonstrated. One approach would be to run the engine slightly rich, producing enough carbon monoxide to react with the nitric oxide to form nitrogen and carbon dioxide over a catalyst. This reaction requires a reducing atmosphere, the chemical antithesis of the oxidizing atmosphere required to treat hydrocarbons and carbon monoxide. A divided catalyst bed would have to be used, with the nitric oxide being reduced in the first stage and hydrocarbons and the remaining carbon monoxide being oxidized in the second stage, which would require air injection to create the necessary oxidizing atmosphere. Work to date suggests that inactivation by lead would be an even greater problem than in catalytic conversion of hydrocarbons and carbon monoxide alone.

Control technology: lead

No emission standards exist now for lead compounds, and no technology exists for removing them from auto exhaust. The amount of lead used in gasoline averages 2.4 grams of the metal (in the form of tetraethyl- and tetramethyllead) per gallon on a national gasoline pool basis. About two thirds of the lead consumed in gasoline is exhausted to the atmosphere, and 25 to 50% of that amount becomes airborne.

The arguments for restrictions on lead include the possible effects of the emissions on human health, the problems that the metal creates in controlling other emissions by methods such as catalysis, and its possible effects on ecology and climate. Extensive research on nonpolluting octane improvers for gasoline has failed to produce any that approach lead in overall effectiveness. Means of removing lead from exhaust gases have been proposed, and at least one, an electrogasdynamic precipitator, has been tested, but no such device has yet been shown to be feasible. Thus the most practical measure, should restrictions on lead be imposed, would be to reduce the amount used in gasoline, and conceivably to use none.

The Panel on Electrically Powered Vehicles of the U.S. Department of Commerce recommended in 1967 that the amount of lead used in gasoline be reduced steadily so as to prevent any increase in the total emitted nationwide as the consumption of leaded gasoline increases. Gasoline consumption is expected to continue to increase at an average rate of 3.5% per year, although the total amount of lead used in gasoline in the next five years is expected either to level off or to grow at a slower rate than in the recent past. The reasons are two: the growth in new manufacturing capacity for high-octane gasoline; and the steadily increasing consumption of jet aircraft fuel, which removes low-octane gasoline stocks from the gasoline pool.

The argument against removing the lead from gasoline is that the economic penalties involved would be unacceptable without the development of much more definitive evidence than now exists of the effects of lead emission, particularly its effect on human health. In 1967 the four U.S. producers of lead alkyls made 685 million pounds of tetraethyl- and tetramethyllead valued at about $254 million. The technology exists for making gasoline of today's octane ratings without using lead, and one petroleum company has been marketing such a gasoline for some years. A petroleum-industry study of the cost of removing lead industrywide (134) concluded that the manufacturing cost for gasoline would rise by amounts ranging from 1.8 to 4.7 cents per gallon, depending on refinery size and location in the U.S. The national average would be 2.2 cents per gallon, based on 1965 data.

Petroleum refiners now use a number of processes that manipulate molecular structures so as to increase octane ratings and otherwise upgrade their feedstocks. An industrywide change to unleaded gasoline of the current octane ratings, however, would require extensive replacements and additions of refinery equipment. The total capital cost, domestically, would be an estimated $4.25 billion, or roughly 40% of present gross investment in refining equipment in the U.S.

Other estimates (120) arrive at somewhat lower costs for changing wholly to unleaded gasoline: 1.1 to 1.5 cents per gallon in added manufacturing cost; $1.5 to $2.0 billion in new capital investment. The costs of such a change, moreover, would strongly stimulate research on new octane-improving processes. Even the lowest cost estimates nevertheless indicate that a sweeping changeover to unleaded gasoline would be a massive technical and economic undertaking to be approached with caution, barring the advent of more definitive evidence of deleterious effects of lead additives in gasoline.

Control technology: costs and future

The Panel on Electrically Powered Vehicles estimated that the systems used now to control hydrocarbons and carbon monoxide in auto exhaust add $25 to $50 to the cost of the car. The panel said that it should become commercially feasible in the next decade to reduce emissions from automobiles using the internal combustion engine to 50 ppm hydrocarbons, 0.5% carbon monoxide, and 250 ppm nitrogen oxides. The systems used, the panel estimated, might add $50 to $300 to the cost of cars produced in 1975-80.

A number of research and development programs on automotive emissions are being pursued by automotive and petroleum companies individually and cooperatively, and NAPCA is partially funding some of them. One such group hopes to achieve in the laboratory in the next few years engine emission levels of 0.3% carbon monoxide, 65 ppm hydrocarbons, and 175 ppm nitrogen oxides. Another cooperative venture is developing an exhaust control system with a catalytic container that could be replaced periodically in the same way as oil filters and other components are replaced.

No significant reduction in automotive air pollution is expected to result in the next decade from the advent of vehicles with unconventional power sources. The most promising low-pollutant power sources for the period 1975-85 appear to be the reciprocating steam engine and the gas turbine. After 1985, the electrically-powered vehicle may become the most attractive. Steam- and electrically-powered autos proved unable originally to compete with cars with internal combustion engines, but the pressures for air pollution abatement have revived interest in them.

The gas turbine is well along in development for vehicular use, but in the next few years will be economically feasible only in heavy duty vehicles, where its high initial cost can be accepted. Relatively little has been done in recent years on the development of steam engines for mass-produced automobiles, but the industry is now working on such engines in the laboratory, and a few experimental steam-driven cars are on the road. High-temperature lubrication and other problems remain, however, and considerably more work will be required to develop an automotive steam engine that can be made for a mass market at reasonable cost. Electrically-powered vehicles seem unlikely to become economically feasible in the next decade except for the special-purpose, short-range tasks for which they are used in some instances today. Among the technological needs are more effective devices for storing and converting electrical energy, such as novel batteries and fuel cells, and improvements in control systems and small motors.

Motor vehicles: diesel

Diesel-powered vehicles are a relatively minor pollution problem compared to gasoline-powered vehicles. Diesel units make up less than 1% of the vehicle population of the U.S. and consume an estimated 3 to 5% of the vehicular fuel. The diesel engine exhausts only about a tenth of the amount of carbon monoxide exhausted by a gasoline engine, although its hydrocarbon emissions may approach those of the gasoline engine. Blowby is negligible in the diesel, since the cylinders contain only air on the compression stroke. Evaporative emissions are also low because the diesel uses a closed injection fuel system and because the fuel is less volatile than gasoline, boiling at 350° to 750° F., compared to 90° to 400° F. for gasoline. Nitrogen oxides emissions by the diesel may be somewhat higher than for gasoline-powered vehicles, and probably would be more difficult to control, but they are not a serious pollution problem at this time. The major problems of the diesel engine are smoke and odor.

Some states have smoke emission standards for diesel engines, and federal standards will take effect Jan. 1, 1970, for new diesel engines for use in heavy duty vehicles. Under the specified test conditions, the smoke emitted must not reduce the transmission of a beam of light more than 20%. Reduction of not more than 40% will be allowed during the acceleration mode of the dynamometer test sequence.

Diesel engine technology can cope with the federal emission standards today. Engines are in use on urban buses that employ relatively high fuel injection pressures and produce little odor and no smoke when operated properly. The operating situation is different for over-the-road trucks and buses. The diesel engines used in such vehicles can create smoke problems both because of faulty maintenance and because the engine can be adjusted to consume fuel at higher than the design rate, thus increasing the power output, but also the smoke output.

Commercially available barium additives for diesel fuel can reduce smoke emission roughly 50%. They are used in concentrations of 0.25% or less and add 1 to 1.5 cents per gallon to the cost of the fuel. Precisely how these additives function is not certain, but they may reduce smoke emission partly by inhibiting the dehydrogenation of hydrocarbons to carbon particles in the combustion process and partly by promoting the oxidation of carbon particles. Three quarters or more of the barium appears to be exhausted from the engine as barium sulfate, the amount depending on the level of sulfur in the fuel. Barium sulfate is insoluble and harmless to humans, but soluble barium compounds are generally toxic. Some soluble barium compounds are formed from the fuel additive but the existing data indicate that the amounts exhausted are too small to be hazardous (47).

No proven technology exists to control fully the characteristic odor of diesel exhaust. The compounds that cause the odor remain unidentified, despite considerable research on the subject. Catalytic mufflers are available on a limited basis to control hydrocarbon and aldehyde emissions from some types of diesel-powered vehicles, and they also change the character of the odor. Their effect on the intensity of the odor thus far appears to be marginal, as is their effect on smoke emission. Fuel additives have also been tried for odor control, but with little success to date. Current evidence suggests that diesel odor is caused by organic compounds of relatively high molecular weight (10 carbon atoms or more), and that a number of different compounds are involved. Since the odor-causing compounds are unknown, and since there is no instrument that measures odor, research on the subject must rely for measurement on the human nose, a sensitive but highly subjective instrument.

Recommendations: motor vehicles

Recommendation A6: *Development of procedures and equipment by government and industry for periodic inspection of emission control systems in normal use should be stimulated to move ahead at the best possible rate.*

Recommendation A7: *The development of improved instrumentation for measuring automotive emissions should be supported by all interests to a degree that will assure rapid progress in the ability to assess emissions in terms of both their amount and their reactivity in the atmosphere.*

Recommendation A8: *Federal emission standards more stringent than those to take effect in 1970 should be developed and promulgated at an early date so that auto makers will have sufficient time to develop the necessary control systems. Such standards should be designed to counteract the effects of the rising population of motor vehicles until at least 1980, and should include standards for nitrogen oxides.*

Recommendation A9: *The effects of the lead compounds in gasoline on possible control systems of the future should be assessed carefully in terms of the emission levels that might be achieved with and without lead, or with reduced amounts of lead, and in terms of the associated costs to the industries involved and to the consumer. Economic studies should include the relationship of lead to projected emission control systems, to the gasoline and lead additive manufacturing industries, and to the design and performance of the internal combustion engine itself.*

Recommendation A10: *The Federal Government should press its assessment of advanced, low-polluting power systems, including steam and electric power, to provide the basis for sound industrial research and development on such systems.*

Recommendation A11: *Control agencies should be encouraged to establish procedures for on-the-road inspection of diesel-powered vehicles for compliance with smoke emission standards.*

Recommendation A12: *More attention should be given to the development of acceptable means of public transportation.*

Industrial facilities

Industrial sources generate a range of air pollutants specific to the processes involved, as well as about a fifth of the total national tonnage of the five most common pollutants, carbon monoxide, sulfur oxides, hydrocarbons, nitrogen oxides, and particles (Table 8). The major indus-

Table 8

Some emissions associated with specific industries [a]

Integrated steel mills: Particles, smoke, carbon monoxide, fluorides.

Nonferrous smelters: Sulfur oxides, particles, various metals.

Petroleum refineries: Sulfur compounds, hydrocarbons, smoke, particles, odors.

Portland cement plants: Particles, sulfur compounds.

Sulfuric acid plants: Sulfur dioxide, sulfuric acid mist, sulfur trioxide.

Grey iron and steel foundries: Particles, smoke, odors.

Ferro-alloy plants: Particles.

Kraft pulp mills: Sulfur compounds, particles, odors.

Hydrochloric acid plants: Hydrochloric acid mist and gas.

Nitric acid plants: Nitrogen oxides.

Bulk storage of gasoline: Hydrocarbons.

Soap and detergent plants: Particles, odors.

Caustic and chlorine plants: Chlorine.

Calcium carbide manufacturing: Particles.

Phosphate fertilizer plants: Fluorides, particles, ammonia.

Lime plants: Particles.

Aluminum ore reduction plants: Fluorides, particles.

Phosphoric acid plants: Acid mist, fluorides.

Coal cleaning plants: Particles.

---

[a] Order of list does not necessarily indicate order of rank of amounts or seriousness of emissions.

SOURCE: Hearings before the Subcommittee on Air and Water Pollution of the Committee on Public Works, U.S. Senate, 90th Congress, 1st Session on S. 780, Part 4, Government Printing Office, Washington, D.C., 1967, p. 2358.

trial contributors of the latter five contaminants are inorganic and organic chemical plants, iron and steel mills, petroleum refineries, pulp and paper mills, and nonferrous metal smelters. Industry is the leading producer of particles and the second leading producer of sulfur oxides.

It is difficult to generalize beyond this point on the status of industrial air pollution abatement because the sources are so diverse. Suffice it to say that despite the burgeoning regulatory effort at the national, state, and local levels, the situation is growing worse because of industrial growth, many instances of failure to apply existing technology, and, in some cases, lack of economically feasible technology. Sulfur oxides emissions alone are growing an estimated 6 to 7% per year overall, and industry is a substantial contributor (Table 9, page 60).

A large fund of air pollution control technology is available to industry and is widely used. Kraft pulp mills, which now produce more than 90% of the U.S. output of chemical pulp, have gradually eliminated an estimated 90% of their emissions of particles industrywide, using devices such as cyclones, wet scrubbers, and electrostatic precipitators. Petroleum refiners often recover hydrogen sulfide from refinery gas and convert it to

Table 9

Emissions of sulfur dioxide from stationary sources—1963 and 1966

PROCESS	SULFUR DIOXIDE [a]			
	1963		1966	
	Millions of tons	% of total emissions	Millions of tons	% of total emissions
Burning of coal				
Power generation				
(211.2 million tons, 1963 data)	9.6	41.0%	11.9	41.6%
Other combustion				
(112.6 million tons, 1963 data)	4.4	19.0	4.7	16.6
Subtotal	14.0	60.0	16.6	58.2
Combustion of petroleum products				
Residual oil	3.7	15.9	4.4	15.3
Other products	1.1	4.8	1.2	4.3
Subtotal	4.8	20.7	5.6	19.6
Refinery operations	1.6	6.8	1.6	5.5
Smelting of ores	1.7	7.4	3.5	12.2
Coke processing	.5	2.0	.5	1.8
Sulfuric acid manufacture	.5	1.9	.6	1.9
Coal refuse banks	.2	0.8	.1	0.4
Refuse incineration	.1	0.4	.1	0.4
Total	**23.4**	**100.0**	**28.6**	**100.0**

[a] A small amount is converted to sulfuric acid mist before discharge to the atmosphere. The rest is eventually oxidized and/or washed out.

SOURCE: "Air Quality Criteria for Sulfur Oxides," U.S. Department of Health, Education, and Welfare, National Air Pollution Control Administration Publication No. AP-50, Washington, D.C., January 1969.

elemental sulfur or sulfuric acid. The open hearth furnace, the steel industry's major emitter of air pollutants, is gradually being replaced by the basic oxygen furnace, which was introduced in the U.S. in the mid-1950's and now accounts for about one third of all steel produced. The basic oxygen furnace is a heavy producer of fumes, but modern pollution control equipment is built into the new plants.

While full utilization of the available economic means of controlling air pollution would markedly improve the quality of the air in many areas, operations remain for which there is no economic control (118). Nitrogen oxides formed in combustion processes cannot be controlled. Emissions from coke ovens in the steel industry cannot be adequately controlled, particularly when the ovens are being charged and discharged. Odor abatement is an unsolved problem in kraft pulp mills, which emit sulfur compounds, such as mercaptans, that can be smelled at concentrations of 1 ppb.

It does not seem likely that emission of sulfur oxides by industrial combustion of fossil fuels can be controlled to any extent by stack gas treatment. The sources are too numerous, too small, and too diverse. Substitution of low-sulfur fuels or development of new combustion processes with reduced sulfur oxides emissions will be required.

Emission of sulfur oxides by nonferrous metals smelters has been rising in the past few years, mainly because of increased production of copper from low-grade ores. Some smelting operations convert waste sulfur oxides to sulfuric acid. Others do not have adequate markets for the acid within economic shipping range and thus continue to emit sulfur oxides. Elemental sulfur can be shipped to distant markets more economically than can sulfuric acid, and processes for making it from smelter waste gases have been developed. However, the prevailing economics do not yet appear to justify the use of such processes in this country.

Industrial air pollution control equipment

A change in process will sometimes solve an industrial air pollution problem, and it is generally true that the tighter process is the better process. Often, however, the solution depends on the use of various devices that collect particles (Table 10, page 62) and gases. These devices fall into seven general classes: filters, electrical precipitators, cyclones, other mechanical devices, scrubbers, adsorbers, and combustion equipment such as afterburners and catalytic units (93). Such equipment must be matched to the emission to be controlled in terms of variables such as flow rate, temperature, nature and concentration of the pollutant, and the necessary degree of control. Custom design and a shakedown period may be required to achieve the desired performance.

Maintaining air pollution control equipment at design efficiency often requires constant attention. It is not unusual to find electrostatic precipitators that appear to be operating properly but are actually performing at 5 to 10% below design efficiency because the operating conditions have changed from the conditions used to design the equipment. Only a few types of control equipment, moreover, will intercept particles smaller than about 2 microns, which are the ones that remain airborne the longest and travel the farthest.

The evolution of the equipment industry has produced a number of relatively small manufacturers, although there are some large ones as well. These companies compete for the business of customers who may regard pollution control equipment as an overhead expense and emphasize first cost at the expense of optimum performance (2). This situation is gradually changing under the impact of increasingly stringent regulation of air pollution. One result of the situation, however, has been that the industry's technical and economic strength has not been sufficiently concentrated to support a range of solid research and development programs on new and existing equipment.

These evolutionary difficulties have not entirely blocked progress. The maximum efficiency of electrostatic precipitators in collecting fly ash has risen from 96 to 99% in the past decade. Precipitators have been oper-

Table 10

Forces influencing small particle collection in air pollution control devices

Class of air pollution control device	Force or mechanism	Particle diameter (microns) [a]
Settling chamber	Gravity	50
Cyclone		
Large diameter	Centrifugal + Impaction	25
Small diameter	Centrifugal + Impaction	> 5
Mechanical centrifugal rotor	Centrifugal + Impaction	> 5
Scrubber		
Simple spray tower	Impaction + Direct Interception	25
Packed tower	Impaction + Direct Interception	5
Wet cyclone	Impaction + Direct Interception + Centrifugal	5
Inertial-power driven	Impaction + Direct Interception + Centrifugal	5
Self-induced spray	Impaction + Direct Interception	5
Venturi	Impaction + Direct Interception	< 1
Filter		
High velocity impingement	Impaction + Direct Interception	10
Spun glass prefilters	Impaction + Direct Interception	5
Deep fiber bed	Impaction + Direct Interception + Diffusion	1
High efficiency cellulose-asbestos or all glass superfine fiber	Impaction + Direct Interception + Diffusion	< 1
Plastic fiber—superfine	Impaction + Direct Interception + Diffusion + Electrostatic	0.1
Cellulose ester membrane	Impaction + Direct Interception + Diffusion + Electrostatic	0.01
Bag or screen woven fabric	Impaction + Direct Interception + Diffusion	< 1
Reverse-jet felt	Impaction + Direct Interception + Diffusion	< 1
Electrostatic precipitators		
Single stage high voltage	Electrostatic	< 1
Two stage low voltage	Electrostatic	< 1

[a] Minimum particle size collected at approximately 90% efficiency under usual operating conditions.

SOURCE: "Air Pollution Manual, Part II—Control Equipment," American Industrial Hygiene Association, Detroit, Mich., 1968.

Table 11

Maximum service temperatures for popular filter media

Medium	Temperature, maximum range, °F
Glass fiber fabrics	500-550
Aromatic polyamide	400-450
Polyesters, acrylics	250-275
Polyamides (nylon)	200-225
Wool	180-200
Cotton	175-200

SOURCE: "Air Pollution Manual, Part II—Control Equipment," American Industrial Hygiene Association, Detroit, Mich., 1968.

ated, either on a pilot scale or full scale, at temperatures as high as 1300° F. and pressures of more than 800 pounds per square inch, both well above the previous limits (137). The heat and chemical resistance of filter fabrics, such as those used in baghouses, have improved steadily in the past decade through the use of such synthetic materials as glass fiber (Table 11). Selective chromatographic absorption of gases on small pellets may offer absorption rates much higher than those achieved in packed towers (131). The efficiencies of packed towers themselves are being improved by the use of new kinds of packing materials. But despite these and other developments, control equipment design is still frequently empirical, based on experience and not on fundamental knowledge of the chemical and physical processes involved. A need exists for more fundamental knowledge of the operating principles of air pollution control equipment and of the effects of the pollutants themselves on the efficiency of the equipment.

Recommendations: industrial facilities

Recommendation A13. *The promulgation of air quality criteria by the Federal Government should be supported in a manner that will allow it to proceed with all possible speed. Without such criteria, and the consequent air quality standards, industry often finds it impractical to select and apply the necessary control methods.*

Recommendation A14: *The development of new and improved control technology and equipment for industrial emissions must be stimulated, particularly for types of industries for which economic means of control do not now exist. Low-cost equipment for small industries is particularly essential.*

Recommendation A15: *More research and development should be undertaken on nonpolluting alternative manufacturing processes, where appropriate, and on the utilization of materials recovered by pollution control equipment, where such equipment must be used.*

Utility power plants

Electric power plants fired with coal or oil are the third largest source of air pollutants in the U.S. in tons emitted annually. Power plants are the leading producer of sulfur oxides, with 46% of the total emitted. They stand second in particle emissions with 25% of the total. Coal-fired power plants produce more than 90% of both the sulfur oxides and the particles. The growing use of nuclear power will reduce the amounts of these pollutants that are emitted in relation to the total amount of power produced, but fossil fuels remain an important and growing source of potential air contaminants. Nuclear plants may account for more than half of U.S. electric power output by the year 2000, but the total output is predicted to be six or seven times the current level, which would make fossil fuel usage roughly triple what it is today.

The flue gas from an electric power plant burning a typical coal containing 2.4% sulfur contains something like 1500 ppm of sulfur dioxide, 10 ppm of sulfur trioxide, 8.5 grams per cubic meter (3.7 grains per cubic foot) of particles, and 400 ppm of nitrogen oxides. The methods used today to manage these contaminants are tall stacks for sulfur oxides and particles, low-sulfur fuels for sulfur oxides, and collection devices for particles. Some methods for removing sulfur oxides from flue gases are available, and others are in development. Nitrogen oxides can sometimes be partially controlled by modifying the combustion process or by fuel substitution, but no generally effective abatement method is available today.

Tall stacks

The tall stack does not reduce the emission of pollutants, but rather reduces the local ground-level concentrations. The average height of power plant stacks to be completed in 1969 for coal-burning power plants will be 609 feet, compared with 243 feet in 1960, and stacks as high as 1000 feet or more are being built. These taller stacks are designed to disperse the emissions from the very large power plants, 500 to 1000 megawatts and up, that today's technology has made possible. Such plants emit very large volumes of contaminants, and the overall effect of using tall stacks to disperse them is not fully clear. One unanswered question is the effect of the practice on ground-level concentrations some miles from the stack. Another is its effect on atmospheric chemistry not obviously related to adverse effects on humans and other receptors. Until such questions are resolved, the tall stack should be regarded conservatively as an interim or partial solution to the pollution problems of power plants.

Low-sulfur fuel: coal

Regulations that have emerged in the past few years in some areas call for sulfur content of 1% or less in power plant fuels in the next few years. The U.S. has substantial reserves of such low-sulfur coal, but much of it is far from the major metropolitan markets. The low-sulfur reserves that are within reach geographically are used largely in premium outlets such as metallurgy. As a result more than 90% of the coal burned in U.S. power plants today contains more than 1% sulfur. The sulfur content of domestic coals ranges up to 6 or 8%, and 20 to 60% of it may be iron pyrites, discrete particles that can be removed at least partially by physical means. The remainder of the sulfur, 40 to 80% of the total, is in the organic form and can be removed only by changing the form of the coal, such as by gasifying it and then cleaning the gas.

The fraction of pyritic sulfur that can be removed from coal depends on the nature of the coal and the size distribution of the pyrite particles that it contains. Conventional coal cleaning processes, which are designed to remove noncarbonaceous material, normally reduce a 3% sulfur coal to between 2 and 2.5% sulfur. The reduction is less for coals of lower original sulfur content (27). Because the process is costly, utilities often use unwashed coals. Laboratory studies have shown that some coals can be reduced from 4% sulfur to less than 2% by pulverizing the coal to about the consistency of talcum powder and removing the pyrites by air classification. In most modern power plants, the coal is pulverized in any case, and deep-cleaning could be inserted as a new step before burning. This process, which could be supplemented by the use of high stacks, is being investigated in a 5 ton-per-hour pilot plant operated by the coal industry (43).

The economic burden of deep-cleaning coal might be eased by finding uses for the pyrites-coal refuse that results, and studies of potential uses are under way. One possibility would be to convert the iron pyrites to sulfur dioxide and iron oxide in a fluid-bed roaster. The sulfur dioxide would be converted to sulfuric acid, and the iron oxide would be used to make steel. An early study of such a process (38) concluded that it would reduce the cost of deep cleaning the coal by about 25%, to $2.81 per ton. (Utility coal averages, nationally, around $6.00 per ton, delivered.)

Exploratory work on removing pyritic sulfur has encompassed magnetic separation, electrostatic separation, froth flotation, and dry centrifugation (88). Some of these methods show promise, but none is considered a complete solution to the sulfur oxides problem. Both pyritic and organic sulfur can be removed by solvent refining (57), which produces a very low-ash liquid or solid fuel that may contain less than 1% sulfur, depending on the original sulfur content of the coal. The process appears to be too costly for general use, but it will be tested further in a pilot plant to be completed probably in 1969.

Low-sulfur fuel: petroleum

The petroleum industry has developed great skill at producing products low in sulfur compounds, which can cause problems such as corrosion, unpleasant odors, and reduction in the effectiveness of the lead alkyls used in gasoline. The average sulfur content of crude oil charged to domestic refineries in 1965 has been estimated to be a relatively low 0.76%, and the average sulfur content of the fuels produced ranged from 0.01% for aviation gasoline to 1.47% for residual fuel oil (36). The average sulfur content of almost all of these fuel products has been declining in the past 15 years. Residual fuel oil is an exception, having risen from 1.18% sulfur in 1950 to the 1.47% of 1965. The reason is that when petroleum is refined, the sulfur tends to concentrate in the residual oil. The more strongly the residual is "milked" for its lighter fractions, the greater the proportion of sulfur that remains behind. The regulations that are being applied to power plant fuels call for 1% sulfur or less, and growing application of desulfurization technology to domestic residual fuel oils can be expected.

The trend among U.S. refiners has been to convert a growing portion of their feedstocks into products higher in value than residual fuel oil, which now averages about 8% of domestic refinery output. The residual fuel oil market, meanwhile, has been served increasingly by imports, which account for well over half of domestic consumption. The meaning of this trend to air pollution lies in the fact that along the East Coast, where the sulfur oxides problem is the most serious, some 85% of the residual fuel oil market is served by Caribbean refineries. Close to 60% of the output of these refineries is residual fuel oil, and its average sulfur content is 2.6%.

The technology is available for desulfurizing Caribbean residual fuel oil, and facilities for doing so are being built. A comprehensive study of the costs involved (30) concluded that to reduce the sulfur content from 2.6% to 0.5% would cost about 80 cents a barrel or about 97 cents on the basis of equivalent heating value. A cost of 80 cents would add about 35% to the cost of No. 6 fuel oil, which, at the time of the study, was selling in New York Harbor for $2.28 a barrel, FOB, with no sulfur guarantee. To reduce the sulfur content to 1% would cost about 58 cents a barrel or 72 cents on the basis of equivalent heating value. The processes used in this study to achieve 0.5% sulfur content would produce about 450 long tons per day of sulfur. The desulfurization costs include a credit for this by-product at $32.00 per long ton. A $5.00 increase in the price of sulfur would reduce desulfurization cost about 1.4 cents per barrel.

The accuracy of these cost calculations could be affected by certain imponderables, such as the lack of process information on feedstocks of high metals content. Caribbean residual fuel oil typically contains about 500 ppm of metals, chiefly iron, nickel, and vanadium. These metals tend to deactivate the catalysts used in hydrodesulfurization of oil, a process in which hydrogen is used to remove the sulfur as hydrogen sulfide. Catalysts are commercially available for hydrodesulfurization, but they are deactivated too quickly when used on feeds of high metals content. Research on hydrodesulfurization catalysts for such feeds (9) has shown that better ones can be developed, and the results suggest that better catalysts offer the best route to lower costs for removing sulfur.

Low-sulfur fuels: future

The use of low-sulfur fuels in conventional power plants is unlikely to be more than a partial solution to the sulfur oxides emission problem. The most plentiful fuel reserve in the U.S. by far is coal, and studies are being made to determine the cleanability of coals that occur in different parts of the country. However, coal of markedly lower sulfur content than is now available is unlikely to be in widespread use by utilities (or other consumers) for some time. Residual fuel oil accounts for less than 10% of utility power production, and the advent of low-sulfur oil will produce only a proportionate effect. Some utilities use low-sulfur natural gas, and NAPCA is studying the feasibility of liquefying natural gas and transporting it in that form to power plants where it would be revaporized and used as fuel. Natural gas is the least abundant of the domestic fossil fuels, however, and overall it appears that low-sulfur fuels will have to be supplemented by other control measures for sulfur oxides.

Stack-gas cleanup: sulfur oxides

A number of processes are being studied for removing sulfur oxides from stack gases (65, 110, 112). In the U.S. they include reaction with limestone or dolomite, catalytic conversion with production of sulfuric acid, sorption by a solid such as alkalized alumina with production of elemental sulfur, and other processes not so far advanced. Processes being studied abroad include absorption by manganese dioxide with production of ammonium sulfate, and absorption by an activated char, a carbonaceous material, with production of sulfuric acid.

Limestone-dolomite. Sulfur oxides removal systems based on limestone and dolomite are under intensive development in this country (94). Limestone and dolomite are cheap and plentiful, and the thermodynamics of their reactions with sulfur oxides are favorable at the temperatures encountered in power plant operation. Some such processes, moreover, appear to be suitable for use on existing power plants, particularly those of small to intermediate size.

In all such processes, pulverized limestone or dolomite is first injected into the boiler, where the heat drives off carbon dioxide, converting the carbonates to the reactive oxide form. The oxides then react with the sulfur oxides to form solid sulfites and sulfates, which are removed from the stack gas by conventional means, such as an electrostatic precipitator, along with unreacted limestone and fly ash. The process can be operated as a simple injection system in which the boiler itself serves as the reaction chamber; a dry reactor system can be added to increase the time available for reaction and intimacy of contact of the reactants; or the reaction can take place largely in a water scrubber. The dry reactor system, the second of these two approaches, probably would not be applicable to existing power plants.

Both the dry and wet systems create waste disposal problems. In the dry systems, the amount of solids to be collected would be two to four times what it would be if limestone were not added to the system. The wet process produces a sludge that is saturated with soluble magnesium sulfites and sulfates, which are potential water pollutants. Studies are under way on utilization of fly ash from the dry processes and on recycling spent limestone-dolomite.

One of several problems with the dry limestone-dolomite processes is that only about a quarter or a third of the stone appears to react. Also, reactivity differs among types of stone found in different parts of the country. Research on reaction kinetics, reactivity of different limestone-dolomites, and other problems is being pursued in the hope of optimizing the dry process. The Tennessee Valley Authority has completed a design study of the dry process (125) and plans full scale tests in 1969.

The wet limestone-dolomite process offers few problems in reaction kinetics, since it does not depend heavily on reactions in the gas phase. The few per cent of sulfur trioxide in the combustion gases reacts completely with the calcium and magnesium oxides, but only about a quarter of the sulfur dioxide appears to react in the gas phase. When the gases enter the scrubber, however, the reactants dissolve in the water where they react to form calcium and magnesium sulfites and sulfates, which dissolve or precipitate. More than 95% of the sulfur dioxide and 99.5% of the particles have been removed in a pilot-scale wet scrubber.

Wet systems have been developed (91, 92), and two have been installed on electric power plants (124). One is on a 140-megawatt plant in St. Louis, and the other is on a 125-megawatt plant in Lawrence, Kan. (Fig. 4). A third unit will be installed on a new 430-megawatt plant in Lawrence that is expected to come into service early in 1971.

Catalytic conversion. A 15-megawatt prototype of a catalytic conversion process (17) has been tested on a power plant in Portland, Pa., and the process is being offered for commercial use. The catalytic converter promotes the oxidation of sulfur dioxide in the stack gas to sulfur trioxide, which combines with water in the stack gas to form a sulfuric acid mist. The acid is trapped in a mist eliminator and removed. Since fly ash would plug the catalytic unit, it is first removed by an electrostatic precipitator operating at the unusually high temperature of 900°F. The process is designed to remove 90% of the sulfur dioxide in the stack gas of a power plant burning coal of 3 to 3.5% sulfur content.

On an 800-megawatt power plant burning coal with 3% sulfur, the process would produce about 750 tons per day of sulfuric acid. Thus the user of the process must be within economic range of markets that can absorb that amount of acid. Currently the process produces 80% acid, a strength which is suitable for many industrial uses, but not for all. It has the capability to produce 90 or 91% acid. Corrosion can also be a problem in the catalytic conversion process.

Alkalized alumina. The alkalized alumina sorption process for removing sulfur dioxide from stack gases is being developed by the U.S. Bureau

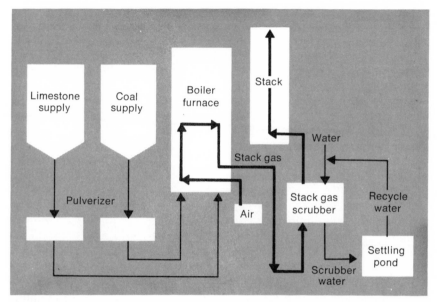

Figure 4

Wet limestone process for removing sulfur oxides from stack gases of utility power plants

In the process shown here, limestone is injected into the boiler furnace, where the heat drives off carbon dioxide, converting the calcium carbonate to the reactive oxide form. The oxide then reacts with the sulfur oxides to form solid sulfites and sulfates. Some of the conversion takes place before the stack gas reaches the water scrubber, but most of it takes place in the scrubber after the reactants dissolve in the water. The resulting solids, as well as the fly ash removed in the scrubber, go to the settling pond, and water from the settling pond is recycled to the scrubber. In the dry limestone process, which is also under development, reaction products and fly ash are removed from the stack gas by an electrostatic precipitator.

of Mines (14). It is operating in a pilot plant that is equivalent to a 0.2-megawatt power plant. The economic feasibility of the process has not yet been established unequivocally, but it appears to be quite promising for the big new power plants of the future.

In this process (Fig. 5, page 70), sulfur oxides in the gas are absorbed by 1/16th inch spheres of alkalized alumina (part aluminum oxide, part sodium oxide) in a bed suspended in the gas stream. In a second unit the sulfur oxides are removed from the spheres by reacting them with a gas containing hydrogen and carbon monoxide to form carbon dioxide and hydrogen sulfide. The alkalized alumina is recycled, and the hydrogen sulfide is converted to elemental sulfur. The process would remove about 90% of the sulfur oxides in the stack gas. On an 800-megawatt

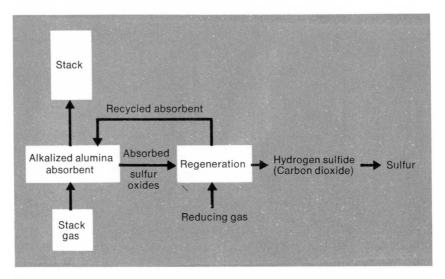

Figure 5

Alkalized alumina process for removing sulfur oxides from stack gases of utility power plants

In the alkalized alumina process, sulfur oxides in the stack gas are absorbed by spheres of alkalized alumina (a mixture of aluminum and sodium oxides) in a bed suspended in the gas stream. The oxides are then removed from the spheres by reaction with a reducing gas containing hydrogen and carbon monoxide, producing carbon dioxide and hydrogen sulfide. The hydrogen sulfide is converted to elemental sulfur, which can be sold, and the regenerated alkalized alumina is recycled.

power plant, burning coal of 3% sulfur content, it would produce about 180 tons per day of sulfur.

One advantage of the alkalized alumina process is that the by-product sulfur could be stored cheaply out of doors while awaiting sale. A problem area is the rate of attrition of the alkalized alumina spheres, and the bureau is seeking cheaper and more efficient forms of that sorbent as well as less costly substitutes. Those that have been studied include oil shale, zinc calcine, phosphate rock, and red mud (a waste from alumina plants).

The bureau plans to test the process at the 30-megawatt level. Such tests should provide the design data for a 1000-megawatt power plant, although such a scaleup would be a calculated risk. Cooperation has been contemplated with the Central Electricity Generating Board in England, which is developing the same basic process, but using a different gas-solid contact method.

Chemical absorption. Also under development is a sulfur dioxide removal process in which a liquid of undisclosed composition absorbs sulfur dioxide from the stack gas and regenerates it as dry, very pure sulfur dioxide. The sulfur dioxide can then be liquefied for sale as such, or it can be converted to sulfuric acid or elemental sulfur. A 500-megawatt power plant burning coal of 3% sulfur content would produce about 68,000 tons of sulfur dioxide annually. The process is designed to remove all of the particulate matter from the stack gas and more than 90% of the sulfur dioxide. A 25-megawatt pilot unit should be operating in 1969 in Baltimore.

Costs. The importance of electrical energy to the U.S. economy makes the cost of sulfur oxides abatement processes a crucial factor. It would be advantageous if such processes were to increase the cost of producing power by only a few per cent. Estimated costs for the processes that are furthest advanced are in this range or not impossibly far above it, but they often reflect local conditions and cannot be applied generally. Firm cost figures will not be available until operating experience at a commercial level has begun to accumulate.

New processes. In addition to sulfur oxides removal processes now in development, new and more economical processes are being sought. NAPCA and industrial contractors are surveying nine broad areas of technology in which such second-generation processes might lie: aqueous scrubbing, solid metal oxides, other inorganic solids, inorganic liquids, organic liquids, organic solids, catalytic oxidation, direct reduction to sulfur, and physical separation.

One second generation process, molten carbonate scrubbing, has been studied in the laboratory, and a small pilot plant has been designed. A prototype system for a 50-megawatt power plant might be operating by 1972. In this process, sulfur dioxide is absorbed from flue gas in a molten carbonate solution. In two further steps the molten carbonate is regenerated for reuse, and the sulfur dioxide is converted to hydrogen sulfide, which can be further converted to elemental sulfur or sulfuric acid. The process would operate at around 850°F., and the high rates of reaction at that temperature should be advantageous.

Stack-gas cleanup: particles

Utility power plants generated an estimated 18 million tons of particles nationwide in 1965, but about 87% of the total was removed from stack gases by electrostatic precipitators and mechanical collectors (76). The amount emitted, 2.4 million tons on the basis of these figures, is expected to shrink to an estimated 820,000 tons in 1980 because of the growing use and efficiency of collection devices and the gradual replacement of older power plants. The trend has been to replace mechanical collectors with electrostatic precipitators, alone or combined with a mechanical collector, to achieve collection efficiencies of 97 to 99% or higher. The guaranteed fly ash collection efficiency of new precipitators has risen from 96% in 1940 to more than 99% today. The performance of newly installed precipitators in actual use has risen from about 75% in 1940 to above 96% today.

Almost all specifications for new power plant electrostatic precipitators today call for collection efficiencies of 99% and up. The use of low-sulfur coal can create a problem, in that the fly ash particles are more resistant to electric charge than those from higher-sulfur coal at the normal operating temperature of the precipitator, 270° to 300° F. New York City will require by 1971 at the latest that all coals used in the city contain no more than 1% sulfur. The effect will be to reduce the efficiency of power-plant precipitators used there from 99% to 98%, and new equipment will have to be added to counteract the effect. At 0.5% sulfur, precipitator efficiency can drop to as low as 50%, and it is not always possible to add new equipment.

At higher operating temperature, low-sulfur coal becomes less troublesome. The first large precipitator in the U.S. to operate at higher temperature is installed at a 1000-megawatt coal and oil fired unit in New York City. Efficiencies of more than 99.6% have been achieved at operating temperatures of 580° to 610° F. when firing coal, whose sulfur content has essentially no effect on the efficiency (23).

A California power company has experimented with both the precipitator and the baghouse (fabric filtration) for controlling visible stack plumes when burning California residual fuel oil (111). The plumes were found to be caused by relatively small amounts of particles and sulfur trioxide aerosol mist. Both are predominantly in the submicron size range and thus produce significant light-scattering effects and the consequent visible plume. A prototype precipitator on a 175-megawatt boiler was unable continuously to meet the local requirements for visible emissions. A prototype baghouse has been operating on a 320-megawatt boiler since 1965 and has proved to be capable of eliminating visible plume. Operating problems have been encountered with the baghouse, however, and it is still not considered a commercially proven control device, although considerable progress has been made. (NAPCA also has been studying the baghouse and plans contract work to evaluate it as a chemical contactor for removing both sulfur oxides and nitrogen oxides.)

Stack-gas cleanup: nitrogen oxides

Work on abatement of nitrogen oxides produced by power plants (and other combustion processes) has been limited, and practical technology for achieving significant control is not available. Emission can be reduced 40 to 50% in some furnaces by two-stage combustion (11), in which air fed to the burner is 90 to 95% of the amount required for complete combustion. The remainder of the air is introduced at a point beyond the burner. The effect is to reduce peak combustion temperature and thus to reduce the amount of nitrogen oxides formed. A few power boilers, all in California, have been designed or modified to use two-stage combustion. In some furnace designs, nitrogen oxides reduction is built in, and two-stage combustion gives very little improvement (108).

A boiler burning natural gas may produce as little as half the amount of nitrogen oxides produced by one burning fuel oil. Some boilers, however, have been found to emit as much or more nitrogen oxides when burning natural gas as when burning fuel oil.

On a laboratory scale, it is possible to convert all of the nitrogen oxides and more than 90% of the sulfur dioxide in simulated flue gas to sulfur and nitrogen (103). The process uses a copper catalyst. The reactions produce the undesirable carbon oxysulfide, but it can be controlled by closely regulating the initial concentration of carbon monoxide. In practice, this would mean operating the furnace at very low excess air (for combustion), even lower than has been achieved today in power plants, which generally try to hold excess air as low as possible consistent with complete combustion.

Fundamental research on the characteristics of flames (109) could develop usable information on the formation and decay of contaminants such as nitrogen oxides and carbon monoxide. Work is also under way on fluid bed combustion of coal, which has potential for controlling both nitrogen oxides and sulfur oxides. NAPCA in addition has contracted for a study that will serve as the basis of recommendations for research and development on control of nitrogen oxides. The agency plans also to evaluate sulfur oxides removal processes, such as the molten carbonate process, for their potential in abating nitrogen oxides.

Recommendations: utility power plants

Recommendation A16: *Translation of federal air quality criteria for sulfur oxides and particles into air quality standards should proceed rapidly so as to speed widespread application of the available means of controlling these emissions.*

Recommendation A17: *Existing research to define the overall effectiveness of the tall stack in meeting air quality standards should consider the effects of mass emissions of pollutants not only on local, ground-level concentrations, but on the local and regional air masses and on ground-level concentrations outside the local area.*

Recommendation A18: *Investigations of techniques for desulfurizing fuels must be carried to the point where economic evaluation is possible. Particularly desirable would be early definition of the amounts and locations of coals that can be cleaned economically of significant amounts of pyritic sulfur. The development of economical coal cleaning processes is a responsibility of the coal industry, and more comprehensive studies should be made than have been made in the past. Further research appears to be required on hydrodesulfurization catalysts that are not deactivated by the heavy metals in residual fuel oils.*

Recommendation A19: *The development of first-generation processes for removing sulfur oxides from utility stack gases should be supported and stimulated so as to achieve early commercialization, particularly in order to offer a control option for existing power plants. Research and* development on new and original methods of removing sulfur oxides from utility stacks should proceed rapidly to the point at which specific processes can be selected for advanced development.

Recommendation A20: Current studies of nitrogen oxides emissions by stationary sources should define the economics and effectiveness of modifying existing power plants, where possible, or of using alternative fuels to reduce such emissions.

Recommendation A21: Research and development on new combustion processes should include pollutant emissions as a basic parameter.

Space heating

Domestic and commercial space heating accounts for only 6% of the weight of total national emissions of the five major air pollutants and for only 12% of the sulfur oxides. The effects of space heating on the quality of urban air, however, are much greater than such figures would indicate, because the emissions enter the air in crowded areas at relatively low heights above the ground. Space heating additionally is a difficult abatement problem because of the large numbers of relatively small sources involved.

The only economic means of reducing sulfur oxides emissions from space heating is the use of low-sulfur fuels. To reduce particle emissions the only economic means are to avoid the use of fuels, such as bituminous coal, that produce relatively large emissions, and to upgrade the efficiency of combustion equipment. One long-range alternative might be to heat domestic and commercial spaces with hot air, electricity, steam, or high-temperature water (400°F., 274 pounds per square inch) from central production units that would be large enough to use advanced pollution abatement technology economically. Heating systems of this kind would not be new to this country, but they have never been widely used.

Recommendations: space heating

Recommendation A22: In its development of national fuels policies and inventories, the Federal Government should take proper account of the needs of present and developing urban areas for low-pollution fuels for space heating.

Recommendation A23: Federal and state governments should insure that objective and up-to-date technical information on the most efficient combustion equipment for space heating is available to municipal authorities.

Recommendation A24: The economics of centralized production of heat for space heating should be re-evaluated. Such studies should consider *the distribution of energy in the form of hot air, electricity, steam, or high-temperature water (400°F. and 274 pounds per square inch).*

Refuse disposal

Refuse disposal, the fifth largest contributor of the five major air pollutants in weight emitted nationwide, is covered in Section III of this report (see page 166).

EFFECTS OF AIR POLLUTANTS

The greatest long-term need for deeper understanding of the air environment lies in the most crucial area: the modes of action and effects of pollutants on man, animals, plants, and inanimate objects. Existing knowledge, buttressed by the clear need for haste, provides the current basis for the establishment of air quality criteria by the Federal Government and the air quality standards already established by some states (130) (Table 12, page 76) and to be set up eventually by all. But the ability to refine and augment such criteria and standards, to predict the effects of pollutants, and to detect such effects at an early stage will require much more penetrating knowledge than now exists of the effects themselves and of the mechanisms of action of contaminants.

Effects on humans

The acute toxicological effects of most air contaminants are reasonably well understood, but the effects of exposure to heterogeneous mixtures of gases and particles at very low concentrations are only just beginning to be comprehended. Two general approaches can be used to study the effects of air contaminants on humans: epidemiology, which attempts to associate the effect, in large populations, with the cause; or laboratory research, which starts with the cause and attempts to determine the effects. Ideally, the two methods should complement each other.

Epidemiology is the more costly of the two, requires great care in planning, and often suffers from incomplete data and lack of controls. One great advantage of epidemiology is that moral barriers do not limit its application to humans as they do with some kinds of laboratory research. The method is thus highly useful and has produced considerable information (45). Laboratory research is less costly than epidemiology, and its results can be checked against controls and verified by repeating the experiment.

The strictures on experimenting with humans can sometimes be bypassed by inventive design of experiments. Scientists in the Soviet Union have done this with experiments that measure the interference of contaminants with human reflexes (128). In the U.S., the electroencephalogram, which measures electrical currents in the brain, is being used to measure the response to a flashing light evoked in animals who have been exposed to pollutants such as carbon monoxide and lead (13).

Table 12

California standards for ambient air quality

POLLUTANT	"ADVERSE" LEVEL[1]	"SERIOUS" LEVEL[2]	"EMERGENCY" LEVEL[3]
PHOTOCHEMICAL POLLUTANTS Hydrocarbons Ozone Oxidant Photochemical aerosols	"Oxidant Index" 0.15 ppm for 1 hour by the potassium iodide method (eye irritation, damage to vegetation and visibility reduction)	Footnote 4 Footnote 5	Footnote 4 Footnote 6
NITROGEN DIOXIDE	0.25 ppm for 1 hour (coloration of the atmosphere during daylight hours)	3 ppm for 1 hour (bronchocon-striction)	Footnote 7
CARBON MONOXIDE	Not applicable	30 ppm for 8 hours, or 120 ppm for 1 hour (interference with oxygen transport by blood)	Footnote 8
SULFUR DIOXIDE	1 ppm for 1 hour or 0.3 ppm for 8 hours (damage to vegetation)	5 ppm for 1 hour (bronchocon-striction)	10 ppm for 1 hour (severe distress in human sub-jects)
HYDROGEN SULFIDE	0.1 ppm for 1 hour (sensory irritation)	Footnote 9	Footnote 10
SULFURIC ACID	Footnote 11	Footnote 11	Footnote 12
ETHYLENE	0.5 ppm for 1 hour or 0.1 ppm for 8 hours (damage to vegetation)	Not applicable	Not applicable
HYDROGEN FLUORIDE	Footnote 14	Footnote 15	Not applicable
LEAD	Not applicable	Footnote 16	Footnote 16
PARTICULATE MATTER	Sufficient to reduce visibility to less than 3 miles when relative humidity is less than 70%	Not applicable	Not applicable
CARCINOGENS	Not applicable	Footnote 13	Not applicable

SOURCE: "California Standards for Ambient Air Quality and for Motor Vehicle Emissions," Revised March 1967, State of California, Department of Public Health, Bureau of Air Sanitation, Berkeley, Calif.

1. Level at which there will be sensory irritation, damage to vegetation, reduction in visibility or similar effects.

2. Level at which there will be alteration of bodily function or which is likely to lead to chronic disease.

3. Level at which it is likely that acute sickness or death in sensitive groups of persons will occur.

4. Hydrocarbons are a group of substances most of which, normally, are toxic only at concentrations in the order of several hundred parts per million. However, a number of hydrocarbons can react photochemically at very low concentrations to produce irritating and toxic substances. Because of the large number of hydrocarbons involved, the complexity of the photochemical reactions and the reactivity of other compounds such as nitrogen dioxide and ozone, it is not yet possible to establish "serious" and "emergency" levels for hydrocarbons. From the public health standpoint, the concentration of those hydrocarbons which react photochemically should be maintained at or below the level associated with the oxidant index defined in the "adverse" standard.

5. Ozone, at 1 ppm for eight hours daily for about a year, has produced bronchiolitis and fibrositis in rodents. Extrapolation of these data to man is difficult. Functional impairment data have been reported; at 1.25 ppm some effect is observed on residual volume and diffusing capacity. The variability of the tests was not reported. Additional data would be needed before a standard is set.

6. A value of 2.0 ppm of ozone for one hour may produce serious interference with function in healthy persons and the assumption is made that this might cause acute illness in sensitive persons.

7. Nitrogen dioxide, at concentrations above 2.5 ppm, causes acute damage to sensitive plants. One ppm for eight hours will produce significant growth reduction, expressed as fresh and dry weight, with no visible lesions of damage. High levels (150-220 ppm) in short exposures produce fibrotic changes in the lungs of man that may end fatally.

8. Given certain assumptions concerning ventilatory rates, acute sickness might result from a carbon monoxide level of 240 ppm for one hour in sensitive groups because of inactivation of 10% of the body's hemoglobin. In any event it is clear that when a population exposure limit has been set for carbon monoxide, because of exposures from other sources, community air pollution standards should be based on some fraction of this limit.

9. Hydrogen sulfide is not known to produce chronic disease in humans but there may be durable sequelae from acute exposures. The disagreeable odor may interfere with appetite in sensitive groups of persons at about 5 ppm. At high concentrations loss of the sense of smell occurs. This has been reported at 100 ppm for exposures lasting two to 15 minutes. Conjunctivitis and mild respiratory tract irritation have been reported at levels of 50-100 ppm for one hour.

10. Acute sickness and death with neurotoxicity may occur at concentrations of several hundred ppm. It is very unlikely these levels will occur in community air pollution.

11. A sulfuric acid mist level of 1 mg/m³ with an average particle size of 1 micron will produce a respiratory response in man. It is not possible to generalize from this for all air pollution conditions, because under natural conditions, particle size will vary. Only with large droplets would sensory irritation be produced without other physiological effects.

12. A level of 5 mg/m³ of sulfuric acid mist for a few minutes produces coughing and irritation in normal individuals. Presumably, it could cause acute illness in sensitive groups of persons in a period of one hour.

13. Carcinogens include a few organic compounds such as some polycyclic hydrocarbons and some metals such as arsenic and chromium. Studies on effects of such substances are currently under way, but there are not sufficient data, at present, to set standards. In the meantime, it is recommended that concentrations of carcinogens in air should be kept as low as possible.

14. Hydrogen fluoride and other airborne fluorides settle upon and some are absorbed into vegetation. When forage crops containing 30-50 ppm of fluoride measured on a dry weight basis are regularly consumed over a long period the teeth and bones of cattle may show changes, depending upon age, nutritional factors and the form of fluoride ingested. Such changes may or may not have any economic effect. Fluorides at these levels do not necessarily cause injury to the forage plants themselves. However, injury may be produced in certain species of vegetation upon long term exposure to low levels of atmospheric fluorides.

15. The irritating properties of hydrogen fluoride in experimental human exposure have been manifested by desquamation of the skin, at concentrations of 2-5 ppm. Mucous membrane irritation also occurs from hydrogen fluorides but quantitative data are not adequate to support a standard.

16. It is clear that lead levels should be set on the basis of average values for long periods. While data are abundant concerning human response to eight-hours-a-day, five-days-a-week exposures, data are insufficient for the effects of the continuous exposure inherent in community air pollution. While laboratory studies will be pursued with vigor, it becomes very important that local agencies collect data on existing lead levels. Since lead exposures are from multiple sources, community air pollution standards should be based on a portion of the total limit for population exposure.

The electroencephalogram is only just beginning to be considered in this country for research on the effects of air pollutants on humans, one problem being the difficulty of analyzing and interpreting the signal that is generated. Another type of behavioral experiment measures the effect of carbon monoxide on the ability of humans to judge short intervals of time (12). Effects have been detected after exposure to 50 ppm of the gas for 40 minutes.

In other work with humans, acrolein, formaldehyde, and peroxyacyl nitrates have been indicted as eye irritants. Eye irritation, and the compounds and their precursors in photochemical smog that cause it, are not fully understood, and the structure of the precursors may be involved (54). The accumulation of lead by the body and its possible effects on health are subjects of vigorous debate (46, 66).

Insufficient knowledge of atmospheric chemistry can contribute to the difficulties of determining the effects of air contaminants on humans. Sulfur dioxide was implicated in the serious pollution incident in London in 1952, and two theories were proposed to explain its behavior. The first is that the gas is oxidized rapidly to sulfur trioxide in a reaction catalyzed by airborne particles, and the sulfur trioxide combines with water in the air to form droplets of sulfuric acid which are inhaled. The second theory is that sulfur dioxide absorbed on airborne particles is inhaled and carried deep into the lungs, where it is desorbed in amounts significantly larger than would be the case if the gas alone were inhaled.

A fundamental question raised by these theories concerns the speed with which sulfur dioxide is converted to sulfuric acid droplets, and how fast the droplets are removed from the air. Research has been done in this area (42, 44, 59, 60), but critics argue that the results cannot be extrapolated to the conditions that actually exist in the air. Sulfuric acid in the air has been studied (16, 132), but the speed and mechanism of oxidation of sulfur dioxide in the atmosphere, and the adsorption of the gas on airborne particles, remain unresolved questions.

Considerable work has been done and is in progress on the effects of pollutants on animals, including, for a few species, experiments involving mixed pollutants and mixed gas-aerosol systems (37, 39, 52). In general, such work has shown that mixed pollutants may act in several different ways: They may produce an effect that is additive, amounting to the sum of the effects of each contaminant acting alone; they may produce an effect that is greater than the simply additive (synergism) or less than the simply additive (antagonism); or they may produce an effect that differs in some other way from the simply additive.

Work with whole animals is further complicated by protective effects (74, 122) and cross tolerances (78). Thus the effects of contaminants on the whole animal are not independent of each other, and the animal's total response involves his past history and his overall response to his environment. Physiological stress, for example, could be a factor in the changes in the alkaline phosphatase activity found in the livers of rats who inhaled acrolein, ozone, nitrogen dioxide, formaldehyde, or sulfur dioxide (80). The same is true of changes in blood serum protein and alkaline phosphatase of the lung found in whole animals exposed to ozone and to nitrogen dioxide (107).

These complexities in research on whole animals have stimulated work on simpler biochemical systems designed to explain the basic mechanisms of the response of cells to toxic or irritating substances. Such work appears to be necessary in order to evaluate the effects of long-term, low-level exposure to individual components of mixtures of gases. It has included research on various bacteria and tissue cultures, using both individual gases and mixtures of gases. Peroxyacyl nitrate and formaldehyde have been found specifically to inhibit enzymes in isolated systems (35, 79). Evidence has been found of correlations between the initial concentrations of reactants in gaseous mixtures and the rate at which the mixtures kill or inhibit the growth of bacteria (34). No correlation was found with the chemical analysis of the mixtures after they had been irradiated and reacted photochemically (33).

Despite the progress made in these and other experiments, the study of mechanisms of action is barely out of its infancy. Research on the biochemistry of the lung, which is crucial to true understanding of many mechanisms, is at about the same point. Subclinical intoxication with consequent predisposition to accident or disease is an uncharted area. Work with biological systems requires analytical chemical methods more precise, more accurate, and more specific than ever required in the past. Although laboratory research and epidemiology have done much to explain the effects of air contaminants on man and animals, what is known is plainly miniscule in the light of what must be learned.

At the other end of the spectrum, little work has been done on those effects on humans generally described as "esthetic" or psychological: depression caused by perpetual grayness, irritation at loss of scenic views, nausea caused by offensive odors, and the like. The few opinion surveys made to date have generally been poorly documented from the standpoint of pollutant concentrations. Often they have lacked adequate controls for the effect of the questioner in bringing to people's attention matters that they might normally ignore.

Effects on vegetation

Vegetation is more sensitive than animals to many air contaminants, and methods have been developed that use plant response to measure and identify contaminants. Among the pollutants that can harm plants are sulfur dioxide, hydrogen fluoride, and ethylene. Plant damage caused by constitutents of photochemical smog has been studied extensively (55). Damage has been attributed to ozone and peroxyacyl nitrates (8, 68), to higher aldehydes (18), and to products of the reaction of ozone with olefins (119). However, none of these cases precisely duplicates all features of the damage observed in the field, and the question remains open to some debate and further study.

The development of air quality criteria and standards depends in part on assessments of economic loss caused by plant damage, and studies have been made that show significant loss. While there is no doubt that severe economic damage can occur, the methods used in many such studies are open to question, and the studies themselves are not amenable to generalization, being confined largely to specific times and places. NAPCA plans field studies designed to define more precisely the economic effects of plant damage.

Of the types of plant damage that air pollutants can cause, acute damage to tissue is the best documented. Only limited information is available on reduction in crop growth and productivity, and very little on chemical and physical changes in plant cells and on interference with plant enzyme systems. Research on such effects, moreover, will be complicated by the effects of light, humidity, temperature, and soil variables on the sensitivity of vegetation to air pollutants, as well as changes in plant susceptibility with age.

Effects on materials

The damage that air pollutants can do to some materials is well known: ozone in photochemical smog cracks rubber, weakens fabrics, and fades dyes (56); hydrogen sulfide tarnishes silver; smoke dirties laundry; acid aerosols ruin nylon hose.

Research on corrosion and accelerated tests of the effects of corrosive substances and conditions (90) have a long history. The chemistry of corrosion is reasonably well understood and can be used in specific instances to solve problems caused by pollution, if not to abate the pollution itself. In the early 1960's in the Los Angeles area, the telephone company began to experience excessive failure of wire-spring relays used in central telephone offices (53). The problem was traced to stress-cracking caused by high concentrations of nitrates in airborne dusts. It was solved by replacing the nickel-brass alloy in the relay with cupro-nickel, and by modifying office ventilating and cooling systems to reduce nitrate intake and to maintain relative humidity at less than 50%.

While the damage to materials is undoubtedly extensive, assigning an accurate dollar value to it is difficult and perhaps impossible except in specific instances. Attempts now being made to define the costs of the damage more precisely include NAPCA's interstate air pollution surveillance program effects network (62). Static "effects packages" at more than 200 monitoring stations gather data on effects such as corrosion, tarnishing of metals, deterioration of textiles and dyes, and deterioration of rubber. In addition NAPCA is involved in research programs on damage caused by pollutants to electrical equipment, building materials, dyes and fabrics, and other materials.

Effects on the ecology

The relationship of air contaminants to the ecology, the aggregate of living things as they exist together in nature, is very nearly a total mystery. It is possible to conceive of ecological cycles in which the specific toxicity of a pollutant for a single species could cause an entire food chain to collapse, but the extent to which this might happen is unknown. Too little is known of the effects of pollutants on too few species to suggest even how such problems might be attacked. That they must be attacked in the long run is certain, but it is equally certain that the attack will require the solution of a variety of difficult problems (31).

One question of ecological concern is the biogeochemical cycles of oxygen, sulfur, carbon, and nitrogen. All organisms, for example, build their protein basically from those four elements and hydrogen. If man were to destroy any of at least half a dozen types of bacteria involved in the nitrogen cycle, say, life on earth could end.

In any ecosystem—a lake, a forest—plants, animals, and microorganisms exist in a complex state of interaction among themselves and with the inanimate phases of the environment. This interaction is affected by climate and by chemical and physical inputs to the system. Scientists are just beginning to study ecosystems on the multidisciplinary basis that is clearly required. Computer simulation and modeling of such systems should be feasible soon, and will be useful. A great deal of research will be required, however, to explain satisfactorily the anatomy and functioning of even relatively small ecosystems.

Recommendations: effects of air pollutants

Recommendation A25: *Epidemiological and laboratory studies of the effects of air pollution on humans, including model experiments on animals, should be carefully coordinated and selectively accelerated. Body burdens and environmental levels of potentially harmful metals should be monitored insofar as is feasible on a systematic and continuing basis.*

Recommendation A26: *Economic and scientific research on the effects of air pollutants on vegetation and materials should be maintained at a level in consonance with work on effects on humans.*

Recommendation A27: *A concerted research program on the ecological effects of air pollutants should be developed and carefully coordinated as a multidisciplinary effort.*

Recommendation A28: *Better experiments must be designed to evaluate the intangible effects of polluted atmospheres, such as annoyance by odors, loss of scenic views, depression at loss of sunlight, and limitations on photosynthesis.*

Recommendation A29: *The establishment of federal air quality criteria, and their continued revision in the light of new evidence, is essential to rational management of the air environment. The effort should be continued at a pace commensurate with the development of knowledge, and the succeeding steps under the federal Air Quality Act of 1967 should be taken as expeditiously as possible.*

ANALYTICAL CHEMISTRY AND INSTRUMENTS

No effort to manage the air resource intelligently can proceed beyond the limits imposed by the ability to detect and measure substances in the air and at the source. Although steady progress is being made in the analytical chemistry of air pollution (6), the fact remains that knowledge of air contaminants today is restricted largely to the more common ones: sulfur dioxide, hydrogen sulfide, nitrogen oxides, total oxidant (including ozone), carbon monoxide, organics such as hydrocarbons, and particles. The analytical methods and instruments that are used to monitor the air (72) can provide useful data, but often they are costly and complex, require highly skilled operators, and are subject to significant limitations and interferences.

Air monitoring

The most sophisticated federal air monitoring system now operating is NAPCA's Continuous Air Monitoring Program (63). CAMP stations in half a dozen major cities continuously monitor and record the concentrations of sulfur dioxide, carbon monoxide, nitric oxide, nitrogen dioxide, total oxidant, methane, total hydrocarbons, particles, and a soiling index (Fig. 6). CAMP equipment was designed to operate automatically, but the stations require an operator as well as an air-conditioned building and a supply of chemicals. Most of the technology used in the CAMP stations is more than 10 years old.

The other, and much larger, federal system is the National Air Surveillance Network, a manual monitoring system. The 200-odd NASN stations collect samples and mail them to the NAPCA laboratories in Cincinnati for analysis. About half the stations sample sulfur dioxide, nitrogen dioxide, ammonia, oxidant, and aldehydes, among the gaseous air contaminants, and the others sample sulfur dioxide and nitrogen dioxide. All stations sample particulate matter, which is analyzed for ammonium, sulfate, and nitrate ions and for some 17 metals (5). NASN methods are subject to improvement, which was made in the past few years in the methods used for nitrogen dioxide and sulfur dioxide (77). As a result, national average values for nitrogen dioxide were about 50% higher in 1966 than in previous years for the same actual concentration of the gas. Sulfur dioxide values were roughly 30% higher. (Comparisons with previous years can be made, when desired, by applying the old and new methods to different parts of the same sample of air.) The remaining techniques are still older than those used in the CAMP stations and certainly can be improved if the effort is made.

An estimated 10,000 sampling stations will be needed to monitor the nation's air adequately. Air sampling activities have been expanding steadily at the federal, state, and local level, but only about 310 state and local air monitoring stations contributed data to NAPCA in 1968. These, plus existing NAPCA stations, thus total something over 500.

Progress is required in standardizing analytical methods, a task undertaken in 1966 by NAPCA's Analytical Methods Evaluation Service

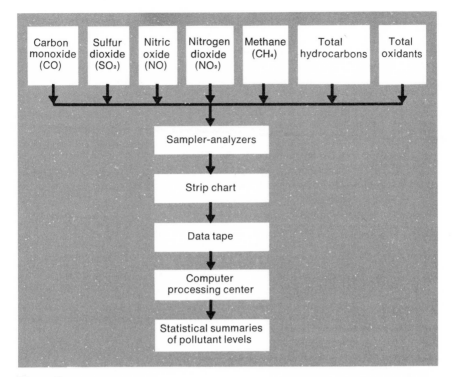

Figure 6

Flow of data from station of Continuous Air Monitoring Program (CAMP)

A space about as big as a large living room is required to house the automatic sampler-analyzers used by a CAMP station to monitor the seven gaseous pollutants shown above. Pollutant concentrations are recorded on strip charts, then transferred onto data tapes. Every week the charts and tapes are sent to a computer processing center in Cincinnati, where statistical summaries of pollutant levels are prepared. The stations also record airborne particles and a soiling index. Six CAMP stations were in the program as of April 1969—in Chicago, Cincinnati, Denver, Philadelphia, St. Louis, and Washington.

SOURCE: Department of Health, Education, and Welfare.

(104). Standardization is necessary to establish the reproducibility of methods of air sampling and analysis when used by chemists in different laboratories. It can help also to optimize the methods. In its first collaborative study, started in 1967, the Analytical Methods Evaluation Service sent two permeation tubes to about 90 laboratories for evaluation as primary standards for methods of determining sulfur dioxide.

The permeation tube is one of the two recently developed solutions (84, 123) to a long-standing problem: generating known amounts of a gas at the very low levels found in polluted atmospheres. Without such a primary standard, the analytical method for the gas cannot be calibrated absolutely. The Teflon permeation tube, which is about the size of a ballpoint pen refill, is filled with the liquefied gas and sealed. The gas escapes through the wall of the tube under its own pressure at a slow but constant rate that can be measured by weighing the tube daily. The gas is picked up in a stream of metered air in which its concentration can be established with great accuracy at well below 1 ppm.

The permeation tube cannot be used for unstable gases, such as ozone and, perhaps, the peroxyacyl nitrates. Ozone generally is measured by methods that are calibrated against dilute ozone that has been standardized by a reaction between ozone and a solution of potassium iodide. The standardization method assumes that the reaction produces one molecule of iodine for each molecule of ozone that reacts. The assumption has never been proved, and if it is wrong the methods calibrated in this way are also wrong.

Both ozone and peroxyacyl nitrates are important constituents of photochemical smog, but there is at present no instrumentation capable of measuring them separately and routinely in the field. Work is in progress on several methods for ozone that should be usable in monitoring, but the methods available now are too complex except for use in research. The best that can be done routinely in the field is to measure total oxidant. The results correlate well with total ozone when the ozone's concentration is high, but not when its concentration is low.

Gas chromatography has been used with some success to determine hydrocarbons and a few inorganic gases and gaseous tracers in the air. Better chromatographic methods are needed in some respects, however, as is more extensive use of chromatography in air pollution work. It should be possible to build gas chromatographic monitoring systems that could be used to obtain large amounts of air quality data.

In addition to measuring air contaminants at specific points, it would be valuable to be able to measure them over a distance and thus derive integrated values for concentrations. Long-path infrared and ultraviolet spectrometers for making such measurements are in development but not in general use. Also in development are instruments that measure particle concentration in the air over a long path by use of Lidar (light detection and ranging by use of pulsed laser source). Lasers whose emitted wavelength can be changed from one frequency to another have been built, and a light source of this kind could be the basis of a number of pollutant detection devices. Practical instruments, however, probably lie some time in the future.

Source monitoring

Sound control of pollutant emissions will require that they be monitored at the source. However, excepting instruments for measuring carbon dioxide, carbon monoxide, and oxygen in boiler plant stacks, very few fully satisfactory devices are available for continuously monitoring gaseous emissions from stacks. Problems with existing instruments include undesirable complexity, inability to perform properly at the high temperatures that may be encountered in stack gases, and clogging by particles and water. Such problems might be solved by optical devices that scan the stack gas rather than sampling it, but such devices are still in the development stage.

Instruments that monitor stack emissions remotely are desirable and in development, although fully successful devices do not appear to be imminent. Both infrared and ultraviolet instruments are being tried for measuring sulfur dioxide in stack plumes. An instrument that would use Lidar to measure particle emissions remotely is in the planning stage.

A major analytical problem is the development of improved methods and instrumentation for measuring automotive emissions. The need exists in three broad areas: research on control devices; certification of new vehicles; and inspection of vehicles in normal use. Of these, the major need is instrumentation that can be used for routine inspection by personnel who are not skilled technologists.

Recommendations: analytical chemistry and instruments

Recommendation A30: *Development of simplified, less costly instrumentation for air monitoring should be accelerated markedly. Means should be found for stimulating industrial research and development in this area.*

Recommendation A31: *The development of better in-stack and remote source-monitoring instrumentation for pollutants is essential and should be accelerated. Federal stimulation may be necessary to achieve adequately rapid innovation and dissemination.*

Recommendation A32: *Standardization of analytical methods and instruments should also be accelerated. Such standardization should include criteria for acceptable methods of sampling and storage as well as for the analytical methods themselves and for the interpretation and use of the resulting data. A program should be considered for certification of air-monitoring instruments on the basis of federally-established standards of performance.*

Recommendation A33: *Current levels of effort in developing new and improved analytical methods for pollutants should be increased. Such methods constitute the input from which monitoring instruments are developed. Analytical methods should not be downgraded solely because they are not adaptable to automatic instrumentation. For some tasks, such as exploratory studies of air pollution, manual methods may be much superior to automatic instruments.*

LITERATURE CITED

1. Agnew, W. G., "Science and Technology in Automotive Air Pollution Research," presented at the Symposium on Science and Technology of Aerosol Pollution in Modern Society, The Royal Society of London, February 1968.

2. "Air Pollution Manual, Part II—Control Equipment," American Industrial Hygiene Association, Detroit, Mich., 1968.

3. "Air Quality Criteria for Particulate Matter," U.S. Department of Health, Education, and Welfare, National Air Pollution Control Administration Publication No. AP-49, Washington, D.C., January 1969.

4. "Air Quality Criteria for Sulfur Oxides," U.S. Department of Health, Education, and Welfare, National Air Pollution Control Administration Publication No. AP-50, Washington, D.C., January 1969.

5. "Air Quality Data from the National Air Sampling Networks and Contributing State and Local Networks, 1964-1965," U.S. Department of Health, Education, and Welfare, National Air Pollution Control Administration, Cincinnati, Ohio, 1966.

6. Altshuller, A. P., "Air Pollution," *Anal. Chem.,* **41** (5), 1R (1969).

7. Altshuller, A. P., Bufalini, J. J., in "Photochemistry and Photobiology," Vol. 4, Pergamon Press, Ltd., London, England, 1965, pp. 97-146.

8. Altshuller, A. P., Cohen, I. R., "Photo-Oxidation of Acrolein-Nitrogen Oxide Mixtures in Air," *Int. J. Air Water Pollut.,* **7**, 1043 (1963).

9. Arey, W. F., Jr., Mayer, F. X., "Desulfurization of Residual Fuel Oils," Division of Petroleum Chemistry Preprints, Vol. 12 (4), A-25, 154th National Meeting of the American Chemical Society, Chicago, Ill., September 1967.

10. "The Automobile & Air Pollution: A Program for Progress," Part I, October 1967; Part II, December 1967, U. S. Department of Commerce, Government Printing Office, Washington, D.C.

11. Barnhart, D. H., Diehl, E. K., "Control of Nitrogen Oxides in Boiler Flue Gases by Two-Stage Combustion," *J. Air Pollut. Contr. Ass.,* **10**, 397 (1960).

12. Beard, R. R., Wertheim, G. A., "Behavioral Impairment Associated with Small Doses of Carbon Monoxide," *Amer. J. Publ. Health,* **57,** 2012 (1967), and subsequent private communication.

13. Behavioral Toxicology Looks at Air Pollutants," *Environ. Sci. Technol.,* **2,** 731 (1968).

14. Bienstock, D., Field, J. H., Myers, J. G., "Process Development in Removing Sulfur Dioxide from Hot Flue Gases. Part 3. Pilot Plant Study of the Alkalized Alumina System for SO_2 Removal," U. S. Bureau of Mines Report of Investigations 7021, Washington, D.C., 1967.

15. Bolin, B., Keeling, C. D., "Large-Scale Atmospheric Mixing as Deduced from the Seasonal and Meridoneal Variations of Carbon Dioxide," *J. Geophys. Res.,* **68**, 3899 (1963).

16. Boone, R. E., Brice, R. M., "Continuous Measurements of Acid Aerosol in the Atmosphere," paper 65-119 presented at the 58th Annual Meeting of the Air Pollution Control Association, Toronto, Canada, June 1965.

17. Bovier, R. F., "Sulfur-Smoke Removal System," *Proc. Am. Power Conf.,* **26**, 138 (1964).

18. Brennan, E. G., Leone, I. A., Daines, R. H., "Atmospheric Aldehydes Related to Petunia Leaf Damage," *Science,* **143,** 818 (1964).

19. Bryson, R. A., "All Other Factors Being Constant—A Reconciliation of Several Theories of Climatic Change," *Weatherwise,* April 1968, p. 56.

20. Cantwell, E. N., Rosenlund, I. T., Barth, W. J., Kinnear, F. L., Ross, S. W., "A Progress Report on the Development of Exhaust Manifold Reactors," Preprint 690139, International Automotive Engineering Congress, Society of Automotive Engineers, Detroit, Mich., January 1969.

21. "Carbon Monoxide—A Bibliography with Abstracts," U.S. Public Health Service Publication No. 1503, Government Printing Office, Washington, D.C., 1966.

22. Clewell, Dayton H., discussion of papers on effects of fuel volatility and composition on automotive emissions, Proceedings, 33rd Midyear Meeting, Division of Refining, American Petroleum Institute, New York, N.Y., Vol. 48, May 1968, p. 743.

23. Consolidated Edison Co. of New York, private communication, 1968.

24. "Control of Air Pollution from New Motor Vehicles and New Motor Vehicle Engines. Standards for Exhaust Emissions, Fuel Evaporative Emissions, and Smoke Emissions, Applicable to 1970 and Later Vehicles and Engines," *Fed. Regist.*, **33** (108), Part II, June 4, 1968.

25. "Control Techniques for Particulate Air Pollutants," U.S. Department of Health, Education, and Welfare, National Air Pollution Control Administration Publication No. AP-51, Washington, D.C., January 1969.

26. "Control Techniques for Sulfur Oxide Air Pollutants," U.S. Department of Health, Education, and Welfare, National Air Pollution Control Administration Publication No. AP-52, Washington, D.C., January 1969.

27. Damon, G. H., "Air Pollution Research and Coal Utilization," preprint No. 68-F-64, American Institute of Mining, Metallurgical and Petroleum Engineers, New York, N.Y., February 1968.

28. Deeter, W. F., Daigh, H. D., Wallin, O. W., Jr., "An Approach for Controlling Vehicle Emissions," preprint 680400, Society of Automotive Engineers, New York, N.Y., 1968.

29. Deevey, E. S., Jr., "Bogs," *Sci. Amer.*, **199** (4), 114 (1958).

30. "Desulfurization Costs—Residual Fuel Oil. Typical Caribbean Refinery, Venezuelan Crude Oil," prepared by Bechtel Corp. for the American Petroleum Institute, New York, N.Y., February 1967.

31. "Ecological Soundings & Awareness," *Environ. Sci. Technol.*, **2**, 1069 (1968).

32. Ehhalt, D. H., "Methane in the Atmosphere," *J. Air Pollut. Contr. Ass.*, **17**, 518 (1967).

33. Estes, F. L., "Analysis of Air Pollution Mixtures: A Study of Biologically Effective Components," *Anal. Chem.*, **34**, 998 (1962).

34. Estes, F. L., "The Effect of Initial Concentration of Reactants on the Biological Effectiveness of Photochemical Reaction Products," *Atmos. Environ.*, **1**, 159 (1967).

35. Estes, F. L., Pan, C., "Response of Enzyme Systems to Photochemical Reaction Products," *Arch. Environ. Health*, **10**, 207 (1965).

36. "Expenditures for Fuel Products Desulfurization," prepared by The Pace Co. for the American Petroleum Institute, New York, N.Y.

37. Fairchild, E. J., Murphy, S. D., Stokinger, H. E., "Protection by Sulfur Compounds Against the Air Pollutants Ozone and Nitrogen Dioxide," *Science*, **130**, 861 (1959).

38. "A Feasibility Study of the Recovery of Sulfur and Iron from Coal Pyrites," Paul Weir Co., Contract No. PH-86-65-29 with U. S. Public Health Service, 1966.

39. Frank, N. R., Amdur, M. O., Whittenberger, J. L., "A Comparison of the Acute Effects of SO_2 Administered Alone or in Combination with NaCl Particles on the Respiratory Mechanics of Healthy Adults," *Int. J. Air Water Pollut.*, **8**, 125 (1964).

40. Friedlander, S. K., Pasceri, R. E., "Measurements of the Particle Size Distribution of the Atmospheric Aerosol: I. Introduction and Experimental Methods, II: Experimental Results and Discussion," *J. Atmos. Sci.*, **22**, 571 (1964).

41. Fristrom, R. M., "The Mechanism of Combustion in Flames," *Chem. Eng. News*, **41** (43), 150 (1963).

42. Gartrell, F. E., Thomas, F. W., Carpenter, S. B., "Atmospheric Oxidation of SO_2 in Coal-Burning Power Plant Plumes," *Am. Ind. Hyg. Ass. J.,* **24,** 113 (1963).

43. Garvey, J. R., testimony at hearings before the Subcommittee on Air and Water Pollution of the Committee on Public Works, U.S. Senate, 90th Congress, 1st Session on S. 780, Part 4, Government Printing Office, Washington, D.C., 1967.

44. Gerhard, E. R., Johnstone, H. F., "Air Pollution Studies—Photochemical Oxidation of Sulfur Dioxide in Air," *Ind. Eng. Chem.,* **47,** 972 (1955).

45. Goldsmith, J. R., "Environmental Epidemiology and the Metamorphosis of the Human Habitat," *Amer. J. Publ. Health,* **57,** 1532 (1967).

46. Goldsmith, J. R., Hexter, A. C., "Respiratory Exposure to Lead: Epidemiological and Experimental Dose-Response Relationships," *Science,* **158,** 132 (1967).

47. Golothan, D. W., "Diesel Engine Exhaust Smoke: The Influence of Fuel Properties and the Effects of Using Barium-Containing Fuel Additive," paper 670092, Society of Automotive Engineers, Automotive Engineering Congress, Detroit, Mich., January 1967.

48. Gunn, R., "The Secular Increase of the World-Wide Fine Particle Pollution," *J. Atmos. Sci.,* **21,** 168 (1964).

49. Haagen-Smit, A. J., "Chemistry and Physiology of Los Angeles Smog," *Ind. Eng. Chem.,* **44,** 1342 (1952).

50. Hamming, W. J., "Inadequate Automobile Control But More Horsepower, More Chrome, and More Red Herring," *Arch. Environ. Health,* **13,** 234 (1966).

51. Hamming, W. J., Dickinson, J. E., "Statistical Survey of Data Relating to Hydrocarbon and Oxides of Nitrogen Relationships in Photochemical Smog," *Int. J. Air Water Pollut.,* **10,** 637 (1966).

52. "Health and Air Pollution Subject of New Studies," *Environ. Sci. Technol.,* **2,** 246 (1968).

53. Hermance, H. W., "Combatting the Effects of Smog on Wire-Spring Relays," *Bell Lab. Rec.,* **44,** 48 (1966).

54. Heuss, J. M., Glasson, W. A., "Hydrocarbon Reactivity and Eye Irritation," *Environ. Sci. Technol.,* **2,** 1109 (1968).

55. Jaffe, L. S., "Effects of Photochemical Air Pollution on Vegetation with Relation to the Air Quality Requirements," *J. Air Pollut. Contr. Ass.,* **17,** 38 (1967).

56. Jaffe, L. S., "The Effects of Photochemical Oxidants on Materials," *J. Air Pollut. Contr. Ass.,* **17,** 375 (1967).

57. Jimeson, R. M., "Utilizing Solvent Refined Coal in Power Plants," *Chem. Eng. Progr.,* **62** (10), 53 (1966).

58. Johnson, K. L., Dworetzky, L. H., Heller, A. N., "Carbon Monoxide and Air Pollution from Automobile Emissions in New York City," *Science,* **160,** 67 (1968).

59. Johnstone, H. F., Coughanowr, D. R., "Absorption of Sulfur Dioxide from Air. Oxidation in Drops Containing Dissolved Catalysts," *Ind. Eng. Chem.,* **50,** 1169 (1958).

60. Johnstone, H. F., Moll, A. J., "Air Pollution . . . Formation of Sulfuric Acid in Fogs," *Ind. Eng. Chem.,* **52,** 861 (1960).

61. Junge, C. E., "Air Chemistry and Radioactivity," Academic Press, New York, N.Y., 1963.

62. Jutze, G. A., Harris, R. L., Jr., Georgevich, M., "The Interstate Air Pollution Surveillance Program Effects Network," *J. Air Pollut. Contr. Ass.,* **17,** 291 (1967).

63. Jutze, G. A., Tabor, E. C., "The Continuous Air Monitoring Program," *J. Air Pollut. Contr. Ass.*, **13**, 278 (1963).

64. Kalkstein, M. I., "Rhodium-102 High-Altitude Tracer Experiments," *Science*, **137**, 645 (1962).

65. Katell, S., "Removing Sulfur Dioxide from Flue Gases," *Chem. Eng. Progr.*, **62** (10), 67 (1966).

66. Kehoe, R. A., "Lead Intake from Food and the Atmosphere," *Science*, **159**, 1000 (1967).

67. Larsen, R. I., Stalker, W. W., Claydon, C. R., "The Radial Distribution of Sulfur Dioxide Source Strength and Concentration in Nashville," *J. Air Pollut. Contr. Ass.*, **11**, 529 (1961).

68. Leighton, P. A., "Photochemistry of Air Pollution," Academic Press, New York, N.Y., 1961.

69. Lettau, H. H., Davidson, B., Ed., "Exploring the Atmosphere's First Mile," Pergamon Press, New York, N.Y., 1957.

70. Lewis, B., von Elbe, G., "Combustion, Flames and Explosions of Gases," 2nd ed., Academic Press, New York, N.Y., 1961.

71. Lodge, J. P., Jr., unpublished data on lead in rainfall.

72. Lodge, J. P., Jr., Pate, J. B., "Section E-44, Analysis of Air for Pollutants," in "Treatise on Analytical Chemistry," Kolthoff, I. M., Elving, P. J., Eds., Part III, Vol. 3, Interscience, John Wiley & Sons, New York, N.Y., in press.

73. Manowitz, B., Smith, M., Steinberg, M., Tucker, W., "Status Report on the BNL Atmospheric Diagnostics Program," USAEC Report BNL 11465, June 1967.

74. Matzen, R. N., "Effect of Vitamin C and Hydrocortisone on the Pulmonary Edema Produced by Ozone in Mice," *J. Appl. Physiol.*, **11**, 105 (1957).

75. McCormick, R. A., Ludwig, J. H., "Climate Modification by Atmospheric Aerosols," *Science*, **156**, 1358 (1967).

76. Moore, W. W., "Reduction in Ambient Air Concentration of Fly Ash—Present and Future Prospects," Proceedings: The Third National Conference on Air Pollution, U.S. Public Health Service Publication No. 1649, Government Printing Office, Washington, D.C., 1966, p. 170.

77. Morgan, G. B., Golden, C., Tabor, E. C., "New and Improved Procedures for Gas Sampling and Analysis in the National Air Sampling Network," *J. Air Pollut. Contr. Ass.*, **17**, 300 (1967).

78. Mountain, J. T., Wagner, W. D., Fairchild, E. J., Stockell, F. R., Stokinger, H. E., "Biochemical Effects of Ozone and Nitrogen Dioxide on Laboratory Animals," paper presented at 138th National Meeting of the American Chemical Society, New York, N.Y., September 1960.

79. Mudd, J. B., "Enzyme Inactivation by Peroxyacetyl Nitrate," *Arch. Biochem. Biophys.*, **102**, 59 (1963).

80. Murphy, S. D., Davis, H. V., Zaratzian, V. L., "Biochemical Effects in Rats from Irritating Air Contaminants," *Toxicol. Appl. Pharmacol.*, **6**, 520 (1964).

81. Newell, R. E., "The Transport of Trace Substances in the Atmosphere and Their Implications for the General Circulation of the Stratosphere," *Geofis. Pura Appl.*, **49**, 137 (1961).

82. Nicksic, S. W., Harkins, J., Painter, L. J., "Statistical Survey of Data Relating to Hydrocarbon and Oxides of Nitrogen Relationships in Photochemical Smog," *Int. J. Air Water Pollut.*, **10**, 15 (1966).

83. Nonhebel, G., "British Charts for Heights of Industrial Chimneys," *Int. J. Air Water Pollut.*, **10**, 183 (1966).

84. O'Keeffe, A. E., Ortman, G. C., "Primary Standards for Trace Gas Analysis," *Anal. Chem.*, **38**, 760 (1966).

85. Patterson, C. C., "Contaminated and Natural Lead Environments of Man," *Arch. Environ. Health*, **11**, 344 (1965).

86. Patterson, C. C., Salvia, J. D., "Lead in the Modern Environment. How Much Is Natural?" *Sci. Citizen*, **10**, 66 (1968).

87. Penner, S. S., "Combustion and Propulsion Research," *Chem. Eng. News*, **41** (2), 74 (1963).

88. Perry, H., "Potential for Reduction of Sulfur in Coal by Other than Conventional Cleaning Methods," preprint 24E at 59th National Meeting of American Institute of Chemical Engineers, Columbus, Ohio, May 1966.

89. Pierrard, J. M., "Photochemical Decomposition of Lead Halides from Automobile Exhaust," *Environ. Sci. Technol.*, **3**, 48 (1969).

90. Pitts, J. W., Moore, D. G., "Apparatus for Studying the Effects of Atmospheric Pollution and Cyclic Dew Formation on the Deterioration of Materials," *Mater. Res. Stand.*, **6**, 328 (1966).

91. Plumley, A. L., Whiddon, O. D., Shutko, F. W., Jonakin, J., "Removal of SO_2 and Dust from Stack Gases," presented at American Power Conference, Chicago, Ill., April 1967.

92. Pollock, W. A., Tomany, J. P., Frieling, G., "Removal of Sulfur Dioxide and Fly Ash from Coal Burning Power Plant Flue Gases," Preprint 66-WA/CD-4 at Winter Annual Meeting and Energy Systems Exposition of American Society of Mechanical Engineers, New York, N.Y., November-December 1966.

93. "Pollution Control Directory," *Environ. Sci. Technol.*, **2**, 799 (1968).

94. Potter, A. E., Harrington, R. E. Spaite, P. W., "Limestone-Dolomite Processes for Flue Gas Desulfurization," presented at the 154th National Meeting of the American Chemical Society, Chicago, Ill., September 1967.

95. "Proceedings: The Third National Conference on Air Pollution," U. S. Public Health Service Publication No. 1649, Government Printing Office, Washington, D.C., 1966.

96. "Progress in the Prevention and Control of Air Pollution. First Report of the Secretary of Health, Education, and Welfare to the United States Congress pursuant to Public Law 90-148, The Air Quality Act of 1967," Senate Document No. 92, 90th Congress, 2nd Session, June 28, 1968.

97. "Progress in the Prevention and Control of Air Pollution," Second Report of the Secretary of Health, Education, and Welfare to the Congress of the United States in Compliance with Public Law 90-148, January 1969.

98. Robbins, R. C., Borg, K. M., Robinson, E., "Carbon Monoxide in the Atmosphere," *J. Air Pollut. Contr. Ass.*, **18**, 106 (1968).

99. Robinson, E., Ludwig, F. L., "Particle Size Distribution of Urban Lead Aerosols," *J. Air Pollut. Contr. Ass.*, **17**, 664 (1967).

100. Robinson, E., MacLeod, J. A., Lapple, C. E., "A Meteorological Tracer Technique Using Uranine Dye," *J. Meteorol.*, **16**, 63 (1959).

101. Robinson, E., Robbins, R. C., "Sources, Abundance, and Fate of Gaseous Atmospheric Pollutants," prepared by Stanford Research Institute for the American Petroleum Institute, New York, N.Y., February 1968.

102. Rohrman, F. A., Steigerwald, B. J., Ludwig, J. H., "Industrial Emissions of Carbon Dioxide in the United States: A Projection," *Science*, **156**, 931 (1967).

103. Ryason, P. R., Harkins, J., "A Method of Removing Potentially Harmful Oxides from Combustion Gases," Division of Petroleum Chemistry Preprints, Vol. 12 (4), A-17, 154th National Meeting of the American Chemical Society, Chicago, Ill., September 1967.

104. Saltzman, B. E., "Air Quality Program Needs Uniform Tests," *Environ. Sci. Technol.,* **2,** 22 (1968).

105. Saltzman, B. E., Coleman, A. I., Clemons, C. A., "Halogenated Compounds as Gaseous Meteorological Tracers," *Anal. Chem.,* **38,** 753 (1966).

106. Schaefer, V. J., "Ice Nuclei from Automobile Exhaust and Iodine Vapor," *Science,* **154,** 1555 (1966).

107. Scheel, L. D., Dobrogorski, O. J., Mountain, J. T., Svirbely, J. L., Stokinger, H. E., "Physiologic, Biochemical, Immunologic, and Pathologic Changes Following Ozone Exposure," *J. Appl. Physiol.,* **14,** 67 (1959).

108. Sensenbaugh, J. D., Jonakin, J., "Effect of Combustion Conditions on Nitrogen Oxide Formation in Boiler Furnaces," paper 60-WA-334, American Society of Mechanical Engineers, New York, N.Y., 1961.

109. Singer, J. M., Cook, E. B., Harris, M. E., Rowe, V. R., Grumer, J., "Flame Characteristics Causing Air Pollution: Production of Oxides of Nitrogen and Carbon Monoxide," U. S. Bureau of Mines Report of Investigations 6958, Washington, D.C., 1967.

110. Slack, A. V., "Air Pollution: The Control of SO_2 from Power Stacks. Part III—Processes for Recovering SO_2," *Chem. Eng.,* **74** (25), 188 (1967).

111. Southern California Edison Co., private communication, 1968.

112. Squires, A. M., "Air Pollution: The Control of SO_2 from Power Stacks, Part II—The Removal of SO_2 from Stack Gases," *Chem. Eng.,* **74** (24), 133 (1967).

113. Stalker, W. W., Dickenson, R. C., Zimmer, C. E., Keagy, D. M., "Sampling Station and Time Requirements for Urban Air Pollution Survey. I. Lead Peroxide Candles and Dustfall Collectors," *J. Air Pollut. Contr. Ass.,* **11,** 270 (1961).

114. Stalker, W. W., Dickerson, R. C., "Sampling Station and Time Requirements for Urban Air Pollution Surveys Part II: Suspended Particulate Matter and Soiling Index," *J. Air Pollut. Contr. Ass.,* **12,** 111 (1962).

115. Stalker, W. W., Dickerson, R. C., "Sampling Station and Time Requirements for Urban Air Pollution Surveys Part III: Two- and Four-Hour Soiling Index," *J. Air Pollut. Contr. Ass.,* **12,** 170 (1962).

116. Stalker, W. W., Dickerson, R. C., Krame, G. D., "Sampling Station and Time Requirements for Urban Air Pollution Surveys Part IV: 2- and 24-hour Sulfur Dioxide and Summary of Other Pollutants," *J. Air Pollut. Contr. Ass.,* **12,** 361 (1962).

117. Stalker, W. W., Kenline, P. A., Paulus, H. J., "Nashville Sulfur Dioxide Emission Inventory and the Relation of Emission to Measured Sulfur Dioxide," *J. Air Pollut. Contr. Ass.,* **14,** 469 (1964).

118. "Status of Current Technology in the Control of Emissions to the Atmosphere," hearings before the Subcommittee on Air and Water Pollution of the Committee on Public Works, U.S. Senate, 90th Congress, 1st Session on S. 780, Part 4, Government Printing Office, Washington, D.C., 1967, p. 2274.

119. Stephens, E. R., Darley, E. F., Taylor, O. C., Scott, W. E., "Photochemical Reaction Products in Air Pollution," *Int. J. Air Water Pollut.,* **4,** 79 (1961).

120. Sterba, M. J., in "Symposium on Environmental Lead Contamination," U. S. Public Health Service Publication No. 1440, Government Printing Office, Washington, D.C., 1966, p. 113.

121. Stern, A. C., Ed., "Air Pollution," Vol. I, 2nd ed., Academic Press, New York, N.Y., 1968.

122. Stokinger, H. E., "Evaluation of the Hazards of Ozone and Oxides of Nitrogen—Factors Modifying Acute Toxicity," *AMA Arch. Ind. Health,* **15,** 181 (1957).

123. Stratmann, H., Buck, M., "Measurement of NO_2 in the Atmosphere," *Int. J. Air Water Pollut.,* **10,** 313 (1966).

124. "SO_2 Control Processes for Stack Gases Reach Commercial Status," *Environ. Sci. Technol.,* **2,** 994 (1968).

125. "Sulfur Oxide Removal from Power Plant Stack Gas," Tennessee Valley Authority, Knoxville, Tenn., 1968.

126. "Sulfur Oxides and Other Sulfur Compounds—A Bibliography with Abstracts," U. S. Public Health Service Publication No. 1093, Government Printing Office, Washington, D.C., 1965.

127. "Survey of Lead in the Atmosphere of Three Urban Communities," U. S. Public Health Service Publication No. 999-AP-12, Government Printing Office, Washington, D.C., 1965.

128. Tarkhova, L. P., "Maximum Permissible Concentration of Chlorobenzene in the Atmosphere," *Gigiena i Sanit.,* **30** (3), 8 (1965).

129. Tebbens, B. D., in "Air Pollution," Vol. I, 2nd ed. Stern, A. C., Ed., Academic Press, New York, N.Y., 1967, Chapter 2.

130. "Technical Report of California Standards for Ambient Air Quality and Motor Vehicle Exhaust," State of California, Department of Public Health, Berkeley, Calif., 1960.

131. Teller, A. J., "Recovery of Sulfur Oxides from Stack Gases," in "New Developments in Air Pollution Control," Metropolitan Engineers Council on Air Resources Symposium, New York, N.Y., 1967, p. 1.

132. Thomas, M. D., "Sulfur Dioxide, Sulfuric Acid Aerosol and Visibility in Los Angeles," *Int. J. Air Water Pollut.,* **6,** 443 (1962).

133. Turner, D. B., "Relationships Between 24-Hour Mean Air Quality Measurements and Meteorological Factors in Nashville, Tennessee," *J. Air Pollut. Contr. Ass.,* **11,** 483 (1961).

134. "U. S. Motor Gasoline Economics. Vol. 1. Manufacture of Unleaded Gasoline," prepared by Bonner & Moore Associates, Inc., for the American Petroleum Institute, New York, N.Y., 1967.

135 U. S. Robert A. Taft Sanitary Engineering Center, "Symposium: Air Over Cities," Report A 62-S, Cincinnati, Ohio, 1962.

136. "Vehicle Emissions," *Progress in Technology,* Vol. 6, 1964; Part II, Vol. 12, 1967, Society of Automotive Engineers, New York, N.Y.

137. Walker, A. B., "New Developments in the Control of Particulate Emission," in "New Developments in Air Pollution Control," Metropolitan Engineers Council on Air Resources Symposium, New York, N.Y., 1967, p. 12.

138. Winchester, J. W., Duce, R. A., in "Nuclear Activation Techniques in the Life Sciences," International Atomic Energy Agency, Vienna, Austria, 1967, pp. 631-643.

The Water Environment

Contents

The Water Environment

INTRODUCTION

T he water environment is confined and unevenly distributed over the earth, and man consequently has been compelled to learn to manage it to a much greater degree than has been the case with air. That the need for water management in the U.S. has outrun the application of the available technology is due more to negligence than to ignorance. Ignorance exists, certainly. The biological processes that have been used for years to treat waste waters are still in many ways highly empirical. The enormously complex chemistry of natural waters (56) is far from being well understood. But notwithstanding the deficiencies in fundamental knowledge, it is technologically feasible today to enhance markedly the quality of the nation's waters.

Organizations such as the Ohio River Valley Water Sanitation Commission, an eight-state compact, have been working successfully for some years to control water pollution. Only in the past decade, however, have the federal legislative and administrative measures evolved that alone can compel comprehensive nationwide use of the available knowledge in upgrading and maintaining the quality of the water environment. To maintain the momentum that these measures have bred, and to augment and refine the technology that they can bring into play, will require, as with the air environment, steady growth in fundamental understanding in four broad areas:

- The flow and dispersion of water pollutants and their degradation or conversion to other chemical and physical forms.
- The means of abating water pollution where generation of the pollutants cannot be avoided.
- The effects of water pollutants on plant and animal life and on inanimate objects.
- The means of detecting and measuring water pollutants and their effects.

BACKGROUND

A body of water, like an air mass, is a dynamic system, steadily absorbing a range of solids, liquids, and gases, both natural and man-made. Natural waters, moreover, normally teem with living organisms, which can powerfully affect the course of events in a given water system. All of these substances, living and nonliving, may flow, disperse, and interact chemically and physically before they reach a sink such as the ocean or a receptor such as a fish. En route from source to receptor they may assume a variety of chemical and physical forms.

Water as H_2O is a chemical compound of unvarying composition, and in this sense natural waters are never pure. Water is considered polluted, by one or more substances, if it is not suitable for its intended use: domestic, industrial, or agricultural water supply; propagation of fish and wildlife; recreation and others.

Determining the relative significance of man-made sources of water pollution is complicated by the fact that contaminants often enter water in complex mixtures of many substances whose specific chemical identities are largely unknown. For practical purposes, this difficulty can be partially bypassed by describing waste streams in terms of certain collective characteristics. One of these characteristics is biochemical oxygen demand (BOD), which is a measure of the weight of dissolved oxygen consumed in the biological processes that degrade organic matter that enters natural waters. Another collective characteristic is the weight of suspended solids, only part of which is settleable, in the waste stream.

In terms of these collective parameters, the leading source of controllable man-made water pollutants in the U.S. is manufacturing, and the second leading source is domestic wastes. Other sources include agricultural and urban runoff, acid mine drainage, watercraft, and livestock feedlots. In 1963, the last year for which figures are available, manufacturing accounted for an estimated 13.1 billion gallons of waste water. Before treatment, these wastes contained 22 billion pounds of BOD and 18 billion pounds of settleable and suspended solids. On these bases, manufacturing generated, before treatment, about three times the amount of wastes produced, before treatment, by the 120 million people (of a total of 189 million) who were served by sewers in 1963 (Table 1). One weakness in such comparisons is that industrial wastes are much more likely than domestic wastes to contain refractory organic chemicals, those that resist biological degradation. (The problem is not confined to the chemical industry.) Industrial wastes may also contain organic compounds that must be converted to other, less harmful compounds before they are discharged, or trace elements that must be removed in the treatment process.

Various agencies have been measuring at least certain aspects of the quality of the nation's waters for some years. The computerized federal storage and retrieval system, STORET (125), now contains such data from roughly 18,000 stations that have sampled water over the years at different points for various lengths of time. Such stations may measure a few or many parameters, depending on their mission (Table 2).

The federal pollution surveillance system started in 1957 with 50 stations. The current system, under the Federal Water Pollution Control Administration (FWPCA) in the Department of the Interior, has about 300 long-term stations, of which about 50 are automatic water quality monitors. FWPCA and other agencies, federal, state, and local, operate a total of 800 to 1000 stations of differing degrees of complexity. An estimated 2500 stations will be required nationwide to fulfill the federal water pollution control mission, and the states are estimated to require at least as many and possibly two or three times that many. The Public Health Service, parent of FWPCA's predecessor agency, published six annual compilations of water quality data, covering through

Table 1

Estimated volumes of industrial and domestic wastes before treatment, 1963

Industry	Waste water (billion gallons)	Standard biochemical oxygen demand (million pounds)	Settleable and suspended solids (million pounds)
Food and kindred products	690	4,300	6,600
Textile mill products	140	890	n.a.
Paper and allied products	1,900	5,900	3,000
Chemical and allied products	3,700	9,700	1,900
Petroleum and coal	1,300	500	460
Rubber and plastics	160	40	50
Primary metals	4,300	480	4,700
Machinery	150	60	50
Electrical machinery	91	70	20
Transportation equipment	240	120	n.a.
All other manufacturing	450	390	930
All manufacturing	13,100	22,000	18,000
Domestic Served by sewers (120 million people)	5,300[a]	7,300[b]	8,800[c]

[a] Number of persons × 120 gallons per person per day × 365 days
[b] Number of persons × 1/6 pound per person per day × 365 days
[c] Number of persons × 1/5 pound per person per day × 365 days
SOURCE: "The Cost of Clean Water, Vol. I, Summary Report," U. S. Department of the Interior, Federal Water Pollution Control Administration, Government Printing Office, Washington, D. C., January 1968.

Table 2

Sample water analysis [a]

Temperature	17.8° C.		Alkalinity	71 milligrams/liter
Dissolved oxygen	8.2 milligrams/liter		Hardness	112 milligrams/liter
			Color	7 (units)
pH (hydrogen ion activity)	8.0		Turbidity	35 (units)
			Sulfate	70 milligrams/liter
Biochemical oxygen demand	5.2 milligrams/liter		Phosphate	0.1 milligram/liter
			Total dissolved solids	200 milligrams/liter
Chemical oxygen demand	19 milligrams/liter		Coliform bacteria	100 per 100 milliliters
Chloride	20 milligrams/liter			

[a] Sample picked at random to indicate nature and order of magnitude of water quality parameters that are often determined. Other data might include plankton populations, trace metals, and organic compounds, both broad classes and specific compounds.
SOURCE: "Water Pollution Surveillance System, Annual Compilation of Data, Oct. 1, 1962—Sept. 30, 1963." Public Health Service Publication No. 663, Vol. 2, Government Printing Office, Washington, D. C., 1963.

Sept. 30, 1963 (140), but none has been published since. The current federal plan is to use the STORET system to supply such data.

The national legislative basis for managing the water environment is the Federal Water Pollution Control Act of 1956, as amended. One of the amendments, the Water Quality Act of 1965, requires the states and four other jurisdictions to establish water quality standards for interstate waters, such standards to be approved by the Secretary of the Interior (57). The water quality standards provide for:

- "Potential and future water uses as well as the present intended use and uses.
- "The upgrading and enhancement of water quality and the use or uses of streams or portions thereof that are presently affected by pollution.
- "The maintenance and protection of quality and use or uses of waters now of a high quality or of a quality suitable for present and potential future uses."

The standards packages include plans for implementation and enforcement. They also include a time schedule for construction of the necessary municipal and industrial waste treatment facilities. By June 1969, the Secretary had approved, with certain exceptions, the standards of all 54 jurisdictions. The exceptions differ with the jurisdiction and are subject to continuing negotiation.

FLOW, DISPERSION, DEGRADATION

A substance moves through a water system by flow or convection and disperses by diffusion or mixing. As the substance travels from source to sink or receptor it may be degraded or converted to other chemical and physical forms by chemical, biological, and physical processes. This overall transport process must be thoroughly understood if the water environment is to be managed soundly in the long run. The transport process determines in large measure the effects of waterborne substances on quality throughout a water system. The transport process is fundamental to the ecology of the system. Clear understanding of degradation phenomena, in particular, is vital in deciding whether specific pollutants should be allowed to enter water systems or even sinks, such as the oceans.

It is possible, though often extremely difficult, to describe the effects of the transport process mathematically, and computer simulation and other high-speed computational techniques can often be brought to bear on such problems. Encouraging progress has been made in developing mathematical descriptions of the physical processes of convection and dispersion in streams, estuaries, and coastal waters. The major uncertainties now in describing pollutant transport mathematically appear to lie in the details of the degradation processes. Proper understanding of these processes requires knowledge not only of the processes themselves, but of the nature and amounts of the substances that are being degraded.

Amounts and composition of wastes

Rational planning for water pollution control in regions or drainage basins requires detailed inventories of the composition and volume of all pollutants from all significant sources. Yet for only a few water systems, such as the Ohio River, the Delaware River, and Lake Erie (36, 68), have such inventories been compiled even partially. For almost no water pollutants, not excepting nutrients such as nitrogen- and phosphorus-containing compounds, have adequate balances been worked out of the amounts that enter the system and the amounts that leave. Gross inventories are available on the sources and amounts of municipal wastes, but data on industrial wastes are less readily available.

The main inorganic constituents of most wastes include ions such as sodium, potassium, ammonium, calcium, magnesium, chloride, nitrate, nitrite, bicarbonate, sulfate, and phosphate. The specific organic compounds in waterborne wastes are less well known. Exceptions include the extensive programs of analysis for pesticides in surface waters, analytical work on synthetic detergents, and a few studies of phenolic substances and carboxylic acids in streams.

Even the major organic chemical groups in domestic wastes and treated domestic wastes are known only partially. One of the relatively few analyses that have been made of domestic sewage could account for only 75% of the total organic carbon (85). The classes of compounds that were detected included carbohydrates, amino acids, fatty acids, soluble acids, esters, anionic surfactants, amino sugars, amides, and creatinine. In other work, more than 40 specific chemical compounds were identified in domestic sewage (62). An analysis of the effluent from secondary sewage treatment could account for only about 35% of the total chemically oxidizable organic materials (17).

The lack of definitive data on the composition of wastes extends to municipal storm water runoff (144), as well as to discharges from combined sewer systems. These systems combine storm water with raw sewage, and the stream bypasses the treatment plant when the system is overloaded. The studies that have been made show that urban storm water runoff at times is equal to or higher than domestic sewage in concentrations of suspended solids, coliform bacteria, chemically oxidizable organics, organic and inorganic nitrogen, and inorganic phosphorus.

Particles, particularly those of colloidal and smaller size, make up a large part of the pollutants discharged from many sources, but important characteristics such as particle size distribution often are not known. Even for municipal waste water and secondary treatment plant effluent, the data on particles are still too scarce to provide the insights that might help to upgrade sewage treatment processes. A particle size classification scheme for waste water has been devised using the electron microscope, centrifugation, and filtration (108). The scheme classifies particulate matter in four size ranges:

Group	Size range
Settleable solids	Larger than 100 microns
Supracolloidal solids	1 to 100 microns
Colloidal solids	1 millimicron to 1 micron
Soluble solids	Less than 1 millimicron

This classification has been used as a basis for developing a rapid means of separating particles in both waste water and treatment plant effluent (104). The separation method, which is based on centrifugation, was applied to two municipal sewage treatment plants. In the waste water entering both plants, 14% of the solids were settleable, 11% were supracolloidal, 6% were colloidal, and 69% were soluble. In both effluents, 93% of the solids were soluble, and most of the remainder were supracolloidal. The influent and effluent particles were largely organic and the soluble solids were largely inorganic.

The electron microscope has been used to study samples of the colloidal fraction of the solids from secondary sewage treatment (34). The samples were separated by centrifugation and freeze-dried to preserve their structure. Colloidal solids in the size range 0.01 to 1 micron fell into two groups: bacteria, viruses, and related compact bodies of definite size and shape; and shapeless, fragmentary material loosely clumped together. The dominant solids found were fragments of bacterial cell walls whose size appeared to range from 0.05 to 0.5 micron. Most of the colloidal material that originated in living cells could be removed by membrane filtration or coagulation with iron (ferric) chloride or lime.

Biological aspects

The processes that degrade and convert substances in water to other chemical and physical forms are extremely complicated because of the effects of aquatic life, mainly microorganisms. Microorganisms may control the soluble concentration of an element in water, notable examples being carbon, nitrogen, and phosphorus, the major elements in cells. Microorganisms may convert organic compounds in the water partly into carbon dioxide. They may convert dissolved carbon dioxide into organic compounds. They may affect the concentrations of inorganic compounds of silicon, aluminum, and other elements. Such effects are multiplied by the very large numbers of different substances in water and the variations in natural populations of microorganisms. Because of these complexities, general descriptions of biological degradation in water systems, particularly mathematical descriptions, seem unlikely to emerge. Research on degradation and its products must thus depend to a large extent on the measurement of specific substances in water, and their degradation products.

Specific chemical methods are not now available for measuring many degradable substances and their reaction products. Reliance must often be placed on the collective parameters such as BOD,* which measures the weight of dissolved oxygen utilized by microorganisms as they degrade or transform the carbon- and nitrogen-containing compounds in organic matter. The biochemical reactions involved in the degradation of carbon compounds are related to the period of incubation. The routine BOD test has been standardized at five days of incubation. The five-day BOD normally measures only 70 or 80% of the biochemical oxygen demand of the sample, and for many purposes this is a reasonable parameter. The test measures the gross five-day oxygen demand of a given sample of waste, and it can be used, for example, to describe the gross quantity of degradable organic matter moving down a stream. It tells little or nothing of the fate of specific organic compounds that enter the stream, including those that resist the biological degradation processes in varying degree.

Other collective parameters have been devised, partly to avoid some of the shortcomings of the BOD test. One of these measurements is chemical oxygen demand (COD), which is based on the fact that most organic compounds can be oxidized to carbon dioxide and water by strong oxidizing agents. COD measures the equivalent oxygen demand of compounds that are biologically degradable and of many that are not. It thus gives higher values for oxygen demand than does the BOD test. Another collective parameter is total organic carbon (TOC). It is based on methods developed recently that involve rapid combustion of carbon and measurement of the resulting carbon dioxide by infrared spectroscopy. Although they measure total oxygen demand, COD and TOC, like BOD, tell little or nothing of the specific organic compounds in the sample of water that is analyzed.

The biological aspects of pollutant transport are important in determining the amount of organic waste that can be discharged to a water system, and at what points it can be discharged. Waste treatment must be managed so that the degradation process does not reduce the level

---

* A more detailed explanation of biochemical oxygen demand is as follows (121): "The oxygen demand of sewage, sewage plant effluents, polluted waters, or industrial wastes is exerted by three classes of materials: (a) carbonaceous organic material usable as a source of food by aerobic organisms; (b) oxidizable nitrogen derived from nitrite, ammonia, and organic nitrogen compounds which serve as food for specific bacteria (e.g., *Nitrosomonas* and *Nitrobacter*); and (c) certain chemical reducing compounds (ferrous iron, sulfite, and sulfide) which will react with molecularly dissolved oxygen. In raw and settled domestic sewage, most—and, for practical purposes, all—of the oxygen demand is due to the first class of materials and is determined by the biochemical oxygen demand (BOD) test. . . . In biologically treated effluents, a considerable proportion of the oxygen demand may be due to oxidation of Class (b) compounds and will also be included in the BOD test. Class (c) materials present may not be included in the BOD test unless the test is based on a calculated initial dissolved oxygen. It should be understood that all three of these classes will have a direct bearing on the oxygen balance of the receiving water and must be considered in the discharge of a waste to such a water.

"If wastes consisted only of raw or treated domestic sewage, measurement of the oxygen load on a receiving water would be simple. Unfortunately, this is not always the case, because most wastes are complex in nature and may contain organic compounds not easily amenable to biologic oxidation. When such compounds are present, the usual methods of seeding and the standard incubation period of 5 days will fail to assess the effect these wastes may have at some point below their point of discharge.

"Complete stabilization of a given waste may require a period of incubation too long for practical purposes. For this reason, the 5-day period has been accepted as standard. . . ."

of oxygen dissolved in the water below the point at which other functions of the water will be impaired. Thus the reaeration capacity, the rate at which water can obtain oxygen from the air, must be known. The determination of reaeration capacity in specific instances has relied generally on indirect methods: mathematical models; and balancing estimated oxygen resources against demands. Lately, however, a method has been developed that measures reaeration capacity directly, using radioactive tracers (135, 136). Field studies on a 17-mile stretch of river have indicated that the method is practical and that it gives reproducible results. They show also that reaeration capacities predicted by mathematical models are in the general range of the observed values, but that in some circumstances the two may differ significantly.

The behavior of microorganisms in degrading chemical compounds can be studied in the laboratory, but such research becomes progressively more complex as the numbers of compounds and types of microorganisms increase. A considerable amount of research has been done on the biodegradability of specific compounds. One notable result was the conversion of the U.S. detergent industry from alkyl benzene sulfonate to the much more degradable linear alkylate sulfonate. It is probably not yet possible, however, to study mixed communities of microorganisms as they exist in nature in the same degree that pure cultures are studied now.

In nature, a dynamic food chain system exists in which one organism may oxidize or hydrolyze a large polymer into smaller polymers, which are then attacked by other organisms, whose products feed a third organism. Many bacteria can work effectively only after wastes have been partly degraded by other microorganisms. The rates at which degradation processes proceed are affected by the buildup of byproducts and other factors. Such processes must thus be studied as systems, which in nature are so complex as generally to defy straightforward investigation.

Laboratory work on relatively simple systems has shown that bacteria may metabolize one nutrient in the water to the exclusion of other compounds, which they metabolize only after the first one is consumed (128). The effect of the microbial community on the nutrients present is thus not necessarily the sum of individual effects, but may be the result of a complicated set of interactions involving both microorganisms and specific chemical compounds. Research on such systems, including the relatively simple ones that have been studied in the laboratory, depends heavily on the ability to detect and measure specific chemical compounds and their rates of disappearance or formation.

Particles

Particles are ubiquitous in natural waters, where they vary widely in size, shape, density, and other physical properties; in concentration; and in chemical and biological properties. Particles can adsorb and otherwise bind various substances, can serve as sites for bacterial growth, and can act in other ways that can strongly affect the transport of pollutants. Detailed data are not extensive on size distributions and properties of particles in water, but a promising start toward deeper understanding has been made using centrifugal methods of separation (69). Such methods have been used to separate particles in natural waters into organic and inorganic fractions and to characterize them on the basis of size, density, sedimentation rate, and other properties. The technique also can determine the distribution of a contaminant among the various fractions.

The transport of pollutants by waterborne particles has been studied to a limited degree. Study of the transport of pesticides, for example, has been stimulated by the fact that some pesticides, such as DDT, are present in almost all surface waters of the U.S., although usually in very low concentrations, parts per billion or less. Pesticides and other organic compounds adsorbed on particles might be deposited in bottom muds. Such compounds are also removed, with the particles, by coagulation-flocculation and filtration as practiced in water treatment processes (107).

Various clay minerals that exist in particulate form in water can sorb large amounts of dissolved organic compounds such as pesticides, although the amounts that actually are sorbed are limited by the very low concentrations of pesticides in surface waters. The sorbed compounds may influence the distribution of other compounds in solution and may also increase the sorptive capacity of the particles. The organophosphorus insecticide, parathion, for example, is sorbed weakly by clay minerals, but the degree of sorption increases if the clays are exposed to organic matter from natural waters.

An important mechanism by which insecticide residues can accumulate in lakes is adsorption by sediments. The degree of adsorption of the chlorinated hydrocarbon insecticide, lindane, has been shown in the laboratory to be affected by several factors, including the amount of sediment in the system, the amount of organic matter in the sediment, and the concentration of lindane in solution (71). Other laboratory work has shown that several clay minerals suspended in dilute solutions of the herbicide, 2,4-D, and the carbamate insecticide, CIPC, adsorb very little of either pesticide (114). On the whole, however, the significance of the transport of specific pesticides by particles has not been clearly defined, and particulate transport of other pollutants is a largely unexplored area.

Transport in soil and ground water

Knowledge of the transport of substances in soil and ground water is growing steadily more important because of the trend toward recharging ground water by spreading treated waste water on soil. Close to two decades of effort has produced sufficient knowledge to permit soil systems to be designed intelligently into water treatment systems in specific instances (6, 74, 106, 134). Much of what is known is empirical, however, and gaps remain in the fundamental understanding of how the soil functions as a filter and biological medium. Even larger gaps exist in the ability to synthesize and exploit existing knowledge of soil systems.

Soil systems appear to be able to remove bacteria and viruses from percolating water quite efficiently by physical means, such as straining and adsorption. They remove particles by physical means and ions and molecules by both physical means, such as ion exchange, and chemical means, such as biological degradation. Overall, however, soil systems have only limited, selective ability to remove chemical compounds such as those in municipal and industrial waste waters. (One exception is phosphate, which usually is held very tightly by soil.) Compounds that are subject to biological degradation may be converted to the stable ions that are found in ground water, such as nitrates, phosphates, carbonates, and sulfates. Under some conditions, which are not yet clearly defined, soils appear to be able to remove chromate ion, phenols, and other compounds from percolating water, but under other conditions the same compounds have been found to move through soil to ground water and travel many miles. Other phenomena that require further study include the flow and reactions of forms of phosphorus, nitrogen, and various organic substances in soil and ground water.

Sinks for waterborne substances

Research on the sources, transport, and effects of water pollutants in the past generally has taken precedence over research on the sinks: oceans, lakes, their sediments, and deep underground formations. In the past decade or so the sinks, particularly the oceans, have begun to receive more attention. The oceans cover some 70% of the earth's surface and constitute an enormous sink that probably contains all of the naturally-occurring chemical elements (23).

The rivers of the world deliver an estimated 4 billion tons of dissolved matter annually to the seas, and there is some evidence that the seas deposit about the same amount as sediment. These river waters contain an average of 120 parts per million (ppm) * of the major dissolved solids, which include ions such as bicarbonate, calcium, sulfate, chloride, sodium, magnesium, potassium, and nitrate. The oceans themselves average about 35 parts per thousand of dissolved salts. They contain in addition large amounts of dissolved gases and dissolved organic matter that ranges from 0.1 milligram per liter (mg/l) in isolated water masses of intermediate to great depth up to 10 mg/l near the shores.

Average composition is not necessarily a sound guide in evaluating the effects of disposing of wastes to the seas. Factors such as currents, mixing processes, geochemical factors, and biological systems must also be evaluated. Extensive biological activity, for example, can cause differences of up to 100-fold between one water mass and another in the concentrations of elements such as oxygen, carbon, phosphorus, iron, silicon, nitrogen, and mercury.

---

* Here, and in water measurements in general, parts per million normally means parts per million by weight, whereas in air measurements, the expression normally means parts per million by volume.

The oceans and other sinks for pollutants are important partly because they also can serve as sources of pollutants. In the oceans, chemical reactions occur unceasingly at the interfaces between water and sediment and between water and air, and the compositions of all three phases are affected accordingly. In lakes, phosphorus compounds in the sediments may participate in equilibria with phosphorus species in the water and thus move from sediment to water and help to support the growth of algae and other life forms. Clays and hydrous oxides of manganese and iron in river sediment may act to remove heavy metals, such as zinc, from the water. The sinks, in brief, are part of the cycle followed by waterborne substances and, at the current level of knowledge, perhaps the least understood part of that cycle.

Recommendations: flow, dispersion, degradation

Recommendation W1: *Regional inventories, on a selective trial basis, should be made of pollutants from all sources that are known or expected to be important. An effort should be made to learn more of the specific chemical compounds, particularly organic compounds, that are present in both wastes and natural waters. Chemical and biological research on natural waters, polluted or not, should be emphasized.*

Recommendation W2: *Fundamental research should be expanded on the action of natural mixed populations of bacteria and other organisms on specific compounds. Such research will require the development of analytical methods for identifying and quantifying specific compounds produced by biological degradation. More and more, the collective chemical parameters now in common use will prove inadequate for understanding the behavior of complex natural systems.*

Recommendation W3: *Comprehensive investigations of naturally-occurring and pollutant particles in water should be undertaken to determine such characteristics as size, charge, composition and adsorptive properties. Expanded knowledge of particles would be important in studies of sedimentation, erosion, and certain waste treatment processes, as well as in work on transport.*

Recommendation W4: *Research on improved mathematical descriptions of natural water systems subject to pollution should be strongly supported. The chemical-biological complexity of those systems requires that such research be highly interdisciplinary, involving scientists from disciplines such as chemistry, chemical engineering, civil engineering, biology, and ecology. Sheer complexity may ultimately limit the generality of the mathematical descriptions that can be developed, but it is essential to find a proper balance between the difficulty of understanding natural water systems and the need to describe them mathematically.*

Recommendation W5: *Systematic studies should be encouraged on the flow and reactions of forms of phosphorus and nitrogen, and various organic substances, in soil and ground water.*

Recommendation W6: *More emphasis should be placed on investigation of the transport and long-term deposition of pollutants in the oceans, lakes, and deep underground formations. The initial requirement is improved analytical methods for identifying and measuring specific chemical compounds.*

MUNICIPAL WASTE WATER TREATMENT

The processes used today in the U.S. to treat municipal wastes before they are discharged to receiving waters are cheap and effective, up to a point, and have been practiced for many years. Incremental improvements have been made in performance, but the basic technology has remained essentially unchanged. Its main purpose is to reduce the amounts of suspended solids, bacteria, and oxygen-demanding materials in waste water. New techniques and processes clearly will be required to remove additional contaminants such as dissolved inorganic compounds. Such methods generally will reinforce, not replace, current technology, for which there is at present no adequate replacement. Pending the advent of new processes, which does not seem imminent, better performance is both desirable and possible for existing methods. These methods fall into two broad classes (Fig. 1):

- Primary treatment: grit removal, screening, grinding, flocculation, sedimentation.
- Secondary treatment: biological oxidation, using processes such as the trickling filter and activated sludge to carry out in a controlled manner the biological assimilation and degradation processes that occur in nature.

Figure 1

Basic primary and secondary treatment of municipal waste water   ▶

The conventional waste water treatment scheme shown here is subject to a number of variations, but the process normally starts with removal of large and fine solids, grease, and scum. Sedimentation in the primary clarifier then removes the remaining settleable solids as primary sludge. Clarified waste water from primary treatment goes to secondary treatment (if it is used). There, microorganisms carry out in a controlled manner the assimilation and degradation process that breaks down organic matter in nature. In the activated sludge process, a widely used secondary treatment, the waste water is aerated to supply oxygen for the microorganisms. The solids or activated sludge formed in the degradation process are removed by sedimentation, and the clarified effluent is discharged to the receiving waters. Some sludge is returned to the aeration tank and mixed with incoming waste water; the rest must be disposed of. A most important fact of life in waste water treatment is that handling and disposing of sludges often accounts for 25 to 50% of the total capital and operating costs of the entire operation.

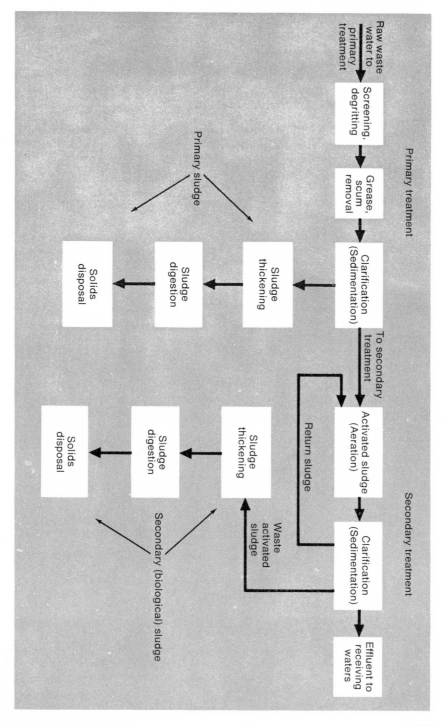

The inventory of municipal sewage treatment works in the U.S. for 1962 showed some 118 million people living in communities served by sewer systems. About 20% of the waste water in these communities was untreated, 28% received only primary treatment, and 52% received some kind of secondary treatment. Currently, about 10% of the waste water in sewered communities is untreated, 30% receives only primary treatment, and 60% receives secondary treatment. The trickling filter and activated sludge processes were by far the most widely used secondary treatment methods, with the activated sludge process slightly ahead. (See Tables 3 and 4 for performance and operating costs of conventional treatment.)

Implementation of the water quality standards now being established by the states and the Federal Government will require secondary treatment for an estimated 90% of the urban population by 1973, and primary

Table 3

Approximate performance and cost of conventional treatment of municipal wastes [a] (Based on raw waste concentrations)

	Removal efficiency of treatment	
	Primary	Primary plus secondary
Biochemical oxygen demand	35%	90%
Chemical oxygen demand	30%	80%
Refractory organics	20%	60%
Suspended solids	60%	90%
Total nitrogen	20%	50%
Total phosphorus	10%	30%
Dissolved minerals	—	5%
Cost/1000 gallons [b]	3-4 cents	5-10 cents

[a] Figures may differ significantly in specific instances.
[b] For industrial wastes, the costs cover a wider range: 2 to 5 cents for primary treatment, 2 to 20 cents for secondary treatment.

SOURCE: Weinberger, L. W., Stephan, D. G., Middleton, F. M., "Solving Our Water Problems —Water Renovation and Reuse," Annals of the New York Academy of Sciences, 136, Art. 5, 131 (1966).
Lesperance, T. W., "Market for Water Pollution Control Equipment Burgeons," Environ. Sci. Technol., 1, 785 (1967).

Table 4

Average composition of effluent from secondary treatment of municipal waste water [a]

Component	Concentration (mg/l)	Average increment added during water use (mg/l) [b]
Gross organics	55	52
Biodegradable organics (as biochemical oxygen demand)	25	25
Sodium	135	70
Potassium	15	10
Ammonium	20	20
Calcium	60	15
Magnesium	25	7
Chloride	130	75
Nitrate	15	10
Nitrite	1	1
Bicarbonate	300	100
Sulfate	100	30
Silica	50	15
Phosphate	25	25
Hardness (as calcium carbonate)	270	70
Alkalinity (as calcium carbonate)	250	85
Total dissolved solids	730	320

[a] Figures may vary significantly in specific instances.
[b] Concentration increase from tap water to secondary effluent.
SOURCE: Weinberger, L. W., Stephan, D. G., Middleton, F. M., "Solving Our Water Problems —Water Renovation and Reuse," *Annals of the New York Academy of Sciences,* 136, Art. 5, 131 (1966).

treatment for the remainder. Building, upgrading, and replacing the necessary treatment plants and interceptor sewers in the period 1969-73 will cost an estimated $8 billion, exclusive of land and associated costs (27, 28).

Conventional processes

It is probably fair to say that more applied research, as opposed to development, has been devoted to the biological assimilation and degradation processes than to any other aspect of waste water treatment (55). Such research has produced results. Improved designs of brush- or blade-type surface aerators and other devices have increased the efficiency with which air is introduced into the aeration tank in the acti- vated sludge process. The use of plastic (polyvinyl chloride) shapes in- stead of rock in the beds of trickling filters roughly doubles the sur- face area on which the biological process takes place (54). Despite these and other advances, however, meaningful general interpretation of the biochemical and biological aspects of research and plant-scale work on the degradation process has been seriously hampered by the use of such collective parameters as BOD and COD (which are never- theless very useful in routine plant operation).

Reliance on such parameters has resulted in a severe shortage of more specific data on the performance of conventional treatment proc- esses. The lack of data is a major problem in FWPCA's effort to de- velop mathematical models of such processes that might be used even- tually to optimize them (2).

One digital computer program that has been developed in this work includes pseudo-steady-state models for preliminary treatment, primary settling, activated sludge treatment, sludge thickening, sludge digestion, sludge elutriation or washing, vacuum filtration aided by addition of chemicals, and sludge incineration. The pseudo-steady-state model re- lates the influent and effluent streams in terms of parameters that fully characterize the stream: flow rate, temperature, and the concentrations of up to 20 species of contaminants. The paucity of specific data on such parameters from operating treatment plants has forced the use in the models of many assumptions that are not fully justified.

Efforts are now being made to develop the necessary data, although it is not certain that optimization and automatic control, based on mathematical models, will affect significantly the costs and effective- ness of conventional treatment processes. Without better data and more refined models, moreover, it cannot be certain which variables should be measured for use in an automatic control system, and there is as yet no on-line instrumentation that could be used to measure some of those that might be selected.

Specific analytical methods, rather than collective measurements, have also been required in research of the past few years on utiliza- tion of specific organic nutrients by mixed populations of bacteria (50). Thus far, three different forms of utilization have been found: The bac- teria consume two compounds simultaneously; they consume first one compound and then the next because of sequential inhibition of the ac- tivity of the enzymes that promote the use of specific compounds; or they consume first one compound and then the next because of sequential repression of the formation of the enzymes. There is no obvious way to reduce such knowledge to practice, but eventually it could have some practical significance for specific waste treatment processes and for in- creasing the knowledge of the degradation of pollutants in nature.

The ability to predict the overall rate at which a biological process removes organics from waste water could be useful in designing treatment units, and a number of mathematical formulations of the process have been developed to that end. These models traditionally have assumed that the overall rate at which the process proceeds is controlled by the rates of the biochemical reactions involved. Work of the past decade has shown that the overall rate might be controlled instead by a mass transfer mechanism or the rate at which organic nutrients diffuse to the organisms. If this is correct, and there are indications that it might be (58), then nutrient uptake rates might be improved by appropriate physical design of the waste treatment process.

Possible improvement in the conventional activated sludge process may lie also in combinations of biological and chemical principles. One approach of this kind combined, on a laboratory scale, a low solids retention system with chemical flocculation of excess sludge (133). Normally, waste water remains in the aeration tank for about six hours, but much of this time is required to allow the excess sludge to flocculate naturally so that it will settle properly later in the process. If the excess sludge is removed and flocculated chemically, the residence time required in the aeration tank can be reduced sharply. Other experiments along these lines indicated that aeration time could be reduced from six hours to one hour. The short aeration time produced a sludge that settled poorly, however, and a final chemical treatment would have been required. The results of this work showed no clear-cut economic advantage for the process over the conventional activated sludge process, except for improved removal of phosphorus in the chemical flocculation and clarification step.

Sludge handling and disposal

Handling and disposing of sludges is the single most troublesome aspect of waste water treatment today. Often it accounts for 25 to 50% of the capital and operating costs of a treatment plant (126). By 1980 the volume of sludge requiring treatment will have grown an estimated 60 to 70% (73), and the increasing costs of labor and land that can be used for ultimate disposal will have rendered the situation even more difficult.

The magnitude of the problem can be seen in the operations of the Metropolitan Sanitary District of Greater Chicago, which serves 5.5 million people plus an industrial equivalent of 3 million. Three activated sludge treatment works process about 1.5 billion gallons of waste water per day and produce more than 900 tons of solids daily on a dry basis (Fig. 2, page 112). Solids disposal costs about $14.5 million per year, or 46% of total operating and maintenance costs (5).

Raw sludge is a semiliquid whose solids content varies with the source. Sludge from primary sedimentation contains 2.5 to 5% solids, that from the trickling filter contains 0.5 to 5% solids, and that from the activated sludge process contains 0.5 to 1% solids. Of these, the latter two are much more difficult to handle because they contain the excess microorganisms that proliferate in biological treatment. These organisms con-

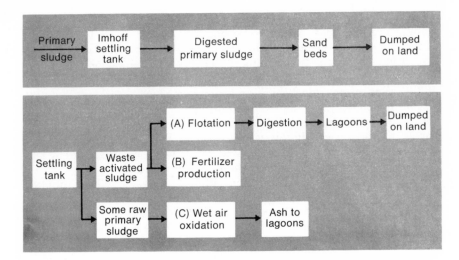

Figure 2

Sludge handling and disposal methods used by Chicago

The two systems shown here are used by the Metropolitan Sanitary District of Greater Chicago to handle and dispose of primary and secondary sludges. The primary sludge system costs about $10 per ton of sludge to operate. Of the three waste activated sludge systems, (A) costs $22 per ton when the sludge feed is 3.5% solids; (B) costs $45 per ton net (allowing for the sale of the fertilizer produced; and (C) costs $50 per ton.

SOURCE: Levin, P., "Disposal Systems and Characteristics of Solid Wastes Generated at Waste Water Treatment Plants," in Proceedings, 10th Sanitary Engineering Conference, Engineering Publications Office, University of Illinois, Urbana, Ill., February 1968, p. 21.

tain water internally and flocculate into a structure that has a strong affinity for water and retains it tenaciously. It is thus difficult and costly to reduce the volume of biological sludges by removing water in the process of preparing them for ultimate disposal.

Sludge handling and disposal has four general objectives:

- To convert organic matter to a relatively stable form.
- To reduce the volume of the sludge by removing liquids.
- To destroy or control harmful organisms.
- To obtain by-products whose use or sale reduces the overall cost of processing the sludge.

The methods commonly used to achieve these ends are shown in Table 5. In some ways they represent technology of a high order, but it is nonetheless true that almost all of them have been known, if not fully developed, for close to four decades. Only in the past few years has a

Table 5

Sewage sludge handling and disposal methods in common use

1. Concentration
   Clarifier thickening
   Separate concentration
   Gravity thickening
   Flotation

2. Digestion
   Aerobic bacteria (which utilize free oxygen)
   Anaerobic bacteria (which utilize oxygen contained in chemical compounds)

3. Dewatering
   Drying beds
   Lagoons
   Vacuum filtration
   Centrifugation

4. Heat drying and combustion
   Heat drying
   Incineration
   Multiple hearth
   Fluidized solids
   Wet oxidation

5. Final sludge disposal
   Landfill
   Soil conditioning
   Discharge to sea

SOURCE: McCarty, P. L., "Sludge Concentration—Needs, Accomplishments, and Future Goals," *J. Water Pollut. Contr. Fed.*, 38, 493 (1966).

scientific base begun to emerge that will allow these processes to be exploited fully and new ones to be developed.

Concentration. The efficiency of the activated sludge process depends strongly on natural flocculation of the microorganisms and their concentration and separation later in the treatment system. Efficiency can be improved by chemically or physically altering the natural process, which is, however, not yet fully understood. A number of mechanisms have been proposed over the years, and prominent among these today is the concept that natural polymers are involved. The bacterium *Zoogloea ramigera* has been found to synthesize large amounts of a specific polymer, poly-β-hydroxybutyric acid (PHB), which is thought to be intimately associated with the flocculation of the organisms (30). Also, the bacteria that the sewage literature reports to be floc formers are polymer formers without exception.

Unidentified polymeric material isolated from a flocculating activated sludge culture has proved capable of flocculating both a specific bacterium and colloidal dispersions of silica (19). The natural polymeric material furthermore appears to create flocs more resistant to dispersive forces than are those created by the synthetic organic polymers used commercially in sludge processing. It is thus conceivable that natural polymers might be isolated and used to improve flocculation of biological sludges.

The synthetic organic polymers, which are mostly of the polyelectrolyte class, have been steadily displacing inorganic chemicals in coagulation or sludge conditioning for waste treatment in the past five years. Inorganics such as lime and salts of iron and aluminum have been used for many years to treat raw sewage and to condition sludges. In raw sewage they cause colloidal and other finely dispersed material to coagulate and settle, thus achieving a degree of treatment that is better than primary, but not so good as secondary. In sludges the inorganics also exert a coagulating effect and thus improve the efficiency of dewatering by such processes as vacuum filtration and drying on sand beds.

The synthetic polymers are now being used in primary treatment, and in sludge conditioning they have replaced the inorganic compounds to a significant degree. One of the problems with the organic polymers has been their cost, but it can be expected to decrease as the market expands. Wider use of the compounds, and the development of better ones, will depend in part on deeper understanding of their mechanism of action (94, 105).

The solids and liquids in treated waste water most often are separated initially by sedimentation in clarifying and thickening basins. Also used is flotation, in which the solids are floated to the surface of the liquid by small bubbles of air or, less often, of biologically-generated gases.

A sharp advance in clarification technology has come quite recently with the successful application of the shallow depth sedimentation theory first proposed more than half a century ago. The theory says that the efficiency of a settling basin depends primarily on its depth, which should be as small as possible, and on the rate at which clarified liquid overflows. Many attempts have been made to apply the theory, often by inserting horizontal trays in conventional basins. These attempts have been frustrated for two reasons: The trays cause hydraulic instability in the basin; and the minimum distance between trays is limited by the vertical clearance required for the equipment that removes the settled material from each tray.

These problems have been solved by using small-diameter tube settlers instead of trays (31). The liquid passes through the steeply-inclined tubes, which are installed in modules, and the solids settle and slide to the bottoms of the tubes. The first plant-scale installation of tubes in an existing secondary clarifier was completed early in 1968 at Aliquippa, Pa., and a second installation was made in 1968 at a 2 million gallon-per-day plant near Miami, Fla. To date, at Aliquippa, the tubes have doubled the rate at which clarified effluent is produced and have substantially reduced the amount of suspended solids in the effluent.

Digestion. A recent development in the digestion of sludges by anaerobic bacteria is the use of the gases produced to fire a gas turbine that generates electricity. Anaerobic digestion is the most commonly used means of processing raw organic sludges for further treatment or disposal, although there is a trend toward processing raw sludges by mechanical dewatering and incineration.

Digestion reduces the volume of the sludge, decomposes organic solids to a more stable form, and in the process produces large amounts of methane and carbon dioxide and smaller amounts of gases such as ammonia and hydrogen sulfide. The methane is commonly burned to produce heat and power for the treatment plant, but it is often impractical to use all of the methane produced.

Since 1966, the County Sanitation Districts of Orange County, Calif., have been burning digester gas in a gas turbine that can also operate on natural gas (61). It is the second such installation in the world, the first having started to operate in England in 1959. At the Orange County works, digester gas, containing about 65% methane and 34% carbon dioxide, is compressed and stored and fed to the turbine as required. The turbine drives a generator rated at 1000 kilowatts. A second unit uses heat in the turbine exhaust to generate steam that drives a 300 kw. generator. The turbine is providing electric power continuously, but it was installed primarily to provide stand-by power for the treatment works in case the public supply was interrupted. (Since standby power must be available and must be paid for whether or not it is used, some communities that have installed power generating facilities waste much of their digester gas by flaring it.)

Anaerobic digestion, followed by dewatering of the digested sludge on sand beds and disposal as landfill or soil conditioner, remains a cheap and simple solution to the sludge processing problem. The process is not well understood at the basic level, however, and more efficient and stable digestion systems are desirable. Among the needs are better analytical tools for controlling the digesters and perhaps changes in the process itself. Digesters have been designed on the basis of essentially the same criteria for more than three decades, and the only major advance in that time has been the introduction of controlled mixing. Results of research on the population dynamics of the microorganisms suggest that the efficiency of the process could be improved by removing solids from the effluent and returning them to the digester (87). The effect would be to increase the digestion capacity of units of a given size and, in some cases, to reduce the amount of heat that is normally applied to the equipment to maintain a desirable rate of digestion.

Dewatering. Of the methods used today to dewater sludge, to reduce it from a fluid to a nonfluid form, drying on sand beds is the most common. However, the increasing costs of land and labor are leading to wider use of mechanical dewatering devices such as vacuum filters and centrifuges, followed by incineration. Incineration normally requires a sludge that contains enough solids, roughly 25% minimum, to support combustion, and mechanical dewatering is the most practical means of producing such a sludge.

Vacuum filtration has been used for some years to dewater sludges, although it fell from favor between World War II and about 1960 because of operating problems and costs. Since 1960, vacuum filtration has come back strongly because of improved filter media, higher costs for competing methods, and the growing popularity of sludge incineration. The main general shortcoming of filtration is that it involves more art than science. Required improvements include equipment that would feed sludge to the filter at a uniform rate and instrumentation that would measure sludge flow and proportion conditioning chemicals accurately. Another improvement would be filters that could adapt readily to unexpected changes in the character of the sludge.

Fly ash has been used successfully to condition specific industrial sludges for vacuum filtration (82), and laboratory work suggests that it would work well on municipal biological sludges (132). The results indicate that, besides improving the filtration characteristics of the sludge, fly ash would upgrade the quality of the filter effluent by removing significant amounts of organic material and phosphorus. Fly ash would replace more costly conditioning chemicals and would thus improve the overall economics of both municipal waste water treatment and fly ash disposal.

Ash from the incineration of sludge is also used as a filter aid in some municipal treatment plants. As with fly ash, amounts approximately equal to the dry solids content of the sludge are used. The use of sludge ash reduces the ash disposal problem significantly and eliminates the need to transport fly ash to the treatment plant.

The centrifuge also has been seeing wider use in the past decade for dewatering sludges, primarily because of improved design based on the solid bowl centrifuge. Although vacuum filtration remains the predominant mechanical dewatering device, the centrifuge has certain inherent advantages, including low capital cost, moderate operating cost, and low space requirement. The chief problem with the centrifuge is that the centrate (the liquid that it returns to the waste water treatment system) often contains undesirable amounts of fine solids that can build up in the system. The problem is greater with the biological sludges from secondary treatment, and the trend is toward more use of secondary treatment. Chemical flocculants can be used to improve the quality of the centrate, but their use can increase operating costs significantly. The centrifuge would benefit from still better design and further research on the use of chemicals and means of disposing of the centrate other than by returning it to the treatment process. Centrifuges alone do not remove enough water from activated or mixed sludges to permit them to be incinerated without using auxiliary fuel. The centrifuged sludge usually ranges from 15 to 20% solids.

A number of unconventional methods have been studied for improving the dewatering characteristics of sludges. They include freezing and thawing, heat treatment, gamma irradiation, solvent extraction, electrical treatment, ultrasonic treatment, and treatment by bacteria. The aims of such work generally have been to increase the rate of production of dewatered sludge and to eliminate the need for conditioning chemicals.

Freezing and thawing improves the dewatering characteristics of sludge, evidently by breaking down the cell walls in the organisms that retain internal moisture. A small plant was built in England to condition water treatment plant sludge by freezing, but the operating costs appear to be impractically high for waste water sludges. The sewage commission of Milwaukee, Wis., is currently developing a freezing process for demonstration and evaluation.

Sludge conditioning by heat treatment, specifically by the Porteous process, is used in a dozen or so treatment plants in Europe, and more are being built (72). The first Porteous unit in the U.S. was installed in Colorado Springs, Colo., in 1968 (93). The sludge is cooked under pressure at about 370°F. Liquid from the pressure cooker is returned to the treatment process, and the sludge, reduced in volume by about two thirds, is dewatered mechanically to a sterile cake containing 45 to 65% solids. Digesters and conditioning chemicals are not required. Of the BOD in the original sludge, 10 to 20% returns to the treatment process in the liquid from the cooker, and 60 to 80% of the nitrogen returns. Although costs and performance data on the Porteous process are not yet available for the U.S., work in England suggests that it will be competitive with alternative processes.

Gamma irradiation is being studied as a means of conditioning sludge (and also for treating waste water). The Metropolitan Sanitary District of Greater Chicago has commissioned a basic layout and construction study for a pilot plant that could irradiate some 2 million gallons per day of sewage sludge (or waste water) with a solids content of about 80 tons per day.

Laboratory work has shown that irradiation of waste activated sludge by doses of about 250,000 RAD can cause a 2.5-fold increase in solids concentration in 50 minutes by settling alone (42). Irradiation had no appreciable effect on the settling properties of other types of sludges including those from primary treatment and anaerobic digestion. It can, however, increase the filterability of digested waste activated sludge. Irradiation appears also to be a likely means of disinfecting digested sludges before applying them directly to land without dewatering. Smaller communities apply nondisinfected, nondewatered digested sludges to land now, but the practice can create a public health hazard.

Electrical conditioning of sludges has been studied, and, although it appears to be effective, it does not appear to be economical. Of the other unusual conditioning methods that have been studied, including solvent extraction, ultrasonic treatment, and bacterial treatment, none has yet shown particular promise.

Drying, combustion. A number of waste water treatment plants have attempted to heat-dry sludges, usually after mechanical dewatering, and sell the product as fertilizer or soil conditioner. Most have abandoned the practice in favor of incineration or landfilling. Heat-drying costs more than incineration, and limited demand for the product has made it difficult to get a high enough return to offset the increased cost. A few cities have sold large amounts of heat-dried activated sludge for some years, but generally the process is considered uneconomical.

Incineration has two aims: to reduce the volume of the sludge, and to sterilize the organic solids. Incineration costs more than some other disposal methods, but it is gaining ground relatively as the costs of alternative methods increase. There is also a trend away from sludge digestion in plants that use incineration. About 50% of the incineration plants installed between 1934 and 1961 burned digested sludges, but only four of the 50 incineration plants built in 1961-67 were designed to burn digested sludge (21).

The most widely used incineration device is the multiple hearth furnace. Use of the newer fluidized bed combustion system for sludge has also been growing since the first commercial unit was installed in the U.S. in 1962 (3). Incineration can cause air pollution problems, but they can be solved by proper design and operation. The process is not truly an ultimate disposal method, since the ash must still be contended with, but disposing of a relatively small amount of ash is considerably simpler than disposing of large amounts of sludge.

The commercial process called wet oxidation or wet incineration produces, instead of a dry ash, a liquid effluent containing an ash that settles readily (131). The wet oxidation plant in Chicago, for example, processes a sludge, containing about 3% solids, at 1750 pounds per square inch and about 500° F. The effluent is pumped to lagoons, where the ash settles. Ash-free liquid from the lagoons, its COD reduced about 70%, is returned to the treatment process. The advantages of wet oxidation include flexibility in the type of sludge handled and the degree of oxidation to be achieved. One disadvantage is that the BOD and nutrients in the ash-free liquid that is recycled impose an extra load on the treatment plant. (A version of the wet oxidation process that operates at 300° to 350° F. and 150 to 300 pounds per square inch has been advocated for treating sludges before dewatering. It accomplishes relatively little oxidation, but produces a solid fraction that filters easily to a sterile filter cake. The solids-free liquid, again, is relatively rich in BOD and nutrients.)

One method of incineration, the atomized suspension technique, has the advantage of being able to handle a relatively dilute sludge, thus eliminating the dewatering step (89). The sludge is thickened, preferably to more than 8% solids, and ground to reduce the particle size.

It is then atomized and sprayed into the top of a vertical reactor where combustion takes place. Relatively little operating experience is available as yet on the atomized suspension technique.

Final disposal. Disposal of liquid sludges on land, in lagoons, or in the ocean are the cheapest methods used today to dispose ultimately of sewage sludge, providing the treatment plant is within economical range of suitable land or the ocean. Disposal by any of these means requires normally that the sludge be digested to avoid problems with odors, insects, and water pollution. Liquid sludges are commonly spread on land, particularly by smaller treatment plants. The sludge contains nutrient values and can be used to fertilize or condition soil and to reclaim waste land for uses such as parks or agriculture (32). Landfill is used to dispose of dewatered sludges of all types. Sludge can be transported to the point of disposal by truck, train, pipeline, or barge.

Despite the utility of these methods of sludge disposal, they are feeling the effects of changing economics, improved technology, and increasing urbanization. The majority of waste treatment plants being designed today in the U.S. are based on one of three processing schemes:

- Dewater digested sludge mechanically and use it for landfill.
- Dewater digested sludge mechanically and dispose of it by thermal means, such as incineration.
- Dewater raw sludge mechanically and dispose of it by thermal means.

Thermal disposal or combustion has good potential, because it seems likely to be able to cope with all of the sludge disposal problems of the future. The ideal would be submerged combustion of sludge in the initial collection basin. The most economical method of sludge disposal depends on local conditions, however, and methods other than combustion seem likely to retain their utility for a long time. The ability to evaluate alternative disposal methods soundly will require thorough investigation of such questions as the value of liquid, dried, or composted sludge as a fertilizer or soil conditioner; underground disposal as in abandoned mines; and pipeline transportation of sludges.

Urban storm water

Precipitation in urban areas creates two potential point sources of pollution: the raw sewage discharged when combined (storm and sanitary) sewer systems overflow; and the storm water discharged by separate storm sewers. Both have come increasingly to be regarded as sources that merit more attention (144). The relatively few studies that have been made of the detailed composition of discharges from combined and separate sewer systems (18) show a clear pollutant potential that will intensify with growing urbanization (Table 6, page 120).

The annual discharge of untreated sewage by combined systems is estimated generally to be about 3% of the amount that enters the system. It can be markedly higher than that during heavy precipitation.

Table 6

Amounts of pollution from urban drainage

(1000 lb/sq mile/yr)

Constituent	Rainfall [a]	Separate sewer runoff [b]	Combined sewer overflow	Raw	Community sewage (mostly domestic) 10 persons/acre [c]		
					3%	5%	10%
Suspended solids	57	366	162	390	12	20	39
BOD	—	27	—	390	12	20	39
Total nitrogen	5.5	5.0	3.9	78	2.3	3.9	7.8
Inorganic nitrogen	3.0	1.6	3.5	58	1.7	2.9	5.8
Total phosphate (as phosphorus)	0.4	0.6	3.2	20	0.6	1.0	2.0

[a] 30 inches/year.
[b] 30 inches/year and 0.37 runoff coefficient.
[c] Population density in Cincinnati. Percentages show magnitude of loss of pollutant to combined sewer overflows at 3%, 5%, and 10% loss.

SOURCE: Weibel, S. R., "Urban Drainage as a Factor in Eutrophication," First International Symposium on Eutrophication, National Academy of Sciences—National Research Council, Washington, D.C., in press.

The problem could be solved by eliminating combined systems, but detailed study has shown that to be often impractical (96). To separate existing combined sewer systems would cost an estimated $48 billion. Also, the lack of specific data on the composition and volume of overflows makes it difficult to assess their importance relative to other sources of pollution. Separation of combined systems may be required in some cases, but other means of abatement must also be used.

Some communities now collect at least part of the overflow from combined sewage systems and send it to the waste water treatment plant in periods of low flow. Skimming and sedimentation may be used to improve the quality of the overflow from detention systems used for this purpose. Polymeric flocculants are being tried as a means of improving such sedimentation. Also under study or development are a number of other means of handling combined system overflow. They include storage in fully or partially flexible underwater tanks with subsequent treatment, storage in deep underground tunnels with subsequent treatment, chlorination, and filtration aided by ultrasonic energy (102).

Work is also under way on small pressure conduits that carry wastes from the home to the waste water treatment plant (75). A unit in the home grinds the wastes and pumps them into the conduit. The concept is basically a new means of separating storm and sanitary sewers, but it could have broader potential. If all organic household wastes were ground and sent to waste water treatment plants, the concentration of solids in waste water might more than triple. The efficiency of removal in the treatment plant, which depends directly on concentration, would rise accordingly.

Relatively little work has been done on treating storm water discharges from separate sewer systems (44). One current project is evaluating the use of ponds of 1 to 2 acres to collect storm water runoff, which then would be treated for various kinds of reuse, including use as potable water (103).

Water treatment plant wastes

Plants that treat water for public water supply produce only a fraction of the amount of sludge produced by waste water treatment. The sludge is largely inorganic and does not normally exert a troublesome oxygen demand in surface waters. Water treatment plants nevertheless are facing today some of the same sludge disposal problems that afflict waste water treatment plants: tighter restrictions on water pollution; and a shrinking supply of cheap land that can be used for disposal. Sludge from water treatment is often discharged to surface waters where it can create turbidity and unsightly sludge banks. Disposal to lagoons is also used, sometimes with subsequent removal of clarified liquid and use of the dried sludge as landfill. Some cities discharge the sludge to the sanitary sewer system. Others have used sand drying beds or vacuum filtration, followed by disposal as landfill.

In some areas, the disposal problem is already critical. An example is the city of St. Paul, Minn., whose purification plant treats about 17 billion gallons of water per year (97). Alum is used to coagulate solids in the raw water, and lime is used to soften the water. These chemicals react with others in the water to produce about 110 million gallons of wet sludge per year in sedimentation basins. The sludge contains about 5% solids or 23,000 tons of dry solids per year made up of 85% calcium carbonate, 9% magnesium hydroxide, 2% aluminum hydroxide, and 4% unclassified solids.

Wet sludge is pumped to lagoons, and clarified liquid pumped from the lagoons is treated in the city's waste water treatment plant. Treated water from the sedimentation basins is stabilized by adding carbon dioxide and then passes through sand filters. Solids that accumulate on the filters are periodically washed off and sent with the wash water to the sewage treatment plant, thus further increasing the solids load that the plant must handle. The lagoons have been nearly filled with sludge solids after more than 25 years of operation, and no additional land is within economic pumping or hauling distance.

St. Paul is now implementing a plan to ease its water treatment sludge problems, basically by recovering and reusing the lime used to soften the raw water. The lime (calcium oxide) appears in the sludge as calcium carbonate. Lime is recovered at a number of water treatment plants, and the practice often has proved less costly than buying lime and discarding the sludge.

In the process to be used at St. Paul, the wet sludge is conditioned, thickened, and calcined at 1600° F., which converts the calcium carbonate to calcium oxide and carbon dioxide. Part of the carbon dioxide is used to recarbonate wet sludge, thereby improving the efficiency of centrifugation in separating magnesium hydroxide, which must be prevented from building up in the lime recycle system. Another part of

121

the carbon dioxide is used to stabilize the treated water before it is filtered. As a result of this and other modifications, St. Paul expects to:

- Recover more lime and carbon dioxide than is needed in the water treatment plant and sell the excess lime.

- Reduce the volume of sludge to be disposed of from 24,600 tons per year to 4200 tons.

- Recover the water used to wash the sand filters, thus avoiding the waste of 1% of the total water treated and reducing the load on the city's waste water treatment plant by the same amount.

Alum can also be recovered, typically by treating coagulation sludge with sulfuric acid to convert insoluble aluminum hydroxide to soluble aluminum sulfate (alum). The aluminum sulfate solution is separated by centrifugation or filtration and stored for reuse in coagulating solids in raw water. Alum recovery is less economic than lime recovery and is not generally practiced in this country. The use of both processes can be expected to grow, however, as the problems of sludge disposal intensify. A potential development that could affect their future would be the use of polymeric flocculating agents instead of the metal ion compounds used today. Such flocculants could change markedly both the volume and characteristics of water treatment sludge.

Recommendations: municipal waste water treatment

Recommendation W7: *Biochemists and biologists should become more involved in research on sewage treatment, primarily to seek radical innovations, based on fundamental understanding of microbiological processes. Emphasis should be laid on the use of adequate chemical tools to develop data that will allow the biochemical and biological aspects of treatment processes to be interpreted more meaningfully and that can be used in process optimization.*

Recommendation W8: *Research should be expanded on new methods of handling waste water treatment sludges and on the fundamental process parameters involved in using synthetic polymers and polyelectrolytes and other novel surface-active chemicals to improve flocculation, sedimentation, and conditioning of such sludges. Comprehensive data should be developed on the economics and technology of complementary and/or alternative means of sludge disposal, such as incineration, use as fertilizer or soil conditioner, underground disposal, and pipeline transportation.*

Recommendation W9: *Systematic studies should be undertaken of the quality of urban storm waters to provide a sound base for assessing alternative means of treatment.*

ADVANCED WASTE TREATMENT

Advanced waste treatment generally describes any treatment that will remove more contaminants from waste water than treatments in common use. It may modify or replace the various steps in conventional treatment, or it may be applied to the effluent from conventional treatment. A narrower term, tertiary treatment, describes limited techniques applied to the effluent from secondary treatment.

Research and development on advanced waste treatment has been under way in an organized fashion in this country for less than a decade, largely in the programs of what is now the Division of Process Research and Development in FWPCA's Office of Research and Development (1, 2). The federal program has two specific objectives:

- To upgrade the effluent from conventional primary-secondary treatment, which adds to receiving waters an increment of roughly 50 mg/l of resistant organic contaminants and 300 to 400 mg/l of dissolved inorganic chemicals.

- To renovate waste water to a level at which it can be reused directly.

An additional aim of the federal program is to develop processes, based on physical and chemical principles, that can supplant biological processes and achieve at least equal effluent quality at comparable cost.

Numerous processes, many of them adapted from other technologies, have been screened for advanced waste treatment potential, and a number of them are in the research or development stages (123). A few are in use on a relatively large scale. At the pilot-plant level, the most advanced integrated system for producing potable water from waste water is installed in a 75,000 gallon-per-day pilot plant at FWPCA's field station at Lebanon, Ohio (Table 7, page 124).

The water treatment system used at any given site may vary with the nature of the waste water and other local factors, but the contaminants to be removed fall into four broad classes: suspended solids; dissolved organic compounds; dissolved inorganic compounds; and the plant nutrients, nitrogen and phosphorus, which in secondary effluent are largely in the inorganic form. Advanced waste treatment processes also must consider the ultimate disposal of the contaminants removed from water, as well as bacteria and viruses in the product water.

Suspended solids

Interest is growing steadily in removing suspended solids from the effluent from secondary sewage treatment. Suspended solids can account for a large part of the residual BOD in the effluent, and they can hamper the operation of other advanced treatment processes. The substances in secondary effluent range from ions and soluble molecules through colloidal materials to visible solids, and it is difficult to classify all of them precisely as soluble or insoluble. However, the processes used to clarify water often will remove 10 to 20 mg/l of the organic

Table 7

Uses and costs of water from sample renovation system [a]

Treatment Sequence	Estimated cumulative capital cost (million dollars)		Estimated cumulative operating cost (cents/1000 gallons)		Uses of treated water
	15 mgd [b]	100 mgd [b]	15 mgd [b]	100 mgd [b]	
Raw waste water	0	0	0	0	None. Highly polluting.
Primary treatment	2.2	9.5	5.2	3.5	Partial pollution control. No direct reuse possible.
Secondary treatment (activated sludge)	4.5	20	11	8.3	Conventional pollution control. Nonfood crop irrigation.
Coagulation-sedimentation	5.1	24	15	13	Improved pollution control. General irrigation supply; low quality industrial supply; recreational water supply; short-term water recharge.

material from secondary effluent and some of the inorganic material as well, and these substances usually are called suspended solids.

The processes that can be used to remove suspended solids include filtration, which is much more effective for organic materials than for inorganic, and treatment with chemicals with or without subsequent filtration. None is used to any extent in this country today on secondary effluent, although chemical coagulation followed by filtration is used commonly in water treatment plants and is just reaching the commercial stage in waste water treatment.

Microscreening, a form of filtration, has been studied at the pilot level on secondary effluent. A screen with openings of 23 microns proved capable of removing an average of 89% of the suspended solids, 81% of the BOD, 30% of the total organic carbon, and 76% of the turbidity.

Treatment Sequence	Estimated cumulative capital cost (million dollars)		Estimated cumulative operating cost (cents/1000 gallons)		Uses of treated water
	15 mgd [b]	100 mgd [b]	15 mgd [b]	100 mgd [b]	
Carbon adsorption	7.3	30	23	17	Complete organic pollution control. High quality irrigation supply; good quality industrial supply; body contact recreational supply; long-term ground water recharge.
Electrodialysis	11	47	37	26	Complete organic-inorganic pollution control.
Brine disposal	25	77	53	33	High quality industrial supply; indefinite ground water recharge.
Disinfection	25	77	54	34	Absolute pollution control; potable water supply.

[a] A 75,000 gallon-per-day system of this configuration is installed at FWPCA's field station at Lebanon, Ohio.
[b] Million gallons per day.

SOURCE: Stephen, D. G., Weinberger, L. W., "Wastewater Reuse—Has It Arrived?" *J. Water Pollut. Contr. Fed.*, 40, 529 (1968).

Pilot work has been done also with a filter aid, diatomaceous earth. A layer of this material, supported on a porous membrane, can filter solids from water more effectively than microscreening, but preliminary estimates indicate that it might cost several times as much. One of the shortcomings of these types of filtration is that they do not remove phosphorus. Chemical coagulation followed by filtration can achieve high removals of both suspended solids and phosphorus and is the process that is currently receiving the most attention for both purposes.

Coagulation-filtration units ranging from pilot plant to full-scale demonstration plant are in the design, construction, or operating stage in the U.S. The coagulants used are alum or lime, often supplemented by synthetic polyelectrolytes. Coagulated material can be removed either in beds containing a single filtration medium, such as sand or coal, or two or more media arranged so that the void spaces grow smaller as the water passes through the bed.

In the rapid sand filter, which is common in water treatment plants, most of the flocculated material collects on the surface of the bed as a result of simple filtration. As the layer of floc builds up, the pressure differential through the filter increases. Eventually the flow must be stopped and the bed cleaned by backwashing with clear water. In a dual or multimedia bed, the flocs penetrate more deeply before simple filtration occurs, and flocculation and sedimentation also can come into play as solids removal mechanisms within the bed. The pressure differential through the filter builds more slowly, the time between backwashes is lengthened, and water can be fed to the filter more rapidly.

A new type of multimedia filter, made by hydraulically blending several materials of different sizes and specific gravities, started to operate with secondary effluent for the first time in the U.S. in July 1965 at Lake Tahoe, Calif. It accepts feed rates two to three times the standard rate for sand filters and reduces suspended solids from a range of 5 to 20 mg/l in the secondary effluent to a range of 0.2 to 3.0 mg/l after filtration.

Dissolved organics

The small amounts of soluble refractory organic compounds that remain in secondary effluent after the suspended solids have been removed can cause tastes and odors. Some such substances may also be toxic to plant or animal life. The method that is furthest advanced for removing these compounds is adsorption on activated carbon, which has been used for many years to remove tastes and odors from water supplies. Its use in that application has been effective, although inefficient, and the past few years have seen a growing effort to upgrade the technology of the process to the level required to permit its widespread economical use with waste water.

Current practice in the few existing units is to pass secondary effluent through vessels filled with granular activated carbon. The carbon gradually loses its adsorptive capacity as it accumulates the organic materials from the water and eventually must be replaced. To make the process economically feasible, the spent carbon must be regenerated and reused, with new carbon being added as necessary to replace that lost in regeneration. Spent carbon is regenerated by heating it to about 1700° F. in an atmosphere of air and steam, thus burning off the adsorbed organics, and returning the regenerated material to the process.

One of the first activated carbon units used to treat waste water was the 0.3 million gallon-per-day pilot plant at Pomona, Calif. (86). One set of data, for more than a year of operation on secondary effluent, showed removal of 77% of the dissolved chemical oxygen demand, which is a measure of dissolved organic material. Most of the carbon was regenerated once during the year, and carbon loss in regeneration averaged about 10%. The quality of the secondary effluent was such that it could be applied without filtration to the carbon columns, which removed more than 90% of the suspended solids. The quality of other secondary effluents might be such that suspended solids would have to be removed before the adsorption step to achieve optimum results.

Activated carbons are made from different starting materials by different methods, and their adsorptive properties can vary widely. They are effective adsorbents primarily because they are porous and provide a very large surface area, but the chemistry of the surface is also an important factor. The results of current research suggest strongly that improved knowledge of the structure and surface chemistry of activated carbon and of the methods used to make it would pay dividends in performance (117).

A need exists also for better methods of designing carbon adsorption beds (37, 65). One possibility is to use fluid bed adsorbers, instead of the fixed bed types used now. In a fluid bed, the water being treated would be pumped through the bed so as to maintain the adsorbent in a suspended or fluidized state. The rate of adsorption increases with decreasing particle size, and a fluid bed should allow smaller particles to be used without the problems, such as high pressure drop, that smaller particles cause in fixed beds.

Powdered activated carbon might be used for adsorption instead of granular material. Because of its much greater surface area, powdered activated carbon adsorbs dissolved organics much more rapidly than does granular material, but it also causes unacceptably high pressure drop in a fixed bed. One alternative means of treatment would be to mix the powdered carbon into secondary effluent. The carbon and other solids could then be flocculated, settled, and filtered, thereby removing suspended solids and dissolved organics at the same time. Such a system is being used in a small pilot plant.

The most important unanswered question is whether powdered carbon can be regenerated with acceptably low loss, and several methods are being studied. One is to centrifuge or filter the water slurry of settled spent carbon, heat-dry the resulting cake to about 75% solids, and regenerate at about 750° F. in a steam atmosphere. Another method is to charge the slurry directly to a continuous reactor operating at about 1600° F. The water in the slurry produces the necessary steam atmosphere, and the carbon is regenerated in as little as one second as it passes through the reactor. Reactivated carbon is separated from the condensed product stream from the reactor as a water slurry and returned to the adsorption process.

Oxidation

Dissolved organics might be removed from secondary effluent by chemical oxidation, as opposed to the biological oxidation used in conventional waste water treatment. Chemical oxidation could be used alone or following treatment by activated carbon. A number of oxidizing agents might be used, including active oxygen species such as ozone, hydrogen peroxide, and hydroxyl free radical; molecular oxygen with or without catalysis; chlorine and its derivatives; and oxy-acids and their salts, such as potassium permanganate. Electrochemical treatment is another possibility. Laboratory work has indicated that a number of oxidation methods are impractical, but research is planned or under way on still others, including ozone treatment, catalytic air oxidation, and light-catalyzed chlorine oxidation.

Of particular interest are means of introducing active oxygen species into water without adding chemicals. One such method, corona discharge, uses a high-voltage, high-frequency, low-temperature electrical discharge to create free radicals and other oxidizing species in moist air. These species are transferred to the water, where oxidation takes place. Laboratory work indicates to date that the method is uneconomic. Gamma irradiation also can be used to produce highly reactive oxidizing species in water, without producing radioactivity. Research on the use of irradiation to degrade waste water contaminants has been fragmentary to date (9, 40, 46), and a clear picture of its potential has not yet emerged.

Dissolved inorganics

Since the effluent from secondary treatment usually contains 300 to 400 mg/l more dissolved inorganic compounds than the municipal water supply, mineral content would build rapidly in a cycle in which water was reused directly. Of the methods that have been investigated for demineralizing secondary effluent, electrodialysis, ion exchange, and reverse osmosis are at the pilot plant stage. Distillation has been studied in the laboratory, but it is costly, and special measures must be taken to prevent volatile materials such as ammonia and foul odors from appearing in the product water. When contaminated water is frozen, the ice that forms is very pure, and a freezing process should remove organic materials as well as inorganics. The results of pilot plant work suggest, however, that freezing is unlikely to be able to compete economically with other purification systems.

Electrodialysis

Electrodialysis is used widely to demineralize brackish ground water, but waste water, because of its organic content, is a somewhat different problem. Electrodialysis is based on the principle that when an electrical potential is impressed across a cell containing mineralized water, the positively charged cations in solution migrate to the negative electrode, and the negatively charged anions migrate to the positive electrode. Certain types of membranes are permeable only to cations or only to anions, and such membranes are placed alternately in the electrodialysis apparatus to form a series of compartments. When the electrical potential is applied, the membranes control the migration of anions and cations so that the concentration of minerals decreases in alternate compartments, from which product water is withdrawn, and increases in the intervening alternate compartments. Charged particles such as large organic ions and colloids also migrate to the membranes, particularly the anionic membranes, but they do not necessarily pass through. They tend instead to accumulate and foul or plug the membranes, thus reducing the demineralizing capacity of the equipment.

At the largest electrodialysis stack in the U.S. now operating on waste water, the 75,000 gallon-per-day unit at Lebanon, Ohio, the most serious problem has been membrane fouling (16). Initially, the secondary effluent fed to the unit was filtered through diatomaceous earth and treated by granular carbon adsorption. Because of the nature of the secondary effluent and the type of pretreatment, the suspected cause of fouling is colloidal organic material and possibly traces of soluble organics. Growth of microorganisms on the membranes may also have some effect. The problem is handled now by shutting down the unit periodically for a day or more, which removes the fouling materials. Chemical clarification and dual media filtration are now being used instead of diatomaceous earth filtration to remove solids from the feed to the electrodialysis unit. This change has significantly improved the performance of the unit, and sustained runs of up to 30 days can now be made with little decrease in the degree of demineralization.

Recent evidence indicates that the membrane-fouling characteristics of the residual turbidity in secondary effluent vary markedly from plant to plant. Sustained operation of the electrodialysis unit at Lebanon requires a turbidity of 0.2 Jackson turbidity unit, but a similar unit is operating with varying degrees of success at Pomona, Calif., on a carbon-treated effluent containing 1 to 2 Jackson turbidity units.

Despite the fact that the fouling problem has not yet been fully solved, electrodialysis today is considered a practical means of removing 40 to 50% of the dissolved inorganics in carefully pretreated secondary effluent. This would be enough to prevent unacceptable mineral buildup in water that is recycled repeatedly without significant dilution.

Ion exchange

The principle of ion exchange is used widely to soften or demineralize water and to recover useful by-products from industrial wastes. It is being studied at the small pilot plant level for demineralizing waste water. A number of natural materials, such as zeolites, as well as certain synthetic resins can exchange ions with ions in water solution. Cation exchange resins, for example, can exchange their hydrogen ions with cations of metals in solution. Anion exchange resins can exchange their hydroxyl ions for anions such as chloride in solution. Eventually, the resins are exhausted and must be regenerated. In a typical system, the cation resin might be regenerated with an acid, such as sulfuric, and the anion resin with a base, such as sodium hydroxide.

Treatment of secondary effluent by ion exchange did not appear initially to be particularly promising compared with some other methods. Certain organic compounds in waste water tend to foul many ion exchange resins, regenerating the resins is costly, and the strong wastes from regeneration present a disposal problem. Progress has since been made, however, in reducing the tendency of some anion exchange resins to be fouled by organic materials. Work has also been done on recovering and recycling the chemicals used to regenerate the resins.

In the laboratory, an ion exchange process has been investigated for renovating secondary effluent (91). In addition to ion exchange, the process involves flocculation with synthetic polyelectrolytes and lime softening, and it simultaneously reduces both the organic and mineral content of the effluent. Ion exchange also can be used to remove phosphates and inorganic nitrogen compounds from waste water, and is of particular interest for removing ammonia, although a practical process has not yet materialized.

Demineralized water produced by ion exchange is usually of much higher quality than is required in waste water treatment. The cost of using the process might thus be reduced by treating only part of an effluent and blending the treated and untreated streams to achieve the required level of dissolved inorganics. Improved methods of reducing the costs of regenerating the resins would also be useful. Since the trend in advanced waste treatment is toward using combinations of processes, ion exchange might best be considered for removing dissolved minerals after other processes have removed the suspended solids and dissolved organic materials.

Reverse osmosis

Reverse osmosis, like electrodialysis, is a membrane process. It is also a very new process, having been developed almost entirely in the past decade. The technique is being evaluated at the pilot plant level in a number of uses, including desalination of water, and is at the small pilot plant stage for tertiary treatment of waste water (51). The process still presents a number of problems, but it is potentially cheap, simple, and capable of producing high quality water.

Reverse osmosis is based on the fact that if two solutions of different concentrations are separated by a semipermeable membrane, water will move through the membrane in the direction of higher concentration. The difference in concentrations provides the driving force or osmotic pressure. Since the membrane will not pass many dissolved substances, the passage of water tends eventually to adjust the two solutions to the same concentration. The process can be reversed by applying pressure to the more concentrated solution. The concentration of dissolved substances will then tend to increase on that side of the membrane and decrease on the other side, where the product water accumulates.

In one of the first extended experiments on treatment of waste water by reverse osmosis, a 5000 gallon-per-day unit operated on carbon-treated secondary effluent at Pomona, Calif., for more than 2000 hours. The feed pressure was 400 pounds per square inch, and 80 to 85% of the feed water was recovered. The contaminant reductions achieved averaged 88% for total dissolved solids, 84% for chemical oxygen demand, 98.2% for phosphate, 82% for ammonia, and 67% for nitrate. The reduction in chemical oxygen demand shows that the process can materially reduce the amount of dissolved organic matter in the carbon-treated effluent as well as remove dissolved inorganics. Some organic compounds evidently can permeate the membrane, but correlations between the ability to do so and the nature of the molecules involved are not well established (79).

Among the aspects of reverse osmosis that require further study are equipment design, membrane fouling, membrane life, and the degree of pretreatment that must be applied to the feed water. Tubular, flat plate, and spiral wound equipment configurations are being evaluated. All reverse osmosis membranes are made of specially processed cellulose acetate, which is relatively porous except for a dense layer, less than 1 micron thick, on one face of the membrane. The dense layer evidently is the part of the membrane that rejects dissolved contaminants, but the mechanism of rejection is not fully understood. Cellulose acetate membranes nevertheless can be tailored for specific applications, and accumulation of experimental data on waste water treatment might lead to more effective membranes for that specific use.

Plant nutrients

The arguments for removing compounds of nitrogen and phosphorus from waste waters are based on their role in eutrophication, in which they support the growth of algae and other plant life, causing accelerated degradation of receiving waters (113). A strong effort is being made to control both nutrients, but particularly phosphorus. One important reason is that certain blue-green algae can utilize atmospheric nitrogen that dissolves in the water and thus can subsist independently of other sources of the element. The technology is available now for removing much of the phosphorus from waste water. The new clean-up plan for Lake Michigan, for example, recommends that by the end of 1972 all cities in the Lake Michigan basin be removing at least 80% of the phosphorus from their waste water (24).

Phosphorus removal

A number of phosphorus removal processes are being studied at levels ranging from the laboratory through the full-scale plant, but chemical treatment is currently the best developed. Operational data show that chemical tertiary treatment can reliably remove 90 to 95% of the total phosphate in municipal waste water at a cost of less than 5 cents per 1000 gallons (88).

In the effluent from secondary treatment, phosphorus occurs largely as orthophosphate ions, with some present in organic compounds. Aluminum sulfate or lime, when added to the effluent, precipitate the orthophosphate in complex inorganic compounds. Aluminum phosphate or aluminum hydroxyphosphates precipitate at neutral and slightly acid pH values; calcium phosphates and hydroxyapatites precipitate at more alkaline pH values (9 to 11). These precipitates can be removed by sedimentation alone or by sedimentation and filtration. Flocculation might be required to remove fine particles effectively.

A curious point in the lime process is that the concentrations of both calcium and phosphate in waste water can far exceed the maximum concentration estimated from the solubility of hydroxyapatite, one of the compounds that might be expected to form when lime is added. If the reason can be found, new phosphate removal processes might result.

Chemical treatment can be combined with biological treatment by adding the chemicals in the primary or secondary tank of a primary-secondary system. Treatment with lime in the primary tank alone has been shown to be capable of removing 80 to 90% of the total phosphorus (20). Addition of sodium aluminate in the secondary tank precipitates phosphorus compounds, which become intimately associated with the activated sludge. The final settling tank can be used to remove the mixture of precipitates and waste activated sludge, which has better settling characteristics than waste sludge alone (13). Phosphorus removals of more than 90% have been achieved by this process.

Biological treatment processes normally remove some phosphorus from waste water, and better than 90% removal of total phosphate has been found in activated sludge plants in some circumstances (137). The phenomenon has been attributed to "luxury metabolic uptake," in which the organisms accumulate much more phosphorus than they need to grow, but it can also be explained on the basis of a chemical precipitation mechanism (77). Phosphate removed from solution in the activated sludge process has also been found to return to solution when the waste sludge is settling (115). Further study of such effects might make it possible to learn to operate the activated sludge process so as to markedly increase phosphorus removal, which normally averages only about 30%.

Other processes that can remove phosphorus include ion exchange and sorption on activated alumina (41). One of the problems with ion exchange is the lack of a resin that is specific for phosphate in the presence of sulfate, which generally is present at four or five times the concentration of phosphate. Activated alumina has been shown to adsorb phosphates very effectively from tap water (147) and in principle should provide economical tertiary treatment. Questions remain, however, on the overall efficiency of activated alumina in the presence of other waste water contaminants, such as organic compounds. Also, about 10% of the alumina is lost each time it is regenerated with sodium hydroxide, and means of reducing this loss are required.

Nitrogen removal

The methods that are being investigated for removing high levels of

132

nitrogen from waste water include some that depend on the interaction of compounds of the element with microorganisms (64). Most of the nitrogen in municipal waste water is in the form of ammonia or compounds that release ammonia during the biological treatment process. Nitrifying bacteria will convert ammonia to nitrite and nitrate if they are populous enough, and if enough dissolved oxygen is present. The population of nitrifiers can be maintained by operating at a ratio of less than about 0.35 between the weight of BOD added to the system per day and the weight of volatile suspended solids in the activated sludge tank. Complete nitrification requires about 50% more air than conventional biological assimilation and degradation. These conditions are not common in the U.S., however, and ammonia is the important form of nitrogen in most secondary effluents.

If the activated sludge process is modified to create nitrifying conditions, the nitrified effluent can be treated by denitrifying bacteria. At low levels of dissolved oxygen, these organisms reduce nitrite and nitrate to nitrogen, which escapes as a gas. The effectiveness of the method has yet to be demonstrated on a large scale, but one four-month pilot-scale study showed average conversions of 95% of the ammonia to nitrate and 86% of the nitrate to nitrogen. The level of organic material in the denitrification system is relatively low, and a nutrient such as methanol or some other source of carbon must be added to support the denitrifying bacteria.

A nitrified effluent can also be denitrified in filters, such as beds of sand or activated carbon. Here, too, a nutrient such as methanol must be added to support the denitrifying bacteria. Denitrification in filtration beds could be a useful process, and research on the technique is continuing.

If the nitrogen in secondary effluent is in the ammonia form, it can be stripped from the water with air. In water, ammonia and hydrogen ion exist in equilibrium with ammonium ion. The state of the equilibrium depends in part on whether the water is acid or alkaline; as the pH rises above 7 (a change in the alkaline direction), the equilibrium shifts in the direction of ammonia. The pH can be increased to the optimum point, which theoretically is 11.5, by adding lime, which thus serves a dual purpose if it is also being added to remove phosphate. If the water is then agitated vigorously in a forced-draft, countercurrent, air stripping tower, the ammonia is driven from solution and leaves in the air exhausted from the tower. Ammonia removals of well over 90% have been achieved in pilot-plant work on air stripping.

Ultimate disposal

Advanced waste treatment, like conventional treatment, produces wastes that ultimately must be disposed of (33). Processes such as microscreening and filtration on diatomaceous earth, applied to secondary effluent, should produce only small volumes of wastes. The solids removed by these processes can be returned to the treatment plant, where they would slightly increase the volumes of sludge from primary and secondary treatment.

The much larger volume of waste produced by chemical treatment for removing solids would be reduced markedly in an advanced treatment system by returning backwash filter water to primary and secondary treatment. The volume could be further reduced by recovering and reusing processing chemicals, such as the lime used to precipitate phosphate.

Adsorption of organics on activated carbon produces little or no solid waste. The adsorbed contaminants are destroyed when the carbon is regenerated.

The liquid wastes from processes such as electrodialysis and reverse osmosis would be a more difficult problem. They may consist of 5 to 10% of the feed and contain from 5000 to 15,000 mg/l of total dissolved solids, compared with sea water at 35,000 mg/l. Concentration of such wastes to smaller volumes during the treatment process appears to be impossible because scale precipitates on membranes and heat transfer surfaces. Disposal in the oceans or salt lakes is one possibility. Another would be concentration by solar evaporation and subsequent disposal of the salts in the oceans or in sealed cavities. Many arid inland areas where demineralization would be required also have low-cost land where solar evaporation ponds could be used.

Bacteria, viruses

Reliable removal, or inactivation, of disease-causing bacteria and viruses from treated waste water is growing more important for two reasons: The waters that receive treatment plant effluent are being used increasingly for recreation, particularly in large urban areas; direct reuse of treated water by humans will require means of preventing the numbers of organisms from building up in recycle systems. Both bacteria and viruses are removed by conventional primary-secondary treatment, sometimes to a high degree, and by some types of advanced waste treatment. For viruses particularly, however, the overall degree of removal is in question.

The conventional activated sludge process can remove 90% or more of the bacteria in raw waste water, and chlorination of the secondary effluent can raise the degree of removal to 99%. Chemical clarification of secondary effluent can also achieve high removals of bacteria, and subsequent filtration can further increase the level of removal. Chlorination is the standard disinfection process for waste water in the U.S., and in a properly operated plant it is effective against bacteria.

The effects of chlorination and other conventional processes on viruses are less well delineated. The indications are that chlorination of secondary effluent, as it is now practiced, does not produce a virus-free effluent (120). Activated carbon has been shown to adsorb certain viruses, but the process is reversible, and the infectious properties of the desorbed viruses are unimpaired (26). Precipitation of phosphate in secondary effluent with lime has been found in the laboratory to remove viruses about as effectively as the activated sludge process. The mechanism appears to be adsorption on the precipitate.

Viruses could be a serious problem in water reuse, and it appears that improved means of removing or inactivating them will be required to achieve virus-free effluents from advanced waste water treatment. Further research is required on disinfection by chlorine or other oxidants, such as iodine, bromine, and ozone. Since relatively high levels of such disinfectants might be required, more should be known of their reactions with the organic compounds in effluent streams. Further work is required also on the efficiencies of removal of viruses by such processes as adsorption, ion exchange, and filtration. Gamma irradiation has been shown to give very high kills of viruses and bacteria as well, and further study of that approach may also be desirable.

Applications of advanced treatment

The economy and effectiveness of advanced or tertiary waste water treatment have not yet reached the levels that continued research and development ought to be able to achieve. It would be injudicious, moreover, to conclude that the existing processes, however improved, will not be displaced in the future by newly discovered or newly adapted methods of treatment. Some, if not all, of the existing advanced or tertiary treatment processes are likely nevertheless to see wide use, and in a few cases they are already being used or contemplated on a large scale.

The most significant large-scale use of integrated advanced treatment today is the water reclamation plant of the South Tahoe Public Utility District at Lake Tahoe, Calif. (116). The new 7.5 million gallon-per-day demonstration plant there combines these processes (Fig. 3, page 137).

- Conventional primary and secondary treatment.
- Flocculation and phosphate removal with lime.
- Nitrogen removal by ammonia stripping.
- Multimedia filtration aided by synthetic polyelectrolytes.
- Organic removal by adsorption on activated carbon.
- Disinfection by chlorination.
- Recovery and reuse of lime used as a flocculant.
- Regeneration of activated carbon.

The new plant was designed on the basis of extensive pilot-plant work, plus experience with an existing 2.5 million gallon-per-day plant that used primary and secondary treatment, chemical coagulation and multimedia filtration, activated carbon adsorption, and chlorination. The performance of the existing plant and the expected performance of the new plant appear in Table 8, page 136. For the first six months of operation, total capital and operating costs for the tertiary section of the new plant were running about 12 cents per 1000 gallons. Costs for the primary-secondary section were about 8 cents, giving a total of about 20 cents per 1000 gallons.

Advanced waste treatment on a considerably larger scale is embodied in the design proposed for the Salt Creek Water Reclamation Plant of the Metropolitan Sanitary District of Greater Chicago (101), which currently is scheduled to be operating in 1970. The proposal for the 30 million gallon-per-day plant included these processes:

- Two-stage activated sludge with nitrification in the second stage.
- Addition of alum or sodium aluminate in the first activated sludge tank to remove phosphate.
- Dual media filtration with nitrogen removal by denitrification in the filters *
- Chlorination.

Table 8

Water quality at South Tahoe Public Utility District water reclamation plant

Parameter	Raw waste water	Existing tertiary plant effluent using alum	Expected of new tertiary plant using lime
BOD (mg/l)	200-400	<1	<1
COD (mg/l)	400-600	1-25	3-25
Total organic carbon (mg/l)	—	<1-7.5	<1-7.5
Color(units)	—	<5	<5
Turbidity (units)	—	<0.5	<0.5
Phosphate (mg/l as PO$_4$)	25-30	0.1-1	0.2-1
Nitrogen			
Organic N (mg/l as N)	10-15	1-2	0.3-2.0
Ammonia N (mg/l as N)	25-35	12-32	.3-1.5
Nitrate and Nitrite N (mg/l as N)	0	0	0
pH	7.2-7.4	6.4-6.8	8.3-8.6
Sodium (mg/l)	60	60	60
Calcium (mg/l as Ca)	15	15	18-25
Alkalinity (mg/l as CaCO$_3$)	110-130	70	250
Sulfate (mg/l)	20	200	20

SOURCE: Slechta, A.F., Culp, G.L., "Water Reclamation Studies at the South Tahoe Public Utility District," *J. Water Pollut. Contr. Fed.*, 39, 787 (1967).

* As of late 1968, it was not anticipated that the receiving water standard would require denitrification of the effluent, although plans for denitrification were being developed.

Figure 3

Water reclamation plant of South Tahoe Public Utility District

The new 7.5 million gallon-per-day advanced waste treatment plant at Lake Tahoe, Calif., shown here in simplified form, is fed the effluent from a conventional primary-secondary (activated sludge) waste water treatment plant. For the first six months of operation, total capital and operating costs for the advanced waste treatment section of the plant were running about 12 cents per 1000 gallons; costs for the primary-secondary section were running about 8 cents per 1000 gallons.

SOURCE: Slechta, A.F., Culp, G.L., "Water Reclamation Studies at the South Tahoe Public Utility District," *J. Water Pollut. Contr. Fed.*, 39, 787 (1967), and subsequent private communication.

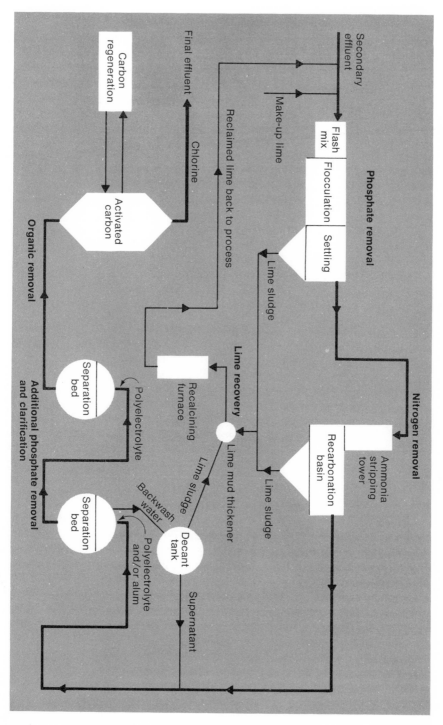

The first large-scale waste water treatment plant designed to produce effluent that could be used to recharge ground water used for municipal water supply has been operating since 1962 at Whittier Narrows in Los Angeles County, Calif. The plant treats up to 15 million gallons of municipal waste water per day and spreads the chlorinated effluent from conventional primary-secondary treatment on flood-water spreading grounds. The effluent percolates through the soil, which provides a form of tertiary treatment, and enters the ground water. Intensive study of the Whittier Narrows operation has produced no evidence of marked or deleterious effects on the ground water at or below Whittier Narrows (139).

Treated waste water is reused for recreation at Santee, Calif. (112). Effluent from primary-secondary treatment is treated further in an oxidation pond, and part of it is then pumped to a spreading area. It percolates through the soil and feeds several lakes that have been used for fishing, boating, and swimming. No public health problems have been detected in the lakes, although problems have arisen with eutrophication and the resulting fish kills caused by low levels of dissolved oxygen. At Lancaster, Calif., a 500,000 gallon-per-day waste water treatment facility is being designed to supply recreational lakes (39). It will use primary treatment, biological treatment in an oxidation pond, chemical coagulation and sedimentation, dual-media filtration, and chlorination.

Recommendations: advanced waste treatment

Recommendation W10: *Chemical and biological characterizations should be made of advanced treatment systems operating at the large pilot-plant or demonstration-plant level, including the identification of specific chemical compounds, studies of the effects of chlorine or other oxidants on organic residues, and other necessary investigations. Such studies should be comprehensive research and development efforts, not simply demonstrations that the systems operate properly in terms of the traditional parameters.*

Recommendation W11: *Adsorbents other than activated carbon, such as inorganic oxide systems, should be considered further for advanced waste treatment. There appears to be no inherent reason to restrict adsorption processes to activated carbons not designed specifically for the chemical species in waste waters. Further knowledge of those species might allow improved adsorbents to be synthesized.*

Recommendation W12: *Research should be maintained at a high level on removal or inactivation of viruses by waste water treatment processes and on other means of preventing virus buildup in recycle systems.*

INDUSTRIAL FACILITIES

Much of the conventional technology used in municipal waste water treatment is used also to treat industrial waste waters. Major industrial establishments, in fact, disposed of about 7.5% of their waste waters to municipal sewers in 1964, and existing data suggest that about half the total volume of waste water treated by municipal plants is of industrial origin. The trend appears to be toward more joint use of waste water treatment plants by industry and municipalities.

It is difficult to generalize on treatment of industrial waste waters because the sources are highly diverse and because only sketchy data are readily available on the specific materials that are treated or discharged (29). The costs of industrial water pollution abatement are certain to rise, however, because the water quality standards now coming into effect generally require the equivalent of municipal secondary treatment. To achieve that level of treatment, if it is taken to be at least 85% removal of BOD and settleable and suspended solids, would require industry to spend an estimated $1.1 to $2.6 billion to upgrade its existing waste water treatment facilities. In addition to this current backlog, industry would have to spend $1.5 to $2.0 billion through 1973 to replace obsolete equipment and build new treatment facilities. The total industrial investment required, in the period 1969-73, is $2.6 to $4.6 billion (Table 9, page 140).

Industrial waste waters generally are likely to be less amenable to conventional treatment than are municipal waste waters because they contain substances such as trace metals and chemical compounds that resist biological degradation. Thus, in addition to its use of municipal treatment, industry must handle its waterborne wastes by various kinds of on-site treatment (including biological), by process changes, or by ground disposal, such as deep well injection (35).

Combinations of these methods must often be used. One large modern petrochemical plant (109) injects strong phenolic wastes into a 6000-foot well, after pretreatment to remove solids. Nitrile wastes are injected into a separate, 7000-foot well. Oily wastes are treated in activated sludge ponds after initial skimming. Other contaminated waters, from hydrocarbon cracking and separation processes, go to a trickling filter along with the plant's domestic wastes and then to an activated sludge tank. Toxic wastes, containing mostly acetonitrile and some cyanides, plus waste hydrocarbons are oxidized completely in incinerators. The annual operating budget for these facilities, including all fixed charges, was $900,000 per year in 1968, when the plant was producing about 3 billion pounds per year of products. A treatment cost of 0.03 cent per pound of product can be derived from these data, but it is not a meaningful figure; waste water from some processes requires extensive treatment, that from others may require practically none.

This plant reuses water extensively, circulating about 1.5 billion gallons per day, but withdrawing only 15 million gallons per day of new water. Of this 15 million gallons of makeup water, only 1 to 2 million gallons per day are discharged, and the rest evaporates. Industry generally is increasing its reuse of water, partly to reduce the costs of pollution abatement (142). Other reasons include reduction of the over-

Table 9

Current and projected waste water treatment needs of major industrial establishments[a]

Industry	Required investment, constant dollars (millions)	
	By expert [b] estimate	By census [b] projection
Current need:		
Food and kindred products	$ 740	$ 670
Textile mill products	170	170
Paper and allied products	320	920
Chemical and allied products	380	1000
Petroleum and coal	380	270
Rubber and plastics	41	59
Primary metals	1500	1400
Machinery	39	56
Electrical machinery	36	51
Transportation equipment	220	160
All other manufacturing	200	290
Total current need	4000	5000
Plant now provided:		
By industry	2200	1800
Through municipal facilities	730	640
Total current backlog	1100	2600
New facilities, fiscal years 1969-73	700	1000
Replacing obsolete equipment	800	1000
Total capital requirement, fiscal years 1969-73	$2600	$4600

[a] Assumes at least 85% removal of BOD and settleable and suspended solids.
[b] All values rounded to two significant figures.
SOURCE: "The Cost of Clean Water, Vol. I, Summary Report," U. S. Department of the Interior, Federal Water Pollution Control Administration, Government Printing Office, Washington, D. C., January 1968.

all cost of water usage and, in some areas, limited water supply. Industry today probably reuses an average of more than 2 gallons of water for every new gallon it takes in, and the figure may rise to 3 gallons by 1980 (143).

New plants and processes generally reduce the ratio of wastes to products, although there are exceptions. In 1963, the pulp and paper industry generated about 200 pounds of BOD per ton of product in plants using "older" technology, about 135 pounds per ton in plants using "typical" technology, and about 80 pounds per ton in plants using "newer" technology. The major process change in the industry has been from sulfite pulping to sulfate or kraft pulping. Kraft pulping's share of industry output was 35% in 1942; it had passed 60% by 1962 and today is more than 90%. In the period 1943-62, effluent from the industry's plants fell from 180 pounds of BOD per ton of product to 68 pounds per ton (15). The shift to kraft pulping, in which processing chemicals are recycled, was a significant factor in the decrease, although other process changes and installation of waste treatment facilities were also important factors. The percentage of pulp output that is bleached, on the other hand, rose from about 25% in 1940 to almost 40% in 1965. Bleaching increases the BOD generated per ton of product by about 25% (66) and thus necessitates additional treatment.

Process modification or change generally seems likely to grow in importance as an economic means of reducing water pollution. By-product recovery, which is practiced widely, may also offer significant opportunities, although it cannot be considered a panacea. In the pulp and paper industry, for example, recycle or sale of processing chemicals, tall oil, and turpentine are self-supporting operations. Spent sulfite pulping liquor, on the other hand, cannot economically be used to a great extent in this country as a source of by-products. This is true despite the fact that on a purely technical basis it can be used to make vanillin, ethyl alcohol, and other chemicals and can serve as a nutrient in making torula yeast.

Product change can also help to abate water pollution. A notable example was the replacement of alkyl benzene sulfonate, a surface active agent used widely in synthetic detergents, by linear alkylate sulfonate, which is much more biodegradable. The change, which took place in 1965 in the U.S., was intended to solve, and did solve, a problem with foam in municipal waste water treatment plants, lakes, streams, and in some cases even in tap water.

Recommendations: industrial facilities

Recommendation W13: *Information should be gathered and made widely available on the technology of joint municipal-industrial treatment of waste waters for the guidance of companies and municipalities who wish to consider such an approach. This task should be managed at the federal level.*

Recommendation W14: *Inventories should be made, on a selective trial basis, of the specific substances in industrial waste waters that are important or potentially important pollutants. This task should be managed at the federal level.*

NONMUNICIPAL, NONINDUSTRIAL WATER POLLUTION

In addition to municipal and industrial wastes, sources of water pollution that are receiving increasing attention include certain agricultural operations, mine drainage waters, and boats and ships. Control technology is available or well along in development for some such sources, but for others it is not.

Agriculture

Agriculture, including the processing of agricultural products, is the source of a number of water pollutants. Among them are sediment from the erosion of crop land, animal wastes, pesticides, and compounds of phosphorus and nitrogen that originate in commercial fertilizers (25, 138). The U.S. Department of Agriculture and other federal agencies, as of early 1968, were spending about $200 million per year on soil conservation programs, about 80% of it to combat sediment from farm land. Such programs solve only part of the problem, and the development of improved land management practices will require deeper insight in many areas, including:

- The detachment and movement of soil particles by raindrop splash and flowing water.
- Means of stabilizing the banks of streams and other soils.
- The physics of the origin of sediments and their movement in watershed systems.

A steadily growing agricultural problem is runoff from areas contaminated by livestock and poultry wastes, particularly feedlots. At any given time in the U.S., an estimated 11 million cattle are on feedlots; in 1964 about 56% of the cattle that were slaughtered spent several weeks on 221,000 feedlots. The capacities of 1635 of these feedlots ranged from 1000 to 35,000 head. On the basis of the five-day BOD, a feedlot with 10,000 cattle is equivalent to a city of about 45,000 people. The production of poultry and swine in confined spaces is a somewhat smaller, though still serious, problem. Overall, waste production by farm animals in the U.S. has been estimated to total about 20 times that of the human population (Table 10).

Animal wastes are disposed of most commonly today by physical means, such as field spreading (130). All such methods require land, which is becoming more costly as urban areas expand into nearby rural areas.

Of the biological treatments that might be used for animal wastes, anaerobic degradation in lagoons has received the most attention from livestock producers. The feedlots that have installed recommended treatment lagoons have found the construction cost to range from $1.00 to $5.00 per head of feedlot capacity. Lagoons, like physical disposal methods, require land, and their design to date has been unsatisfactory. For swine and poultry wastes, however, lagoons may prove to be one of the best disposal methods if research can develop design criteria and means of controlling odors and eliminating mosquito breeding and the hazard of ground water pollution. Among other biological methods being studied are composting, anaerobic digestion with recovery of methane, and cultivation of algae, which could be used as a source of protein.

Table 10

Production of wastes by livestock in the U.S., 1965

Livestock	Population (millions)	Annual production of solid wastes (million tons)	Annual production of liquid wastes (million tons)
Cattle	107	1004.0	390.0
Horses[a]	3	17.5	4.4
Hogs	53	57.3	33.9
Sheep	26	11.8	7.1
Chickens	375	27.4	—
Turkeys	104	19.0	—
Ducks	11	1.6	—
TOTALS		1138.6	435.4

[a] Horses and mules on farms as work stock.

SOURCE: "Wastes in Relation to Agriculture and Forestry," U. S. Department of Agriculture, Miscellaneous Publication No. 1065, Government Printing Office, Washington, D. C., March 1968.

Disposal on land remains the most economical choice for animal wastes. Already, however, in the most populous states, only highly treated wastes can be disposed of in that way. Livestock producers need waste disposal methods that require little labor, cause little nuisance, and improve sanitation, but the new, experimentally proven ideas that are required to solve the problem have not yet materialized. Among specific requirements are improved data on the volume of manures and their plant nutrient content and biochemical oxygen demand. Also required are data on the chemical composition of manures and of the gases produced by their uncontrolled biological degradation.

Compounds of phosphorus and nitrogen that originate in chemical fertilizers enter natural water systems, but the importance of fertilizers relative to other sources, such as barnyard and feedlot runoff, raw or treated sewage, or nitrate formed naturally in soils, generally is not known with precision. The concern over phosphorus is due to its role as a nutrient for algae and other water plants whose excessive growth degrades surface waters. Nitrogen, too, is an important nutrient, but concern is growing also over the nitrate and small amounts of nitrite in ground water in many parts of the country. Both infants and ruminant livestock have become ill and sometimes died after drinking well water containing nitrate. The stomachs of both reduce nitrate to nitrite, which in infants causes methemoglobinemia (blue babies). From 1947 to 1950, Minnesota alone reported 139 cases of methemoglobinemia, including 14 deaths, caused by nitrate in farm well water. The U.S. Public Health Service has assigned a limit of 45 mg/l for nitrate in drinking water (99).

There is evidence that much of the phosphorus in surface waters comes from sewage treatment plants, and that phosphate in chemical fertilizers is only a secondary source. Phosphate is bound tightly to soil particles, and it enters surface waters from farm land mainly as a result of erosion and runoff. Extensive data are not available, however, on the relationship of the phosphate in agricultural runoff and drainage water to soil type, fertilizer and cultural practices, and other factors.

Nitrate, unlike phosphate, leaches through soil into tile drainage and ground water. There is evidence that chemical fertilizers are, in fact, a significant source of nitrate in ground water, and there is evidence to the contrary. Further data are required to resolve the question. Domestic sewage may be a major source of nitrate in ground water in rural communities. There is also evidence that leachate from cattle pens and feedlots may be important, particularly in restricted areas, but the overall significance of this source is unknown.

Analyses of data on nitrate and phosphate in surface waters in Illinois (59) suggest that nutrient problems caused by nitrogen and phosphorus might be expected to become common throughout the state. The data do not establish to date that nitrate in surface waters is becoming a widespread hazard to health, although the concentrations are tending to increase as time passes. The sources of nitrate and phosphate vary with the stream discharge and often are difficult to identify. Significant amounts of nitrogen have been found in precipitation, however. Known sources of both nitrogen and phosphorus include treated domestic sewage, drainage from cultivated land, and runoff from livestock feedlots. The data for one Illinois river, the Sangamon, show that treated waste water appears to contribute less than 1% of the nitrate found in April and most or all of that found in October. The heavy contributor of nitrate in April is tile drainage systems on cropland fertilized by nitrogen. Overall, the level of nitrate in Illinois surface waters is high in the spring, when water flow is high and reservoirs are filled, and low in the fall, when water flow is low.

Acid mine drainage

Acid mine drainage, almost all of it from coal mines, pollutes an estimated 10,000 miles of streams in the U.S. An estimated 60 to 70% of the drainage comes from abandoned mines, and about 85% of that amount comes from exhausted underground mines. Mine drainage can be alkaline as well as acid, but acid drainage is the more serious problem. The formation of acid mine water involves initially the oxidation of iron sulfide or pyrite to form, in a series of reactions, sulfates, sulfuric acid, iron oxides, and probably other compounds (12). Water that enters the mine dissolves oxidation products, and the resulting acidic solution, which may by now contain compounds of several different metals, runs eventually into surface waters. Three forms of oxidation are believed to be involved: chemical, electrochemical, and bacterially-catalyzed. The key to the overall rate of oxidation is the reaction of exposed pyrites with moist air.

One means of dealing with acid mine water is to prevent or minimize its formation at the source, and this is being practiced by industry (95). Measures that can be used include flooding or sealing, to prevent air from entering the mine and oxidizing the pyrite; and preventing water from entering acid-producing strata and minimizing its time of contact with reactive or reacted surfaces when it does enter.

Prevention at the source holds the best long-term hope, but it must be supplemented meanwhile by methods of treating acid (or alkaline) mine water after it forms (81, 148). Most of the work on treatments for acid mine water has involved neutralization with lime, which is generally available and costs less than any other neutralizing agents except limestone and waste alkaline material. In Pennsylvania, about 135 lime treatment plants were operating in late 1968. The solids, mostly hydrated iron oxide, and water in the voluminous sludge that is produced are separated mainly in settling lagoons (22). Solids may then be disposed of by a variety of means: in old strip-mine cuts, in underground mines, and in new-fill areas.

The cost of lime has stimulated research and development on the use of the cheaper limestone as a neutralizing agent. One of the problems with limestone is that insoluble iron (ferric) hydroxide or calcium sulfate can precipitate on the surface of the stone, preventing further reaction. The difficulty can be minimized by grinding the limestone and agitating the reaction mixture during neutralization, and a pilot plant of this type has been operated by the U.S. Bureau of Mines (80). The cost added by these two steps can be held down by using water power, where it is available, to operate the grinding and agitation equipment, and by using autogenous grinding, in which the pieces of stone grind against themselves instead of against an added grinding medium. This approach is being used at an installation in West Virginia.

Ion exchange has been studied for reclaiming acid mine water (90), and Pennsylvania expects in 1969 to ask for bids on ion exchange plants to convert acid mine water to potable water for two small towns. The capacity of each of the two plants will be roughly 500,000 gallons per day. The state also is planning a 5 million gallon-per-day flash distillation plant, but does not expect to ask for bids until after 1969.

Wastes from watercraft

The more than 8 million watercraft that navigate U.S. waters discharge a variety of pollutants, including sanitary wastes, oil, litter, and ballast and bilge waters (92). No federal legislation deals squarely as yet with watercraft pollution, although more than half of the states have laws of different degrees of effectiveness. The cost of bringing all U.S. watercraft into compliance with pollution regulations that would control boat pollution adequately has been estimated to be on the order of $600 million.

Watercraft operated by several federal agencies and other organizations already treat their wastes before discharge. The technology is not highly developed, however, at least in terms of adapting it to use on watercraft. The available equipment includes holding tanks, incinerators, biological treatment devices, and macerator-disinfectors. In development are systems that remove solids from sewage, disinfect the clarified water, and incinerate or store the solids for disposal on shore.

Recommendations: nonmunicipal, nonindustrial water pollution

Recommendation W15: *Basic research should be encouraged on economic means of treating and disposing of animal wastes in agriculture.*

Recommendation W16: *Basic data should be gathered systematically to delineate the relative importance of the various agricultural and rural sources of compounds of nitrogen and phosphorus in surface waters and ground waters.*

EFFECTS OF WATER POLLUTION

Research on the effects of water pollutants has developed a very large body of knowledge, which is reflected in existing and recommended water quality criteria (100, 141). Much remains to be done, however, in establishing the scientific bases for such criteria, which in turn supply the bases for water quality standards and the required abatement measures. The effects of pollutants depend on a variety of interrelated factors: the acidity or alkalinity of the water, its temperature, the degree of dilution and mixing, chemical and biochemical effects, the rate of flow of the water, and the reinforcing or counteracting effects of contaminants on one another. Further complexity is introduced by the economic need to relate water quality standards to water uses: recreation, public water supply, aquatic life and wildlife, agriculture, and industry. Among those areas in which the state of knowledge can be improved are effects on human health, tastes and odors, and eutrophication.

Human health

Very little is known of the possible effects on human health, at environmental levels, of the variety of largely unidentified chemical compounds that enter sources of water supply in municipal and industrial wastes, both treated and untreated. It is thus impossible to be entirely sanguine about the ability of water treatment plants to cope with steadily increasing chemical pollution as water reuse increases. At the present levels of exposure, water pollutants do not seem likely to have significant acute effects on human health, with the exception of nitrates, which can cause methemoglobinemia and death in infants. Less well defined, however, is the potential for chronic effects caused by long-term, low-level exposure.

Substances that may exert long-term effects include organic carcinogens, asbestos, and selenium (124). Excess intake of selenium, which is widespread in nature, has been linked to bad teeth, gastrointestinal disturbances, and skin discoloration. Statistical correlations suggest that death

146

rates due to degenerative cardiovascular disease may be reduced by some factor that is either present in "hard" water or missing from "soft" water. Efforts to identify such a factor have shown thus far that excess cadmium in the kidneys can cause hypertension in animals, and that a deficiency of chromium (in the trivalent state) favors atherosclerotic disease.

As water reuse grows more common, it will become increasingly important to single out potentially harmful substances and remove them at the source or by water treatment. Determination of those substances that might be harmful in long-term, low-level exposures will require improved knowledge of the specific compounds that are entering receiving waters. It will also require considerably more research, including research in epidemiology and on laboratory animals.

For example, the evidence that supports the present Public Health Service standard for nitrate in drinking water, 45 mg/l, is not strong. As of 1962, there had been no reports of methemoglobinemia in infants who drank water from public water supplies, which in some cases may routinely contain more than 45 mg/l of nitrate. Unlike public water supplies, wells are not monitored, and practically nothing is known of how nitrate concentration varies in the same well. Since well water is normally sampled only after nitrate injury occurs, it is conceivable that the nitrate concentration can change so that the analysis does not show the concentration that caused the injury. Nitrate is being found in more and more waters and is a good example of the need for better epidemiological, toxicological, and other kinds of evidence in setting water quality standards.

Bacteria, viruses

The prospect of increased reuse of water by humans intensifies the need to know more of the enteric viruses, those that occur in the gastrointestinal tract and feces of man and many lower animals. Recent years have seen increased concern over waterborne viral diseases [145]. This concern exists despite the fact that, of the enteric-virus diseases, only infectious hepatitis has been shown to be waterborne, and no large outbreaks of that disease have occurred in the U.S.

It might be possible to use ground water basins for water treatment and dilution, but the opportunity cannot be assessed intelligently because remarkably few studies have been made of viruses in reuse systems for protracted periods [78]. Data on the movement of viruses in ground water are extremely limited [38]. The ability of water treatment processes to remove or inactivate viruses has not been fully explored. Knowledge of the infectious hepatitis virus in particular is limited by the lack of suitable means of culturing it in the laboratory. Intensive research on the potential for viral disease is required in order to evaluate the soundness of proposed and possible systems for water reuse.

One of the major forces behind the drive to control water pollution is the demand for clean water for recreation. Public health officials have worked for years to maintain certain bacterial quality standards at bathing beaches. These standards commonly are based on counts of the coliform group of bacteria, the same group that is used to assess the quality of drinking water. The feces and urine of warmblooded animals are the major sources of bacteria and viruses that are capable of infecting man, and counts of total coliforms are taken to indicate a proportional level of fecal coliforms and contamination. Coliforms can come from many sources, however, and the fraction of the total in water that is of fecal origin may range from less than 1% to more than 90%. There is in fact no significant epidemiological basis for the total coliform standards used to assess the quality of bathing waters.

Only three epidemiological studies have ever been made in this country that were designed to relate the bacterial quality of natural bathing waters to human health (146). None of the three was conclusive or even highly suggestive as to a suitable standard. Eye, ear, nose, and throat ailments were the dominant illnesses reported. Gastrointestinal disturbances, the type that would be caused by fecal bacteria, accounted for 20% or less of the complaints. Swimmers showed distinctly higher rates of illness than nonswimmers, regardless of the bacterial quality of the water, a point that has been noted in other studies of the illness experience of swimmers. Very large sums of money are likely to be spent in the next decade primarily to meet bacterial quality standards for recreational waters. There can be no assurance that the money will be spent wisely unless a sound basis is established for such standards. Research is badly needed on correlation of currently-used or new indicator organisms with waterborne disease. Key questions include the rates of dispersion and inactivation of viruses in recreational waters.

Tastes and odors

A number of substances, both man-made and naturally occurring, can cause tastes and odors in water and impart off-flavors to fish and shellfish. Only traces of some organic compounds are required to cause a noticeable effect. The Public Health Service drinking water standards, for example, limit the content of phenols to 0.001 mg/l. The reason is that water treatment plants customarily disinfect water by chlorination, and the chlorophenols that form when phenols are present can cause an unpleasant taste at extremely low concentrations. Chlorophenol has been found to produce unpleasant taste in fish at a concentration of 0.0001 mg/l (14).

Current research is directed in part at isolating and identifying the specific chemical compounds that cause tastes and odors and determining the sources of those compounds (60). One instance is the musty, earthy odors, typical of freshly plowed soil, that often occur in water supplies. In the past few years, a specific organic compound believed to be responsible for such odors has been isolated from bacteria of the actinomycetes group (53) and from two species of blue-green algae (76, 111). It has also been detected in the effluent from secondary sewage treatment plants. It has been found to be a dimethyl decalol (52).

The available evidence suggests that the earthy odors in nature may be caused by several compounds that have some common structural features. If this is true, the number of variables involved in preventing or removing such odors might be considerably reduced.

Eutrophication

Eutrophication can be simply defined as the process of enrichment with nutrients (43), although the word is used often to describe the effects of the process when it occurs to excess in lakes and other waters. The effects are the same whether eutrophication occurs naturally over geologic time or is accelerated by the activities of man. They include excess growth of algae and other plant life; depletion of dissolved oxygen, which causes fish kills and the development of anaerobic zones where bacterial action produces foul odors; problems in water treatment plants, such as clogging of filters by algae, and undesirable tastes and odors (4); and a general lowering of aesthetic and recreational values. Notable examples of accelerated eutrophication include Lake Erie (67), Lake Washington in Seattle, Wash., the Madison lakes in Wisconsin, and Lake Zurich in Switzerland.

Eutrophication supports the photosynthetic process in which algae and other plant life synthesize new plant protoplasm using the energy in sunlight and a range of nutrients (48, 98, 127). The nutrients used in relatively large amounts are carbon, hydrogen, oxygen, sulfur, potassium, calcium, magnesium, nitrogen, and phosphorus. The growth process also requires trace amounts of other nutrients, both organic and inorganic. It is affected by many factors, including temperature, turbulence, toxins in the water, and the effects exerted by organisms on the growth of other organisms.

The measurement of eutrophication and its effects is highly complex and must rely on a variety of chemical, physical, and biological tools (49). Clarification of the variables involved and their relative importance in a given body of water requires that measurements be made over a period of years, but relatively few long-term studies have been made. Of the known variables, however, the only one that has appeared to be subject to preventive control by man is the supply of nutrients. Green plants consume differing amounts of the nutrients on which they subsist, and Liebig's Law of the Minimum states that the essential nutrient that is present in the lowest relative amount limits the amount of growth. Of the nutrients utilized by aquatic plant life, only nitrogen and phosphorus have been studied in any depth, and the evidence is strong that both can be important limiting nutrients.

One of the difficulties in controlling nitrogen and phosphorus, as well as other nutrients, is that they can enter a body of water from many sources: municipal and industrial waste waters, both raw and treated; tributary streams; rainfall; urban runoff; agricultural drainage; ground water; bird and animal wastes; decomposition of dead plant and animal life; and nitrogen fixation (83, 118).

Nitrogen and phosphorus may be removed from a body of water in flowing streams or ground water. They may also be removed in food consumed by animal life, such as birds, insects, and fish. The nutrients can be deposited in the sediments, creating a reserve that may be returned to the water to support plant growth if the input of fresh nutrients is shut off (47). It is possible that some inland waters already contain amounts of nutrients, such as phosphorus, so large that source control would be ineffective. For most regional water systems in the U.S., however, the data do not exist that could be used to establish phosphorus or nitrogen budgets with reasonable precision.

The nutrient control measures that have been invoked against eutrophication to date have involved chiefly diversion of waste waters. Domestic waste waters may contain not only nitrogen and phosphorus, but all other known nutrients as well, and industrial waste waters may contain one or two nutrients in relatively high concentrations. Early indications are that diversionary measures will succeed in arresting or reversing eutrophication in some cases at least. The main limiting factor appears to be the amounts and availability of nutrients in the sediments. The more recent techniques, removal of nitrogen and phosphorus from waste waters, have yet to come into use on a large scale, and their effectiveness probably will not be known for some years.

The current emphasis on phosphorus is based on several interrelated arguments. The control technology for phosphorus is better established than for nitrogen, which in addition can be obtained from the air by nitrogen-fixing blue-green algae. The ratio of phosphorus to nitrogen has been found in some cases to be the growth-limiting factor. Where this is true, removal of phosphorus would reduce the ratio to the point at which phosphorus became the limiting nutrient for green algae. The latter would then reduce the concentration of phosphorus to the point at which the nitrogen-fixing blue-green algae could not grow. Some authorities consider this overall argument too simplistic. It rests, they believe, on inadequate knowledge of eutrophication and its effects.

Limiting nutrients and their critical concentrations are likely to differ in different bodies of water and must be determined individually for each. Analyses of the waters of 17 Wisconsin lakes led to the suggestion that annual average concentrations of 0.015 mg/l of inorganic phosphorus and 0.3 mg/l of inorganic nitrogen were critical levels above which algal blooms could be expected. Excessive growth has been found elsewhere, however, at much lower phosphorus levels and has not occurred at much higher levels. Determination of critical concentrations is complicated by the fact that algae can take up and store excess phosphorus and subsist on this luxury uptake if the supply in the water is depleted. Algae have also been found capable of luxury uptake of nitrogen, but it is not known if this is an important factor in nature.

The best current means of studying critical concentrations of nutrients appears to be the biological assay using mass, optical density, and chlorophyll or carbon-14 uptake to measure the response of the algae. In various waters, phosphorus, nitrogen, molybdenum, iron, and other nutrients have been found to be limiting.

The emphasis on phosphorus in nutrient control has resulted in proposals that phosphates be removed from household detergents, in which they are currently essential ingredients. If the available data are correct, about 280 million pounds of phosphorus per year would thus be withheld from surface waters, but at least 680 million pounds per year would continue to enter from other sources (45). If the latter amount were distributed equally in the total annual stream flow of the U.S., it would produce an average concentration more than 10 times the amount believed to induce excessive growth of algae.

The validity of extrapolations of this kind may be arguable. It is possible that removing phosphates from detergents could be beneficial in at least some cases, but it is also evident that the soundness of decisions for or against phosphates in detergents would benefit from further knowledge of the sources of phosphorus and of its relative importance in promoting algal growth. A nonphosphorus compound, nitrilotriacetic acid, is being studied as a possible partial replacement for phosphates in detergents. It has been found in the laboratory to be essentially completely degraded in the activated sludge process (129).

Chemical control of algae, chiefly with copper sulfate, is practiced, and one organic compound, 2, 3-dichloronaphthoquinone, has been studied as a specific toxin for blue-green algae. Questions have been raised on the effects of copper sulfate on the ecology of the waters to which it is applied, and some algae appear to develop a tolerance to the compound. Another difficulty with chemical control of algae and other aquatic plants is that when they decompose they release more nutrients to the water. Other research has isolated a virus that selectively destroys blue-green algae (110). The aim of such research is to find agents that destroy only nuisance organisms without disrupting the overall biological community.

Recommendations: effects of water pollution

Recommendation W17: *Research should be strongly encouraged on the effects of known water pollutants in long-term, low-level exposure. Both laboratory and epidemiological work will be required.*

Recommendation W18: *Studies should be maintained on enteric viruses and their movement in soil and ground water.*

Recommendation W19: *Correlations of bacterial indicator organisms with waterborne disease, particularly in recreational waters, should receive high priority.*

Recommendation W20: *Public water supply treatment methods should be upgraded through research on removal and destruction of potentially*

*harmful substances not removed by waste treatment practices, or by-
passed with insufficient dilution during plant outage periods or in times
of disaster such as power failures.*

Recommendation W21: *Investigations should be pursued of the fundamental chemical and biological parameters of eutrophication and its effects. Development of effective and economic long-term controls will depend on considerably improved knowledge of factors such as mass balances for significant nutrients; the forms in which those nutrients exist
in water; natural population dynamics; potentially limiting nutrients in
specific situations; and algal, bacterial, and plant physiology in general.*

ANALYTICAL CHEMISTRY AND INSTRUMENTS

Progress in analytical chemistry and instrumentation is vital to
both water pollution research and surveillance (11), and research on
eutrophication is a notable example of the need. The identification
and measurement of limiting nutrients would be greatly eased by improved analytical methods for low levels of the forms of phosphorus compounds (70), the various forms of nitrogen compounds, trace metals, and
trace organic growth factors in water. Improved procedures may help to
distinguish phosphorus in water in at least four different forms: in true
solution as orthophosphate; as a component part of suspended mineral
material; adsorbed on suspended material; and in soluble organic material. More must be known particularly of the availability of adsorbed
and organic phosphorus as a plant nutrient.

Improved procedures are required also for traces of organic compounds, which may be important in three problem areas: toxicity to
man and animal life; color; and taste and odor (7, 8). Current methods such as carbon adsorption and solvent extraction have limitations
that need to be understood more fully, and new and improved methods
should be sought directly. Techniques are required that will identify
and measure organic contaminants in water at concentrations of from

---

Figure 4

Automatic water quality monitor installation ▶

An estimated 250 automatic water quality monitors of the type shown here are
in use in the U.S. Data can be recorded and telemetered to a central point. The
Ohio River Valley Water Sanitation Commission pioneered the concept of using
a network of such instruments to monitor water quality in a river basin automatically on an integrated basis.

SOURCE: "A Program Guide to Automated Instrumentation for Water Pollution Surveillance,"
U.S. Department of the Interior, Federal Water Pollution Control Administration, Cincinnati, Ohio, 1966.

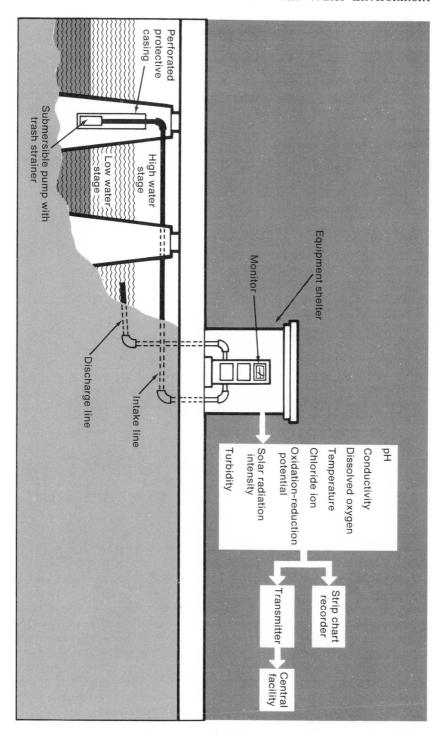

milligrams per liter down to micrograms per liter or lower. Chromatographic and spectrographic methods are the most promising today, but often they are not sensitive enough to determine organic contaminants at the levels at which they occur in natural and waste waters. Preliminary concentration methods are required that do not alter the organic compounds to be measured or their relative distributions in complex mixtures. Methods used in biochemical analysis can perhaps be adapted to analysis of trace organics in water.

Among more specific requirements are a simple, reliable, specific test for hydrogen sulfide and its ionic forms in water; more sensitive and quantitative techniques for measuring turbidity; an organic nitrogen method to replace the method published by Kjeldahl in 1883; and a means of measuring oxygen demand in undisturbed lake bottoms (122).

In the past decade, interest has grown rapidly in the condition of estuaries in the U.S., but efforts to determine the quality of estuarine waters have been hampered by lack of suitable analytical methods (63). Techniques are required that can be used on turbid waters of high and variable salinity, containing many substances in far higher concentrations than are found in the open ocean.

Automatic continuous monitoring of rivers and streams is a growing trend, and an estimated 250 automatic water quality monitors are now in use (10, 119). Such equipment (Fig. 4, page 153) is largely of the probe type today and can be equipped to measure dissolved oxygen, pH, temperature, conductivity, chloride, fluoride, turbidity, oxidation-reduction potential, and solar radiation. Data can be recorded and telemetered to a central point, such as a computer center. Work is in progress on extending automatic monitoring capability to sulfates, phenols, iron, manganese, and calcium. It would be desirable also to extend the capability to magnesium and other ions as well as inorganic and organic carbon. In addition there is a need to be able to monitor microorganisms (84).

There is an increasing contribution of acidic and noncarbonate mineral components in wastes from domestic, industrial, and agricultural sources. A need thus exists to develop corrosivity criteria to assess the gradual impact of such substances on water handling facilities.

Continuous monitoring is relatively costly, and the current equipment generally measures water quality characteristics rather than specific pollutants. For these reasons, such methods probably will continue to supplement analyses of samples in the laboratory, rather than replace them.

A general requirement in analytical chemistry is standardization of methods. The methods that serve today as the legal standard in pollution control hearings and legal actions (121) are used in most water pollution control laboratories, but in some cases the methods are not sufficiently sensitive and/or accurate or are outmoded. The establishment of a method, moreover, does not guarantee that it will produce the same results when used by different chemists in different laboratories. A strong effort is required in evaluating and improving the analytical chemical methods used on water and waste water.

Recommendations: analytical chemistry and instruments

Recommendation W22: *Emphasis should be placed on the development of analytical methods for specific organic pollutants at all concentrations and in all waste sources and receiving waters, including estuaries and the oceans. Similar effort should be devoted to developing methods for low levels of phosphorus, nitrogen, and other nutrients that are involved in eutrophication.*

Recommendation W23: *Analytical methods for gathering basic data, monitoring, research, and treatment control should be actively and continuously upgraded by systematic evaluation and standardization.*

LITERATURE CITED

1. "Advanced Waste Treatment Research. Summary Report. January 1962-June 1964," U.S. Public Health Service Publication No. 999-WP-24, Washington, D.C.

2. "Advanced Waste Treatment. Summary Report. July 1964-July 1967," U.S. Department of the Interior, Federal Water Pollution Control Administration, Publication WP-20-AWTR-19, Washington, D.C.

3. Albertson, O. E., "Low-Cost Thermal Oxidation of Sewage Sludge," presented at 36th Annual Meeting of the Water Pollution Control Federation, Seattle, Wash., October 1963.

4. "Algae in Water Supplies," U.S. Public Health Service Publication No. 657, Government Printing Office, Washington, D.C., 1962.

5. Bacon, V. W., Dalton, F. E., "Professionalism and Water Pollution Control in Greater Chicago," *J. Water Pollut. Contr. Fed.,* **40**, 1586 (1968).

6. Bailey, G. W., "Role of Soils and Sediment in Water Pollution Control. Part 1. Reactions of Nitrogenous and Phosphatic Compounds with Soils and Geologic Strata," U.S. Department of Interior, Federal Water Pollution Control Administration, Southeast Water Laboratory, Athens, Ga., March 1968.

7. Baker, R. A., "Trace Organic Analyses by Aqueous Gas-Liquid Chromatography," *Int. J. Air Water Pollut.,* **10**, 591 (1966).

8. Baker, R. A., Malo, B. A., in "Proceedings, the National Symposium on Quality Standards for Natural Waters," Continued Education Series No. 161, School of Public Health, University of Michigan, Ann Arbor, Mich., July 1966, p. 275.

9. Ballantine, D. S., Miller, L. A., Bishop, D. F., Rohrman, F. A., "The Practicality of Using Atomic Radiation for Wastewater Treatment," *J. Water Pollut. Contr. Fed.,* **41**, 445 (1968).

10. Ballinger, D. G., "Automated Water Quality Monitoring," *Environ. Sci. Technol.,* **2**, 606 (1968).

11. Ballinger, D. G., "Effecive Water Pollution Control Requires Accurate Data," *Environ. Sci. Technol.,* **1**, 612 (1967).

12. Barnes, H. L., Romberger, S. B., "Chemical Aspects of Acid Mine Drainage," *J. Water Pollut. Contr. Fed.,* **40**, 371 (1968).

13. Barth, E. F., Ettinger, M. B., "Mineral Controlled Phosphorus Removal in the Activated Sludge Process," *J. Water Pollut. Contr. Fed.,* **39**, 1362 (1967).

14. Boetius, J., "Foul Taste of Fish and Oysters Caused by Chlorophenol," Medd Denmarks Fishlog Havundersdg. N.S.1, 1 (1954).

15. Bower, B. T., in "Water Research," Kneese, A. V., Smith, S. C., Eds., Resources for the Future, Inc., Johns Hopkins Press, Baltimore, Md., 1966.

16. Brunner, C. A., "Pilot Plant Experiences in Demineralization of Secondary Effluent Using Electrodialysis," *J. Water Pollut. Contr. Fed.*, **39**, R1 (1967).

17. Bunch, R. L., Barth, E. F., Ettinger, M. B., "Organic Materials in Secondary Effluents," *J. Water Pollut. Contr. Fed.*, **33**, 122 (1961).

18. Burm, R. J., Krawczyk, D. F., Harlow, G. L., "Chemical and Physical Comparison of Combined and Separate Sewer Discharges," *J. Water Pollut. Contr. Fed.*, **40**, 112 (1968).

19. Busch, P. L., Stumm, W., "Chemical Interactions in the Aggregation of Bacteria. Bioflocculation in Waste Treatment," *Environ. Sci. Technol.*, **2**, 49 (1968).

20. Buzzell, J. C., Jr., Sawyer, C. N., "Removal of Algal Nutrients from Raw Wastewater with Lime," *J. Water Pollut. Contr. Fed.*, **39**, R16 (1967).

21. Cardinal, P. J., Jr., "Discussion and Review of the United States Sewage Solids Disposal Techniques," Advanced Waste Treatment Seminar, Osaka, Japan, Bartlett-Snow-Pacific, Inc., San Francisco, Calif., May, 1967.

22. Charmbury, H. B., Maneval, D. R., "Mine Drainage Pollution Abatement, Pennsylvania Style," preprint No. 68-F-18, annual meeting of American Institute of Mining, Metallurgical and Petroleum Engineers, New York, N.Y., February 1968; and subsequent private communication.

23. "Chemistry and the Oceans," *Chem. Eng. News*, **42** (22), 1A (1964).

24. "Clean-up Program Approved for Lake Michigan," *Environ. Sci. Technol.*, **2**, 397 (1968).

25. "Control of Agriculture-Related Pollution," a Report to the President, Submitted by the Secretary of Agriculture and the Director of the Office of Science and Technology, Washington, D.C., January 1969.

26. Cookson, J. T., Jr., North, W. J., "Adsorption of Viruses on Activated Carbon. Equilibria and Kinetics of the Attachment of *Escherichia coli* Bacteriophage T4 on Activated Carbon," *Environ. Sci. Technol.*, **1**, 46 (1967).

27. "The Cost of Clean Water and Its Economic Impact," U.S. Department of the Interior, Federal Water Pollution Control Administration, Government Printing Office, Washington, D.C., 1969.

28. "The Cost of Clean Water. Vol. I, Summary Report," U.S. Department of the Interior, Federal Water Pollution Control Administration, Government Printing Office, Washington, D.C., January 1968.

29. "The Cost of Clean Water. Vol. III. Industrial Waste Profiles," U.S. Department of the Interior, Federal Water Pollution Control Administration, Government Printing Office, Washington, D.C., 1968.

30. Crabtree, K., Boyle, W., McCoy, E., Rohlich, G. A., "A Mechanism of Floc Formation by *Zoogloea ramigera*," *J. Water Pollut. Contr. Fed.*, **38**, 1968 (1966).

31. Culp, G., Hansen, S., Richardson, G., "High Rate Sedimentation in Water Treatment Works," *J. Am. Water Works Assoc.*, **60**, 681 (1968); and subsequent private communication.

32. Dalton, F. E., Stein, J. E., Lynam, B. T., "Land Reclamation—A Complete Solution of the Sludge and Solids Disposal Problem," *J. Water Pollut. Contr. Fed.*, **40**, 789 (1968).

33. Dean, R. B., "Ultimate Disposal of Waste Water Concentrates to the Environment," *Environ. Sci. Technol.*, **2**, 1079 (1968).

34. Dean, R. B., Claesson, S., Gellerstedt, N., Boman, N., "An Electron Microscope Study of Colloids in Waste Water," *Environ. Sci. Technol.*, **1**, 147 (1967).

35. "Deep Wells for Industrial Waste Injection in the United States. Summary of Data," U.S. Department of the Interior, Federal Water Pollution Control Administration Publication No. WP-20-10, November 1967.

36. "Delaware Estuary Comprehensive Study, Preliminary Report and Findings," U.S. Department of the Interior, Federal Water Pollution Control Administration, Washington, D.C., July 1966.

37. Dostal, K. A., Harrington, J. J., Clark, R. M., Robeck, G. G., "Development of Optimization Models for Carbon Bed Design," *J. Am. Water Works Assoc.*, **58**, 1170 (1966).

38. Drewry, W. A., Eliassen, R., "Virus Movement in Groundwater," *J. Water Pollut. Contr. Fed.*, **40**, R257 (1968).

39. Dryden, F. D., Stern, G., "Renovated Waste Water Creates Recreational Lake," *Environ. Sci. Technol.*, **2**, 268 (1968).

40. "The Effects of Radiation on Chicago Metropolitan Sanitary District Municipal and Industrial Wastewater," by Pacific Northwest Laboratories, Battelle Memorial Institute for The Metropolitan Sanitary District of Greater Chicago, March 1968.

41. Eliassen, R., Tchobanoglous, G., "Chemical Processing of Wastewater for Nutrient Removal," *J. Water Pollut. Contr. Fed.*, **40**, R171 (1968).

42. Etzel, J. E., Born, G. S., Stein, J., Helbing, T. J., Baney, G., "Sewage Sludge Conditioning and Disinfection by Gamma Irradiation," paper at 96th Annual Meeting, American Public Health Association, Detroit, Mich., November 1968.

43. "Eutrophication—A Review," State of California, State Water Quality Control Board Publication No. 34, 1967.

44. Evans, F. L., III, Geldreich, E. E., Weibel, S. R., Robeck, G. G., "Treatment of Urban Stormwater Runoff," *J. Water Pollut. Contr. Fed.*, **40**, R162 (1968).

45. Ferguson, F. A., "A Nonmyopic Approach to the Problem of Excess Algal Growths," *Environ. Sci. Technol.*, **2**, 188 (1968).

46. Fleischman, M., Price, R. H., "Gamma Irradiation of Dilute Aqueous Alkyl Benzene Sulfonate Solutions," *Environ. Sci. Technol.*, **1**, 573 (1967).

47. Frink, C. R., "Nutrient Budget: Rational Analysis of Eutrophication in a Connecticut Lake," *Environ Sci. Technol.*, **1**, 425 (1967).

48. Fruh, E. G., in "Advances in Water Quality Improvement," Gloyna, E. F., Eckenfelder, W. W., Jr., Eds., University of Texas Press, Austin, Tex., 1968, p. 49.

49. Fruh, E. G., Stewart, K. M., Lee, G. F., Rohlich, G. A., "Measurements of Eutrophication and Trends," *J. Water Pollut. Contr. Fed.*, **38**, 1237 (1966).

50. Gaudy, A. F., Jr., "Induction and Repression in Activated Sludge Systems," *Appl. Microbiol.*, **10**, 264 (1962).

51. Gentry, R. E., Jr., "Reverse Osmosis—A Pleasant Inversion," *Environ. Sci. Technol.*, **1**, 124 (1967).

52. Gerber, N. N., "Geosmin, from Microorganisms, Is Trans-1, 10-Dimethyl-Trans-9-Decalol," *Tetrahedron Lett.* No. 25, 2971 (1968).

53. Gerber, N. N., Lechevalier, H. A., "Geosmin, an Earthy-Smelling Substance Isolated from Actinomycetes," *Appl. Microbiol.*, **13**, 935 (1965).

54. Germain, J. E., "Economical Treatment of Domestic Waste by Plastic-Medium Trickling Filters," *J. Water Pollut. Contr. Fed.*, **38**, 192 (1966).

55. Gloyna, E. F., Eckenfelder, W. W., Jr., Eds., "Advances in Water Quality Improvement," University of Texas Press, Austin, Tex., 1968.

56. Gould, R. F., Ed., "Equilibrium Concepts in Natural Water Systems," Ad-

vances in Chemistry Series No. 67, American Chemical Society, Washington, D.C., 1967.

57. "Guidelines for Establishing Water Quality Standards for Interstate Waters (Under the Water Quality Act of 1965, Public Law 89-234)," U.S. Department of Interior, Federal Water Pollution Control Administration, Washington, D.C., May 1966.

58. Gulevich, W., Renn, C. E., Liebman, J. C., "Role of Diffusion in Biological Waste Treatment," Environ. Sci. Technol., 2, 113 (1968).

59. Harmeson, R. H., Larson, T. E., "Interim Report on the Presence of Nitrates in Illinois Surface Waters," Proceedings, 1969 Illinois Fertilizer Conference, University of Illinois, Illinois Fertilizer Industry Association, Champaign, Ill., 1969, p. 33.

60. Henley, D. E., Glaze, W. H., Silvey, J. K. G., "Isolation and Identification of an Odor Compound Produced by a Selected Aquatic Actinomycete," Environ. Sci. Technol., 3, 268 (1969).

61. Hunt, H. H., Clarke, W. N., Sr., "Design and Operation of the First Digester Gas Turbine in the U.S.A.," J. Water Pollut. Contr. Fed., 40, 1346 (1968).

62. Hunter, J. V., Heukelekian, H., "The Composition of Domestic Sewage Fractions," J. Water Pollut. Contr. Fed., 37, 1142 (1965).

63. Jenkins, D., "Analysis of Estuarine Waters," J. Water Pollut. Contr. Fed., 39, 159 (1967).

64. Johnson, W. K., in "Advances in Water Quality Improvement," Gloyna, E. F., Eckenfelder, W. W., Jr., Eds., University of Texas Press, Austin, Tex., 1968, p. 178.

65. Keinath, T. M., Weber, W. J., Jr., "A Predictive Model for the Design of Fluid-Bed Adsorbers," J. Water Pollut. Contr. Fed., 40, 741 (1968).

66. Kneese, A. V., Bower, B. T., "Managing Water Quality: Economics, Technology, Institutions," The Johns Hopkins Press, Baltimore, Md., 1968, p. 48.

67. "Lake Erie—Dying But Not Dead," Environ. Sci. Technol., 1, 212 (1967).

68. "Lake Erie Report. A Plan for Water Pollution Control," U.S. Department of the Interior, Federal Water Pollution Control Administration, Washington, D.C., August 1968.

69. Lammers, W. T., "Biophysical Limnology. Separation of Suspended and Colloidal Particles from Natural Water," Environ. Sci. Technol., 1, 52 (1967).

70. Lee, G. F., Clesceri, N. L., Fitzgerald, G. P., "Studies on the Analysis of Phosphates in Algal Cultures," Int. J. Air, Water Pollut., 9, 715 (1965).

71. Lotse, E. G., Graetz, D. A., Chesters, G., Lee, G. B., Newland, L. W., "Lindane Adsorption by Lake Sediments," Environ. Sci. Technol., 2, 353 (1968).

72. Lumb, C., "Heat Treatment as an Aid to Sludge Dewatering—Ten Years' Full-Scale Operation," Inst. Sewage Purif. J. Proc., Part I, 5 (1951).

73. McCarty, P. L., "Sludge Concentration—Needs, Accomplishments, and Future Goals," J. Water Pollut. Contr. Fed., 38, 493 (1966).

74. McGauhey, P. H., Krone, R. B., "Soil Mantle as a Wastewater Treatment System," Sanitary Engineering Research Laboratory Report No. 67-11, University of California, Berkeley, Calif., December 1967.

75. McPherson, M. B., "ASCE Combined Sewer Separation Project Progress," Conference Preprint 548, American Society of Civil Engineers Meeting, New York, N.Y., October 1967.

76. Medsker, L. L., Jenkins, D., Thomas, J. F., "Odorous Compounds in Natural Waters. An Earthy-Smelling Compound Associated with Blue-Green Algae and Actinomycetes," Environ. Sci. Technol., 2, 461 (1968).

77. Menar, A. B., Jenkins, D., "The Fate of Phosphorus in Sewage Treatment Processes. II. Mechanism of Enhanced Phosphate Removal by Activated Sludge," SERL Report No. 68-6, Sanitary Engineering Research Laboratory, University of California, Berkeley, Calif., August 1968.

78. Merrell, J. C., Jr., Ward, P. C., "Virus Control at the Santee, Calif., Project," *J. Am. Water Works Assoc.*, **60**, 145 (1968).

79. Merten, U., Nusbaum, I., "Organic Removal by Reverse Osmosis," Division of Water, Air and Waste Chemistry Preprints, **8**, (2), 156th National Meeting of the American Chemical Society, Atlantic City, N.J., September 1968.

80. Mihok, E. A., Deul, M., Chamberlain, C. E., Selmeczi, J. G., "Mine Water Research. The Limestone Neutralization Process," U.S. Bureau of Mines Report of Investigations 7191, Washington, D.C., 1968.

81. "Mine Drainage Treatment—State of the Art and Research Needs," U.S. Department of the Interior, Federal Water Pollution Control Administration, Cincinnati, Ohio, December 1968.

82. Moehle, F. W., "Fly Ash Aids in Sludge Disposal," *Environ. Sci. Technol.*, **1**, 374 (1967).

83. "Nutrient-Associated Problems in Water Quality and Treatment," Task Group Report, *J. Am. Water Works Assoc.*, **58**, 1337 (1966).

84. Oleniacz, W. S., Pisano, M. A., Rosenfeld, M. H., Elgart, R. L., "Chemiluminescent Method for Detecting Microorganisms in Water," *Environ. Sci. Technol.*, **2**, 1030 (1968).

85. Painter, H. A., Viney, M., "Composition of a Domestic Sewage," *J. Biochem. Microbiol. Technol. Eng.*, **1**, 143 (1959).

86. Parkhurst, J. D., Dryden, F. D., McDermott, G. N., English, J., "Pomona Activated Carbon Pilot Plant," *J. Water Pollut. Contr. Fed.*, **39**, R70 (1967).

87. Pfeffer, J. T., Leiter, M., Worlund, J. R., "Population Dynamics in Anaerobic Digestion," *J. Water Pollut. Contr. Fed.*, **39**, 1305 (1967).

88. "Phosphate Removal Processes Prove Practical," *Environ. Sci. Technol.*, **2**, 182 (1968).

89. Pinder, K. L., Gauvin, W. H., "Applications of the Atomized Suspension Technique to the Treatment of Waste Effluents," Proceedings, 12th Industrial Waste Conference, Purdue University, Lafayette, Ind., 1957, p. 217.

90. Pollio, F., Kunin, R., "Ion Exchange Processes for the Reclamation of Acid Mine Drainage Waters," *Environ. Sci. Technol.*, **1**, 235 (1967).

91. Pollio, F. X., Kunin, R., "Tertiary Treatment of Municipal Sewage Effluents," *Environ. Sci. Technol.*, **2**, 54 (1968).

92. "Pollution from Vessels Threatens to Negate Clean Water Goals," *Environ. Sci. Technol.*, **2**, 93 (1968).

93. "Porteous Process Unit Readied for Startup," *Environ Sci. Technol.*, **2**, 1068 (1968).

94. Priesing, C. P., "A Theory of Coagulation Useful for Design," *Ind. Eng. Chem.*, **54**, 38 (1962).

95. "Principles and Guide to Practices in the Control of Acid Mine-Drainage," Ohio River Valley Water Sanitation Commission, Cincinnati, Ohio, March 1964.

96. "Problems of Combined Sewer Facilities and Overflows, 1967," Federal Water Pollution Control Administration, Water Pollution Control Series WP-20, Government Printing Office, Washington, D.C., July 1968.

97. Proudfit, D. P., in "Waste Disposal from Water and Wastewater Treatment Processes," Proceedings, Tenth Sanitary Engineering Conference, Engineer-

ing Publications Office, University of Illinois, Urbana, Ill., February 1968, p. 125.

98. Provasoli, L., in "Algae and Metropolitan Wastes; Transactions," U.S. Public Health Service, Robert A. Taft Sanitary Engineering Center, Cincinnati, Ohio, 1960.

99. "Public Health Service Drinking Water Standards," U.S. Public Health Service Publication No. 956, Government Printing Office, Washington, D.C., 1962.

100. "Report of the Committee on Water Quality Criteria," U.S. Department of the Interior, Federal Water Pollution Control Administration, Government Printing Office, Washington, D.C., 1968.

101. "Report on Salt Creek Water Reclamation Plant," The Metropolitan Sanitary District of Greater Chicago, Camp, Dresser & McKee, Boston, Mass., January 1968.

102. "Research and Development Programs, Division of Engineering Development," U.S. Department of the Interior, Federal Water Pollution Control Administration, Washington, D.C., August 1968.

103. "Reusing Storm Runoff," Environ. Sci. Technol., 2, 1001 (1968).

104. Rickert, D. A., Hunter, J. V., "Rapid Fractionation and Materials Balance of Solids Fractions in Wastewater and Wastewater Effluent," J. Water Pollut. Contr. Fed., 39, 1475 (1967).

105. Ries, H. E., Jr., Meyers, B. L., "Flocculation Mechanism: Charge Neutralization and Bridging," Science, 160, 1449 (1968).

106. Robeck, G. G., Bendixen, T. W., Schwartz, W. A., Woodward, R. L., "Factors Influencing the Design and Operation of Soil Systems for Waste Treatment," J. Water Pollut. Contr. Fed., 36, 971 (1964).

107. Robeck, G. G., Dostal, K. A., Cohen, J. M., Kreisse, J. S., "Effectiveness of Water Treatment Processes in Pesticide Removal," J. Am. Water Works Assoc., 57, 181 (1965).

108. Rudolfs, W., Balmat, J. L., "Colloids in Sewage. I. Separation of Sewage Colloids with the Aid of the Electron Microscope," Sewage Ind. Wastes, 24, 247 (1952).

109. Sadow, R. D., "Waste Treatment at a Large Petrochemical Plant," J. Water Pollut. Contr. Fed., 38, 428 (1966).

110. Safferman, R. S., Morris, M., "Control of Algae with Viruses," J. Am. Water Works Assoc., 56, 1217 (1964).

111. Safferman, R. S., Rosen, A. A., Mashni, C. I., Morris, M. E., "Earthy-Smelling Substances from a Blue-Green Alga," Environ. Sci. Technol., 1, 429 (1967).

112. "The Santee Recreation Project. Final Report," U.S. Department of the Interior, Federal Water Pollution Control Administration, Publication No. WP-20-7, 1967.

113. Sawyer, C. N., "The Need for Nutrient Control," J. Water Pollut. Contr. Fed., 40, 363 (1968).

114. Schwartz, H. G., Jr., "Adsorption of Selected Pesticides on Activated Carbon and Mineral Surfaces," Environ. Sci. Technol., 1, 333 (1967).

115. Shapiro, J., Levin, G. V., Zea, G. H. "Anoxically Induced Release of Phosphate in Wastewater Treatment," J. Water Pollut. Contr. Fed., 39, 1810 (1967).

116. Slechta, A. F., Culp, G. L., "Water Reclamation Studies at the South Tahoe Public Utility District," J. Water Pollut. Contr. Fed., 39, 787 (1967).

117. Snoeyink, V. L., Weber, W. J., Jr., "The Surface Chemistry of Active Carbon," Environ. Sci. Technol., 1, 228 (1967).

118. "Sources of Nitrogen and Phosphorus in Water Supplies," Task Group Report, J. Am. Water Works Assoc., 59, 344 (1967).

119. "Specifications for an Integrated Water Quality Data Acquisition System," U.S. Department of the Interior, Federal Water Pollution Control Administration, 8th ed., January 1968.

120. Sproul, O. J., Larochelle, L. R., Wentworth, D. F., Thorup, R. T., in "Water Reuse," *Chem. Eng. Progr. Symp. Ser.*, **63**, (78), American Institute of Chemical Engineers, New York, N.Y., 1967, p. 130.

121. "Standard Methods for the Examination of Water and Wastewater," American Public Health Association, American Water Works Association, and Water Pollution Control Federation, New York, N.Y., 12th ed., 1965.

122. Stein, J. E., Denison, J. G., "In Situ Benthal Oxygen Demand of Cellulosic Fibers," paper presented at Third International Conference on Water Pollution Research, Munich, Germany, 1966.

123. Stephan, D. G., Weinberger, L. W., "Wastewater Reuse—Has it Arrived?" *J. Water Pollut. Contr. Fed.*, **40**, 529 (1968).

124. Stokinger, H. E., "The Spectre of Today's Environmental Pollution—USA Brand: New Perspectives from an Old Scout," *Am. Ind. Hyg. Assoc. J.*, **30**, 195 (1969).

125. "The Storage and Retrieval of Data for Water Quality Control," U.S. Public Health Service Publication No. 1263, Government Printing Office, Washington, D.C., 1966.

126. "A Study of Sludge Handling and Disposal," U.S. Department of the Interior, Federal Water Pollution Control Administration Publication WP-20-4, May 1968.

127. Stumm, W., Morgan, J. J., "Stream Pollution by Algal Nutrients," *Trans. 12th Sanit. Eng. Conf.*, University of Kansas, Lawrence, Kans., 1962, p. 16.

128. Stumm-Zollinger, E., "Substrate Utilization in Heterogeneous Bacterial Communities," *J. Water Pollut. Contr. Fed.*, **40**, R213 (1968).

129. Swisher, R. D., Crutchfield, M. M., Caldwell, D. W., "Biodegradation of Nitrilotriacetate in Activated Sludge," *Environ. Sci. Technol.*, **1**, 820 (1967).

130. Taiganides, E. P., in "Agriculture and the Quality of Our Environment," Brady, N. C., Ed., American Association for the Advancement of Science, Publication 85, Washington, D.C., 1967.

131. Teletzke, G. H., "Wet Air Oxidation," *Chem. Eng. Progr.*, **60**, 33 (1964).

132. Tenney, M. W., Cole, T. G., "The Use of Fly Ash in Conditioning Biological Sludges for Vacuum Filtration," *J. Water Pollut. Contr. Fed.*, **40**, R281 (1968).

133. Tenney, M. W., Stumm, W., "Chemical Flocculation of Microorganisms in Biological Waste Treatment," *J. Water Pollut. Contr. Fed.*, **37**, 1370 (1965).

134. Thomas, R. E., Schwartz, W. A., Bendixen, T. W., "Soil Chemical Changes and Infiltration Rate Reduction Under Sewage Spreading," *Soil Sci. Soc. Amer. Proc.*, **30**, 641 (1966).

135. Tsivoglou, E. C., Cohen, J. B., Shearer, S. D., Godsil, P. J., "Tracer Measurement of Stream Reaeration. II. Field Studies," *J. Water Pollut. Contr. Fed.*, **40**, 285 (1968).

136. Tsivoglou, E. C., O'Connell, R. L., Walter, C. M., Godsil, P. J., Logsdon, G. S., "Tracer Measurements of Atmospheric Reaeration. I. Laboratory Studies," *J. Water Pollut. Contr. Fed.*, **37**, 1343 (1965).

137. Vacker, D., Connell, C. H., Wells, W. N., "Phosphate Removal Through Municipal Wastewater Treatment at San Antonio, Texas," *J. Water Pollut. Contr. Fed.*, **39**, 750 (1967).

138. "Wastes in Relation to Agriculture and Forestry," U.S. Department of Agriculture, Miscellaneous Publication No. 1065, Government Printing Office, Washington, D.C., March 1968.

139. "Wastewater Reclamation at Whittier Narrows," State of California, State Water Quality Control Board Publication No. 33, 1966.

140. "Water Pollution Surveillance System, Annual Compilation of Data, Oct. 1, 1962-Sept. 30, 1963," Public Health Service Publication No. 663, Government Printing Office, Washington, D.C., 1963.

141. "Water Quality Criteria," 2nd Ed., State of California, State Water Quality Control Board Publication No. 3-A, 1963.

142. "Water Reuse," Cecil, L. K., Ed., *Chem. Eng. Progr. Symp. Ser.*, **63**, (78), American Institute of Chemical Engineers, New York, N.Y., 1967.

143. "Water Re-Use," *Chem. Eng. News,* **40** (12), 90 (1966).

144. Weibel, S. R., "Urban Drainage as a Factor in Eutrophication," in "Proceedings, First International Symposium on Eutrophication," National Academy of Sciences—National Research Council, Washington, D.C., in press.

145. Weibel, S. R., Dixon, F. R., Weidner, R. B., McCabe, L. J., "Waterborne Disease Outbreaks, 1946-60," *J. Am. Water Works Assoc.,* **56**, 947 (1964).

146. Woodward, R. L., "Environmental Hazards: Water Pollution," *New England J. Med.,* **275**, 819 (1966).

147. Yee, W. C., "Selective Removal of Mixed Phosphates by Activated Alumina," *J. Am. Water Works Assoc.,* **58**, 239 (1966).

148. Zawadzki, E. A., "Status of Mine Drainage Technology," hearings before the Committee on Public Works, U.S. House of Representatives, 90th Congress, 2nd Session, on H.R. 15906 and Related Bills, Government Printing Office, Washington, D.C., 1968, p. 219.

Section 3

Solid Wastes

Contents

Solid Wastes

INTRODUCTION

The technology used to handle and dispose of solid wastes in the U.S. lags well behind that used to control air and water pollution. Less than 10 years ago, far fewer than half of the cities and towns in this country with populations of more than 2500 were disposing of community refuse by approved sanitary and nuisance-free methods (29). Municipalities have resorted primarily to open dumps, with relatively few using incinerators or improved disposal methods, such as sanitary landfills. Industry often has followed a like course.

As recently as 1965, the Federal Government was spending only an estimated $300,000 annually on research on solid waste disposal. In the few years since that time, and largely under federal stimulus, solid wastes management has come under increasing scrutiny, and the situation has begun slowly to change (16, 40, 44). The basic science of solid waste handling and disposal remains in relatively primitive condition, but advanced technology from other fields is being brought increasingly to bear on the many problems that must be solved. The need is clear. Even disposal methods that are now acceptable cannot be counted on to deal fully with the refuse from a growing industry and from 22 highly urbanized areas, containing some 240 million people, the situation expected in the U.S. by the year 2000.

BACKGROUND

Current estimates (Table 1) show that public and private agencies in the U.S. collect an average of 5.32 pounds per person per day of solid wastes, nationwide, or more than 190 million tons per year (3). By 1980,

Table 1

Average solid waste collected, pounds per person per day

Solid wastes	Urban	Rural	National
Household	1.26	0.72	1.14
Commercial	0.46	0.11	0.38
Combined	2.63	2.60	2.63
Industrial	0.65	0.37	0.59
Demolition, construction	0.23	0.02	0.18
Street and alley	0.11	0.03	0.09
Miscellaneous	0.38	0.08	0.31
Totals	5.72	3.93	5.32

SOURCE: Black, R.J., Muhich, A.J., Klee, A.J., Hickman, H.L., Jr., Vaughan, R.D., "An Interim Report. 1968 National Survey of Community Solid Waste Practices," presented at 1968 annual meeting, Institute for Solid Wastes, American Public Works Association, Miami Beach, Fla., October 1968, Bureau of Solid Waste Management, U.S. Department of Health, Education, and Welfare, Washington, D.C.

some 235 million people are expected to be generating 8 pounds per person per day of solid wastes or more than 340 million tons per year. These figures, moreover, cover only those wastes that are handled by collection agencies. Overall, the nation is generating today an estimated 10 pounds per person per day of household, commercial, and industrial wastes, or more than 360 million tons per year. In addition, about 7 million passenger cars, trucks, and buses are junked annually in this country. More than 80% of them may be salvaged in varying degree, but the excess contributes to an accumulation of abandoned vehicles that has been estimated at from 9 million to 16.5 million. The mineral industries alone in 1965 generated an estimated 1.1 billion tons of solid wastes in the form of mine waste, mill tailings, washing plant rejects, processing plant wastes, and smelter slags and rejects (but not including the overburden from surface mining).

The first federal effort to deal directly with the solid wastes problem was the Solid Waste Disposal Act of 1965. The act has two purposes: to start and accelerate a national research, development, and demonstration program on solid wastes; to give technical and financial support to interstate, state, and local agencies in planning, developing, and conducting solid waste disposal programs. The act authorized appropriations rising from not more than $10 million in fiscal 1966 to not more than $32.5 million in fiscal 1969. The money is divided between what is now the Bureau of Solid Waste Management in the Department of Health, Education, and Welfare, and the Solid Waste Research and Economic Resource Evaluation Studies Programs of the Bureau of Mines, in the Department of the Interior. Under the act, the Bureau of Solid Waste Management would receive 60 to 70% of the total when both agencies receive the maximum allowable appropriations.

MUNICIPAL REFUSE

Municipal refuse is a complex heterogeneous substance, both physically and chemically (Table 2). Measurements and standards that can be used to characterize municipal refuse do not now exist, and the Bureau of Solid Waste Management is working to establish suitable parameters. The bureau is also developing statistics on the use of different disposal methods (Fig. 1, page 168). Of the 5.32 pounds per person per day of solid wastes handled by collection agencies, about 8% is disposed of in some 300 municipal incinerators in the U.S. More than 90% goes to some 12,000 land disposal sites. Hog feeding and composting account for relatively small fractions of the solid waste disposal load. Of the 300 incinerators, only about 30% have adequate air pollution control devices. Of the 12,000 land disposal sites, only about 6% are sanitary landfills, defined as having daily cover, no open burning, and no water pollution problems. The remaining 94% of the land disposal sites are considered inadequate.

The aim of solid waste disposal processes is to reduce primarily the

Table 2

Sample municipal refuse composition—U. S. East Coast

Weight per cent

Physical		Rough Chemical	
Cardboard	7%	Moisture	28.0%
Newspaper	14	Carbon	25.0
Miscellaneous paper	25	Hydrogen	3.3
Plastic film	2	Oxygen	21.1
Leather, molded		Nitrogen	0.5
plastics, rubber	2	Sulfur	0.1
Garbage	12	Glass, ceramics, etc.	9.3
Grass and dirt	10	Metals	7.2
Textiles	3	Ash, other inserts	5.5
Wood	7		100.0
Glass, ceramics, stones	10		
Metallics	8		
Total	100		

SOURCE: Kaiser, E. R., "Refuse Reduction Processes," in "Proceedings, The Surgeon General's Conference on Solid Waste Management for Metropolitan Washington," U.S. Public Health Service Publication No. 1729, Government Printing Office, Washington, D.C., July 1967, p. 93.

volume and secondarily the weight of the refuse, so that it can be disposed of more readily, and to convert it to a less offensive form. Sanitary landfilling will reduce municipal refuse from an initial volume of about 7 cubic yards per ton to about a third of that volume. Incineration can reduce the volume 80 to 85% if the refuse is uncompacted and about 95% if cans and similar material are compacted. In composting, the organic matter in the refuse is reduced about 40% in weight by biological degradation and marketed as compost. If the uncomposted residue is used in landfill, the process achieves an overall volume reduction similar to that of incineration.

Composting involves the concept of cost recovery, since the compost itself is sold, and materials such as paper and rags may be salvaged and sold. The concept can also be applied to refuse incineration by using the heat produced to generate steam. There is very little evidence to suggest that cost-recovery will be a panacea. The importance of the concept lies in its recognition that municipal refuse can be treated as an asset rather than a nuisance, even though no net profit is realized, and this idea can be applied even in upgrading simple dumping to the sanitary landfill.

Sanitary landfill

Modern practice in sanitary landfill (Fig. 2, page 169) can be seen in those operated by the Sanitation Districts of Los Angeles County, Calif. (4). Refuse is spread in thin layers, and each is compacted by a bulldozer before the next is spread. When about 10 feet of refuse has been

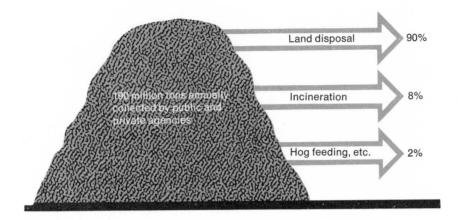

Figure 1
Methods used to dispose of solid wastes

Public and private agencies in the U.S. collect an average of 5.32 pounds per person per day of solid wastes, or more than 190 million tons annually. About 90% of the wastes collected go to some 12,000 land disposal sites, of which only about 6% are considered adequate sanitary landfills. About 8% is disposed of in some 300 municipal incinerators, of which only about 30% have adequate air pollution controls.

SOURCE: Black, R. J., Muhich, A. J., Klee, A. J., Hickman, H. L., Jr., Vaughan, R. D., "An Interim Report. 1968 National Survey of Community Solid Waste Practices," presented at 1968 annual meeting, Institute for Solid Wastes, American Public Works Association, Miami Beach, Fla., October 1968, Bureau of Solid Waste Management, U.S. Department of Health, Education, and Welfare, Washington, D.C.

laid down in this way, it is covered by a thin layer of clean earth, which also is compacted. The operation is repeated until the landfill has reached the desired depth. At the end of each working day the fill is sealed with a thin layer of compacted earth, and the completed fill is sealed with 2 or 3 feet of compacted earth. There is no burning and no serious problem with odors, flies, or rats. Water pollution is minimized by the small amount of rainfall.

Los Angeles County has used the landfill technique to reclaim land and convert it to parks, golf courses, and other types of recreational areas. The county has found that it can haul refuse for up to 50 miles in large trailers and bury it in landfills at costs competitive with those of operating municipal incinerators that would meet the local air pollution regulations. The 13 municipal incinerators that were operating in the county in 1955 have since closed down because they could not meet the regulations economically.

Air does not penetrate a well-compacted landfill to any extent, and oxygen inside the fill is utilized rapidly by aerobic microorganisms as they decompose organic matter. When the oxygen is depleted, decomposition

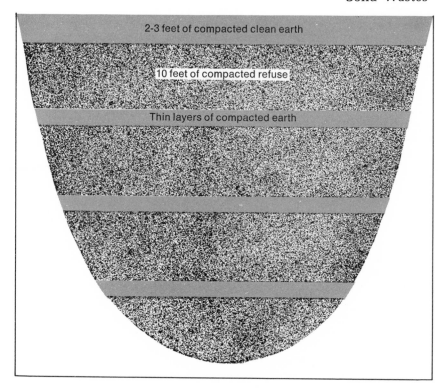

2-3 feet of compacted clean earth

10 feet of compacted refuse

Thin layers of compacted earth

Figure 2
Modern practice in sanitary landfill
In a modern sanitary landfill, refuse is spread in thin layers, each compacted by a bulldozer before the next is spread. When about 10 feet of refuse has been laid down in this way, it is covered by a thin layer of clean earth, which is also compacted. At the end of each working day, the landfill is sealed with a thin layer of compacted earth, and the completed fill is sealed with 2 or 3 feet of compacted earth. An adequate sanitary landfill should have no burning and no serious problems with odors, flies, rats, or water pollution.

by anaerobic microorganisms begins and accounts for the degradation of most of the organic matter in the landfill. Methane and carbon dioxide are among the products of anaerobic decomposition. Methane tends to escape over the surface of the fill, but at rates that are not troublesome in open recreation areas. Buildings can trap methane, however, creating an explosion hazard, and this, plus settlement of the fill, are two factors of concern in erecting buildings on or next to sanitary landfills. Carbon dioxide produced inside a landfill can dissolve in ground water, making it weakly acidic. The water can then dissolve any limestone and other rock that it contacts, thus increasing the dissolved solids content of the water. For such reasons, sanitary landfills must be carefully designed and operated to avoid difficulties with gases and ground water pollution. Current research is directed at upgrading the knowledge of the products of decomposition and improving methods of construction and operation. The movement of contaminants into ground water is also being studied, and further research is required on bacterial pollution of ground water.

Gas chromatographic analyses of the gases and acids produced by refuse decomposing anaerobically in steel cylinders indicate that the most pronounced changes in the organic materials occur in the first 60 days of decomposition (5). The accumulation of intermediate products of decomposition indicates further that the process is not complete even after two years. In addition to carbon dioxide and methane, decomposition produces hydrogen and organic acids of from two to six carbon atoms. Leachate created by percolating water through large concrete cylinders filled with anaerobically decomposing refuse was found to be rich in both organic and inorganic substances.

Other work is designed to demonstrate the feasibility of pumping air into a landfill and thus achieving aerobic instead of anaerobic decomposition of the organic matter (42). Previous study of aerobic landfills indicates that they might have several advantages, including more rapid settling than anaerobic landfills, and thus more waste disposal capacity; elimination of methane and hydrogen in explosive concentrations; and more rapid stabilization of the landfill, so that the land can be reclaimed more quickly for conventional construction.

Abandoned strip mines are being investigated as sites for sanitary landfills (1). This approach may have the additional advantage of reducing acid mine drainage in some cases.

Well-planned and well-operated sanitary landfill should offer at least a partial solution to the municipal refuse problem for some years to come. The method requires that suitable land be within economic range of the source of the refuse, however, and that the site be of such a nature that pollution of ground water can be prevented by application of the available technology. Where these requirements cannot be met, incineration will be most often the best alternative for disposing of municipal refuse, and use of incineration seems likely to grow.

Incineration

U.S. incinerator technology was largely empirical for many years, but it is moving now into an era of rapid evolution. The air pollution requirements that are beginning to appear for incinerators make scrubbers or electrostatic precipitators mandatory. The effect has been almost to double the cost of smaller units (from 240 to 450 tons of refuse per day) and to add up to 30% to the cost of larger units (500 tons per day and higher) (19). Other current developments include more sophisticated design, more careful examination of the economics of recovering waste heat, and an incipient trend toward large regional incinerators rather than small local units. U.S. practitioners also are looking more closely at incinerator and other solid waste management practices in Europe (37, 41). Urban pressures there have compelled the application of technology that is available in the U.S., but is not yet used widely in this country for disposing of municipal refuse.

In modern U.S. incinerators, refuse burns on moving grates in refractory-lined chambers, and combustible gases and entrained solids burn in secondary combustion chambers or zones. Combustion is 85-90% complete for the combustible materials. Up to three times as much air is introduced into the incinerator as would be needed to supply the oxygen required to oxidize the refuse completely. The temperature in the bed of burning refuse may reach 2500° F. or more, and the excess air is required mainly to hold the temperature in the furnace at 1400° to 1800° F. Above 1800° F., slag formation in the furnace can become a problem. The incinerator produces the normal primary products of combustion, carbon dioxide and water, as well as oxides of sulfur and nitrogen and whatever other gaseous air pollutants might be generated (Table 3). It also produces fly ash, unburned solid residue, and the heat from combustion.

A large body of technology has grown up around this process, and a variety of mechanical designs is available in incinerators. The scientific principles that underlie this technology often are not well defined (12), partly because the heterogeneous nature of refuse and its variable moisture

Table 3

Typical products of incineration of municipal refuse

Stack gases:	Pounds per ton of refuse	Fraction by volume, dry
Carbon dioxide	1,738	6.05%
Sulfur dioxide	1	22 parts per million
Carbon monoxide	10	0.06%
Oxygen	2,980	14.32%
Nitrogen oxides	3	93 parts per million
Nitrogen	14,557	79.57%
Total dry gas	19,289	100%
Water vapor	1,400	
Total	20,689	
Solids, dry basis:		
Grate residue	471	
Fly ash	20	
Total, pounds per ton of refuse	21,180	

SOURCE: Kaiser, E. R., "Refuse Reduction Processes," in "Proceedings, The Surgeon General's Conference on Solid Waste Management for Metropolitan Washington," U.S. Public Health Service Publication No. 1729, Government Printing Office, Washington, D.C., July 1967, p. 93.

content make analysis of the combustion process extremely complex. For example, although useful combustion and heat calculations can be made, no scientific basis is yet available for estimating a refuse incinerator's maximum capacity in weight of refuse that can be burned per hour (13, 22). Progress might be made also in the chemistry of the slags that form in incinerators and their reactions with the refractories that line the combustion chambers (9).

Air pollution

The most immediate problem in municipal incineration today is control of air pollutants, chiefly fly ash (48). Odors caused by gaseous air pollutants can normally be prevented by proper furnace design and operation. Emissions of noxious gases such as oxides of sulfur and nitrogen are quite low compared with those from other sources, and do not appear currently to offer serious difficulty. Questions have been raised about incinerating plastics, whose concentration in municipal refuse now is estimated to be only 1.5%, but is growing (34). The widely-used packaging material polyvinyl chloride, for example, is about 50% chlorine, and that element is emitted as the toxic hydrogen chloride upon incineration. Very little data are available, however, on the overall air pollution potential of plastics incineration, although it might cause clogging and corrosion in the incineration equipment.

Emission of fly ash and other solid particles is more clear-cut. Typical practice in large municipal incinerators today produces up to 4 pounds of particulate matter per 1000 pounds of stack gas when the weight of the gas is adjusted to what it would be at 50% excess air instead of the 200 to 300% used normally. The regulatory trend in the U.S. today is to reduce particulate emissions to as low as 0.2 pound per 1000 pounds of stack gas. (In some parts of Europe, maximum allowable emissions of even less than 0.2 pound are in force.) Currently in this country there are three general levels of allowable particulate emission. These levels, the particle collection efficiencies that they require, and the collection capability of the available equipment appear in Table 4.

All of the devices shown in Table 4 are used routinely in industry. The devices used most commonly on municipal incinerators in this country are the settling chamber and wetted baffles. Cyclone collectors and direct impaction scrubbers have also been used, but to a lesser degree (14). The direct impaction scrubber is the least efficient device that is known to be able to meet better-than-intermediate particulate emission codes. The water used in the scrubber produces a stack plume, however, unless the gases are cooled to condense the water and reheated to make the dried stack gas sufficiently buoyant. Also, the scrubber uses a large amount of water, which can introduce a water pollution problem.

Of the two remaining devices, the electrostatic precipitator and the bag filter, the former is the more advanced for use on incinerators. Both devices require that the gases they treat be cooler than about 600° F., whereas uncooled gas from a refractory-lined incinerator may

Table 4

Particulate emission restrictions, required collection efficiency, collection efficiency of available equipment

Emission limit (lb./1000 lb. gas at 50% excess air)	Stringency of limit	Approximate collection efficiency required, %
0.85	Nonexistent or lenient	74
0.65	Intermediate	80
0.20	Strict	94
Clear stack: refractory furnace	Strict	96-97
Clear stack: water-cooled furnace	Strict	98.5

Type of collector	Maximum demonstrated efficiency, %
Settling chamber	35
Wetted baffles	53
Cyclone collectors	75-80
Direct impaction scrubbers	94-96
Electrostatic precipitators	99+
Bag filters	99+

SOURCE: Walker, A. B., "Air Pollution Control Equipment for Incinerators," in "Incineration of Solid Wastes," Metropolitan Engineers Council on Air Resources, New York, N.Y., March 1967, p. 75.

range from 1200° to 1500° F. or higher. (It is now possible, however, to build electrostatic precipitators that will operate at considerably higher than 600° F.) The gas can be cooled by using a waste heat boiler, a water-wall (instead of refractory-lined) furnace and boiler, or by water sprays. Air cooling is uneconomical because of the large volume of air required. The bag filter has been tried to only a limited extent on municipal incinerators because of relatively high first cost and space requirements, and because the available filter fabrics had too short a life at the prevailing operating temperatures. Bag filters also might not withstand the flash high-temperatures that may occur when a batch of plastic or similar material enters the furnace. New materials might solve these temperature problems. Glass fabric filter bags, for example, have long life at 500° F., only about 100° F. below the temperature to which gases from refractory-lined furnaces are cooled by the normal means. Bag filters remain promising for use on incinerators, but require further research and development.

Water-wall incinerators

It appears today that to meet stringent particle emission codes for incinerators the U.S. will most likely follow the European practice of using electrostatic precipitators. These devices are performing at efficiencies of 99% or higher in Europe, but they are installed mostly on water-wall incinerators, which can produce steam and also produce a stack gas that is automatically preconditioned to enter the precipitator. Although large, steam-generating incinerators are operating in Europe (11), waste-heat recovery from municipal incinerators in the U.S. has been limited to relatively small, inefficient units that use waste heat boilers with refractory-lined incinerators. The water-cooled furnace wall is not a new concept, but for municipal incinerators it has been better adapted to conditions in Europe. Fuel is relatively costly there, which helps to justify the recovery of heat from incinerators. Also, urban pressures are greater in Europe than in the U.S., and the need is thus greater to convert refuse to the lowest-volume, most-readily-disposable form. This need is generally best filled by incineration, and, in addition, the auxiliary fuel used typically in heat-recovery incinerators can increase the efficiency of combustion of refuse to well over 90%.

The water-cooled furnace wall absorbs enough of the heat from combustion so that the incinerator can be operated at about 50% excess air, compared to the 200 to 300% used on refractory-lined furnaces. Gas handling equipment such as stacks and fly ash collectors can thus be much smaller. The heat of combustion also converts the cooling water in the water-wall furnace (with boiler) to steam, whose energy content can be recovered as heat or power. Stack gas from the water-wall furnace, moreover, is cool enough to enter the precipitator without further cooling. The water-wall furnace may cost more to build than the refractory-lined type, and the use of a boiler may require more highly-trained operators. Depending on the economic context, however, these costs can be offset by heat-recovery and lower costs for gas handling equipment and particle emission control. Another factor, if the heat recovered is to be used to generate power, is that a refuse incinerator is designed to operate 85 to 90% of the time, and a power plant is designed to operate 95 to 98% of the time. In any economic context, the difference must be reconciled. In any event, conditions in some parts of North America are beginning to converge with those of Europe, and European incineration practice is taking root on this continent.

Status of advanced incineration practice

The U.S. Naval Station at Norfolk, Va., started to operate a water-wall incinerator early in 1967 (28) (Fig. 3). It has a steam capacity of 100,000 to 120,000 pounds per hour, and the boilers can be fired with oil when the supply of refuse is inadequate. The new water-wall incinerator in Montreal, the first to be built by a municipality in North America, will be rated at 1200 tons of refuse per day and 400,000 pounds of steam per hour. It will use four electrostatic precipitators. The city of Chicago has contracted for a water-wall incinerator with a refuse capacity of 1600 tons per day. The plant will be rated at 440,000 pounds of steam per hour and will use electrostatic precipitators. Braintree, Mass., is building a water-wall incinerator with a refuse capacity of 240 tons per day.

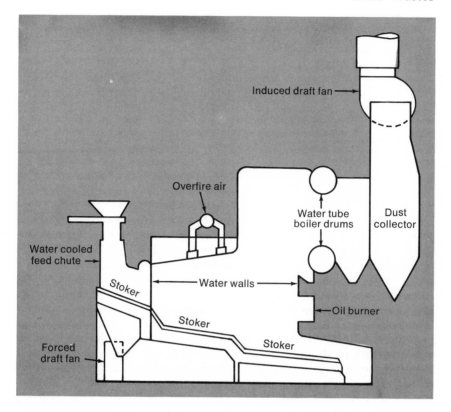

Figure 3

Water-wall incinerator at U.S. Naval Station, Norfolk, Va.

A water-wall incinerator, shown here in simplified form, has been used to burn refuse at the Norfolk Naval Station since 1967. The heat of combustion is recovered in cooling water and boilers to produce about 100,000 pounds of steam per hour at design conditions. Fuel oil can be used to augment the supply of refuse when necessary. Water-wall incinerators have been in use in Europe for some time, but are only just beginning to be used in the U.S.

SOURCE: Moore, H. C., "Refuse Fired Steam Generator at Navy Base, Norfolk, Va.," in "Incineration of Solid Wastes," Metropolitan Engineers Council on Air Resources, New York, N.Y., March 1967, p. 10.

The plant will produce 60,000 pounds per hour of steam and will use electrostatic precipitators. Two electrostatic precipitators are expected to come into operation on municipal incinerators in New York City in 1969.

Commercial buildings, apartments

Not all of the particulate control measures that might be used on big municipal incinerators can be applied to the smaller units used in commercial buildings and apartment houses. Attempts to use dry collectors such as filters or cyclones have failed because the equipment is fouled rapidly by condensation of fats. However, proper incinerator design and use of a wet scrubber can reduce particle emissions by at least 90% (and noxious gas emissions by up to 60%). The problem is more economic than technical, particularly where old incinerators must be modernized. The capital cost of modernizing old equipment in New York City has been estimated at $1500 to $5000 per unit, depending on size. The New York City Housing Authority in early 1967 was experiencing an average unit cost of about $2000 for upgrading flue-fed apartment house incinerators.

Incineration research and development

Among the concepts being investigated for use in municipal incineration is the fluidized bed, which has long been used for a variety of purposes in the chemical and other industries and is being used successfully to incinerate sewage sludge (15). Refuse is fed into a bed of hot sand supported by an upward flow of air. The bed may be characterized as a violently agitated fluid, and the process provides both the heat transfer and gas-solid contact required for good incineration. A potential advantage of the fluid bed incinerator is that it may be able to operate with as little as 5% excess air, thus greatly reducing the size of the gas handling equipment required. Problems with the equipment include feed preparation and feeding, as well as ash removal. Considerable development remains to be done, but pilot-plant results to date suggest that the concept can be the basis of a compact incinerator for solid wastes with relatively clean stack gases.

Another concept that is being studied is to use hot gases from incineration to drive a gas turbine that generates electricity. Refuse would be shredded, dried, and burned under pressure, and the resulting hot gases would drive a turbocompressor and turbogenerator. A waste heat boiler would reclaim part of the heat from the turbine exhaust and generate steam that would drive an auxiliary turbogenerator. If the feasibility of process is demonstrated, a pilot plant could be operating sometime in 1971.

Incinerator residue. The chemical and physical nature of the residue from municipal incinerators is of interest for two reasons: The residue must normally be disposed of by landfill, where its stability, a function of carbon and hydrogen content, might be important; and the residue may contain salvageable material. Work is under way on the composition of incinerator residue, and means of characterizing it have been developed (25, 36). Analysis of residues from municipal incinerators in Washington, D.C., showed them to contain about 30% metals, mostly tin cans and other iron-based materials, 45% glass, 15% ash, 8% paper and charcoal, and less than 1% putrescible organic matter (Table 5). Incineration of a ton of municipal refuse produces up to 500 pounds of such residue. In Europe, the iron-based materials are sometimes salvaged from the residue, baled, and sold as scrap. The tin content usually makes such scrap unsalable in the U.S., although shredded, detinned cans find a limited market in the copper industry, where they are used to reclaim copper from dumps. There is reason to believe, however, that the use of plastic coatings and painted cans, plus lighter deposits of tin on cans, will increase the salability of iron scrap in incinerator residue.

The residue from the 300-odd municipal incinerators now operating in the U.S. can be viewed as a mineral resource, containing annually some 3 million tons of iron and 250,000 tons of nonferrous metals, including aluminum, zinc, copper, lead, and tin. The economic incentive to recover and recycle these metals does not exist today, but research is under way on the complex metallurgical problems that would be involved (33).

Composting

Composting municipal refuse to produce a soil conditioner and low-grade fertilizer has been generally unsuccessful in the U.S. Of nine composting plants built in this country in 1951-66, six were shut down or forced into intermittent operation, one important reason being in-

Table 5

Average composition of residues from five municipal incinerators in Metropolitan Washington, D.C.

Material [a]	Weight %, dry
Tin cans	17.2%
Mill scale and small iron	6.8
Iron wire	.7
Massive iron	3.5
Nonferrous metals	1.4
Stones and bricks	1.3
Ceramics	.9
Unburned paper and charcoal	8.3
Partially burned organics	.7
Ash	15.4
Glass	44.1

[a] Sample weighed 951.2 pounds, of which 33.4% was moisture.

SOURCE: Kenahan, C. B., Sullivan, P. M., "Let's Not Overlook Salvage," *APWA Rep.*, *34* (3), 5 (1967).

ability to sell the compost at a realistic price. Interest in composting appears nevertheless to be growing to a degree, partly because of the benefits that might be derived from the compost, partly because of the contention that the composting process is the best way to recycle the minerals and other resources in solid wastes.

Composting operations in the U.S. include three basic steps: refuse preparation; stabilization of organic material by aerobic microorganisms; and product upgrading (17). Refuse is presorted to remove noncompostible materials or those that might have salvage value, such as paper, cardboard, rags, metals, and glass. The refuse is then ground to improve the efficiency of the aerobic digestion process. The ground material is stacked in long, narrow piles (windrows) on the ground or placed in mechanical systems where it is degraded biologically to a humus (much like the organic portion of soil) that contains about 1% or less of the primary plant nutrients: nitrogen, phosphorus, and potassium. The finished product may be cured, ground, and bagged. Of the waste that enters a composting plant, more than 75% goes into the digestion process, and one third to one half of the latter amount becomes compost.

Windrow composting costs less than mechanical systems, but it requires six or seven weeks, compared with five or six days for mechanical systems. A windrow plant large enough to serve 100,000 people would require perhaps 30 acres, compared with 5 acres for a mechanical system.

The largest composting plant yet built in this country is a mechanical system that has been operating in Houston, Tex., since early 1967 (32). It is rated at 360 tons of municipal refuse per day, and the city guarantees the operator a delivery of 300 tons per day (Houston generates about 2000 tons of refuse daily). The plant was producing about 200 tons per day of compost in mid-1968, and its capacity was being expanded by 50%. Most of the compost is retailed in bags. Salvaged material, such as paper, rags, and metal, is available for sale.

In the spring of 1968, the Public Health Service and the Tennessee Valley Authority started to operate a windrow composting plant at Johnson City, Tenn. (38). The plant handles refuse mechanically, but composts it on a 7-acre area in long windrows 7 feet wide and 5 feet high. The PHS-TVA plant was designed to compost about 60 tons per day of refuse and produce about 25 tons of compost. Before composting, the refuse is mixed with sewage sludge, which supplies nutrients and the moisture required for optimum composting. The plant was designed basically to study the technology and economics of windrow composting, and TVA will work on the development of markets for the product.

Little is known about the chemical constituents of compost that might be essential plant nutrients, excepting the three primary nutrients. Furthermore, there is no agreement on the point at which degrading organic material becomes "compost." Research on the chemical and biological changes that occur in composting waste is being hampered seriously by the lack of a fully satisfactory method for determining the extent to which the waste has been degraded. Plant design is hampered

178

in turn, because logically it should depend on the degree of treatment that is being given to the waste.

New approaches to municipal refuse

A variety of unconventional means of using municipal refuse are being investigated, although few have moved out of the laboratory. Research is being done on transformation of organic material in solid wastes into sugars or protein. Heating of organic refuse out of contact with air to produce useful gases and liquids has also been studied (23). A plant is operating in Japan that compresses refuse into building blocks that can be sheathed in iron or other material, and the process is being investigated in this country. Another compression project under study will produce small bricks, for use as fill to reclaim submerged land, using a mixture of shredded refuse, fly ash, dried sewage sludge, incinerator residue, and river and lake dredgings.

Research and development on handling and disposal must take account of the fact that the nature of municipal refuse is changing. Per capita consumption of packaging materials, for example, is predicted to increase more than 25% in the decade 1966-76 (35). The growing use of paper is increasing the carbon content of municipal refuse, and this could have practical consequences in composting. The aerobic organisms use 30 to 35 carbon atoms for each nitrogen atom, and if excess carbon is present, the digestion process is delayed until enough nitrogen becomes available from dead microorganisms to support further growth. One of the potential benefits of adding sewage sludge to refuse before composting is that it will add enough nitrogen to maintain the ratio of carbon to nitrogen at the optimum level.

Collection and transportation. Collection and transportation of municipal refuse, which account for an estimated 75% of the total cost of handling and disposal, are the subjects of several studies. One of them involves the use of paper bags, instead of trash cans, by the householder. The bags have a capacity of about 30 gallons and, when full, are closed and placed at the curb. They speed the collection process because they can simply be thrown into the vehicle at curbside. They resist water, so that municipal incinerators need not cope with masses of wet paper. The bags keep out flies, resist rats to a fair degree, and minimize spillage in the streets.

Collection vehicles that operate more rapidly and do a better and less noisy job of compaction are desirable. Vehicles that are superior to U.S. models in these respects are available in Europe.

The efficiency of trash collection is susceptible to improvement by operations analysis of vehicle routes and schedules, and this approach is being studied in the U.S. Also under study are the transport of ground refuse as a liquid slurry in pipelines, and short-range transport of dry refuse in pneumatic tubes, a method developed in Sweden. The American Public Works Association is studying the use of unit trains to haul solid wastes from urban areas to disposal sites, such as land reclamation areas.

Recommendations: municipal refuse

Recommendation S1: *The appropriate federal, state, and local government agencies should press their efforts to define the nature and magnitude of the solid wastes problem both now and in the future. Education, research, and demonstration, and local and regional planning for solid wastes management, utilization, and disposal are all necessary for progress in this neglected area.*

Recommendation S2: *The use of known peripheral science and technology in developing improved methods for sanitary landfill and incineration should be encouraged and supported. Efforts to develop a more scientific basis for composting should also be supported, particularly in the area of the biochemistry and related aspects of the degradation process, so that the potential of the method, which appears to date to be quite limited, can be assessed more definitively.*

Recommendation S3: *Research and development on utilization and recycle of components of municipal refuse and incinerator residue should be maintained at a level that will insure that radically new approaches are not overlooked or inadequately investigated.*

Recommendation S4: *Continuing attention should be paid to collection and transportation of municipal refuse, both in the development of improved technology and in mechanisms for promoting the application of such technology by local agencies who are responsible for handling and disposing of municipal refuse.*

JUNKED AUTOMOBILES

Despite the backlog of unreclaimed junked automobiles that has accumulated over the years, a large fraction of junked cars actually is being processed by industry. A study of areas with a total junk car inventory of 510,000 vehicles showed that in 1965 about 73% of them were in the hands of auto wreckers and 6% in the hands of scrap processors (2). About 21% were in auto graveyards, abandoned on public or private property, or held on the owner's property. An investigation of problems in the iron and steel scrap business (21) showed that the gap between the number of cars junked and the number reclaimed was due in large measure to the difficulty of marketing scrap contaminated by nonferrous metals.

The discarded automobile typically goes first to the auto wrecker, who removes parts that can be sold for further use, sometimes after rebuilding. The scrap processor then may sell the battery for its lead content, the radiator, electric motors, and some other parts for their copper content, the engine block and other cast-iron components for use in foundries, and heavy components such as the frame for use as heavy melting stock. The remaining hulk, weighing 1000 to 1500 pounds, is cleaned of combustible or other nonmetallic material by hand stripping or burning and is then converted to scrap by baling, shearing, or shredding.

Traditionally, most auto hulks have been compressed into No. 2 bundles, which yield 85 to 90% iron and contain 0.5% copper, the most troublesome impurity. Another technique is to compress the hulk into a slab and shear it into sections of about 150 pounds each. Since about 1962, the shredding process has been gaining ground rapidly and in 1966 accounted for an estimated 16% of the 6.4 million cars that were consumed as scrap. In this process, the hulk is torn into small fragments by hammer mills, and ferrous material is separated magnetically from nonferrous and nonmagnetic material. The iron yield of shredded scrap ranges up to 97%, and copper content is 0.2% or less. A maximum of 0.15% copper is desirable, and one recent study concludes that that goal can be achieved consistently if the hulk is prepared properly before shredding and the shredder discharge is segregated carefully (7).

Auto scrap processors suffer from the cost of transporting hulks to processing points. They also have faced a generally lower demand for scrap, particularly impure automobile scrap such as No. 2 bundles, owing to the steel industry's adoption of the oxygen-enriched open hearth and the basic oxygen furnace. In addition, for auto hulk incinerators there is no effective smoke-control equipment whose cost can be borne by small auto wreckers and scrap processors (24, 31). Some authorities believe nevertheless that the junk car problem conceivably can be solved in perhaps a decade because of changes in steel-making techniques and the general upgrading of scrapping methods to yield a more salable product.

Research on scrap processing

The Bureau of Mines is seeking new ways to utilize automotive and other ferrous scrap using chemical and metallurgical methods as well as mechanical methods (10). At Salt Lake City, the bureau is working in two complementary areas: dismantling and chemically analyzing selected cars; and developing hydrometallurgical or chemical leaching methods for making clean scrap from cars or the by-products of scrap processing yards. One aim of this work is to develop less costly means of separating autos into light steel components, which could be shredded, and heavy components, which could be cut up and sold as heavy melting stock. Shredding only the light metal would reduce the cost of the required equipment. It might also allow the development of portable shredders that could be moved to rural areas to process auto hulks accumulated there.

A second aim of the work at Salt Lake is a system in which the stripped, incinerated hulk would be partly compacted and then leached with cupric ammonium carbonate or nitric acid to remove residual nonferrous metals. It would then be compacted further and sheared into slabs essentially free of impurities. Rough cost estimates for the process show that a plant handling 25,000 cars per year could produce scrap for $9.30 per ton minimum; at 100,000 cars per year, production cost would be $6.00 per ton. In August 1968, high-quality scrap of the type that would be made by this process was selling for about $25 per ton, and

No. 2 bundles for about $18. Costs other than production costs that would be incurred in using such a process have not been worked out.

In the Mesabi range in Minnesota, the Bureau of Mines had planned to operate a demonstration plant that would have processed a mixture of nonmagnetic taconite and automobile, refrigerator, and other kinds of ferrous scrap. In the process, the mixture is heated to about 1000°C. The iron oxide in the nonmag..etic taconite is reduced to the magnetic form, and the scrap is oxidized at the same time to the magnetic form (26). The discharge from the process is treated magnetically or by flotation to produce a concentrate containing 62% iron or more for use as blast furnace feed. By converting nonmagnetic taconite to the magnetic form, in which it can be converted to blast furnace feed by the normal means, the process would both increase the nation's iron resources and provide a use for scrap. The Bureau of Mines stopped work on the project in 1968 for budgetary reasons, but as of mid-1969 was hoping to resume the work as a joint government-industry effort.

Building blocks. A nonmetallurgical use of auto scrap would be as a core material in light-weight concrete building blocks. Prototype scrap-cored blocks have been made and show promise for use in light commercial buildings, bridge abutments and piers, foundations, and retaining walls. To make the blocks, the hulk is incinerated and the scrap is cut into sections, compressed, and encased in 2 inches of concrete, which is steam cured using the heat from the incineration process. The scrap accounts for more than half the volume of the block.

Vehicle tires

Of the 100 million vehicular tires that are discarded annually in the U.S., about 30% are reclaimed, and the remaining 70 million must be disposed of in some way. One potential method would be to grind up the tires, remove the cord, and incorporate the ground rubber in paving materials such as asphalt to improve such properties as resiliency and life. The use of various forms of rubber, including ground tire tread, in roads has a long history, particularly abroad (45), but it presents certain technical problems. Official specifications in the United Kingdom, for example, point out that the composition of ground tire tread is variable, and that the material is not recommended for use in roads unless its composition can be guaranteed. In this country, the Bureau of Solid Waste Management is supporting an intensive study of solid waste management in the rubber industry, including scrap and reclaim. One objective of the work is to determine whether changes in the distribution of facilities, or new processes or techniques, would improve the market for scrap rubber. Another is to identify all forms of scrap rubber that lend themselves to some form of reuse or that present a disposal problem.

Recommendations: junked automobiles

Recommendation S5: *Efforts by private industry to improve the economics of the auto scrap processing industry should be stimulated. The de-*

velopment of scrapping methods that would permit the use of less costly equipment, and of radically new scrapping methods, should be pursued at all levels. The development of new means of utilizing junked vehicles should also be encouraged and supported, with emphasis on methods of recycling the metals.

INDUSTRIAL SOLID WASTES

Industrial solid wastes differ sharply from municipal solid wastes in that they are much more varied, both chemically and physically. They are more likely to release toxic substances when burned, and their heating values may cover a much wider range. Industry, moreover, recycles large amounts of the materials of production, both in-plant and through the operations of the secondary materials industries. A distinction should be made between scrap, those solid materials that can be recycled at a profit, and solid wastes, those that are beyond the reach of today's technology.

Recycle by industry

The secondary materials industry includes roughly 9000 recognized establishments with total annual sales of more than $5 billion. In 1966, in the U.S., secondary aluminum accounted for about 20% of total consumption, secondary copper for about 42% of consumption, secondary iron and steel for about 45%, and secondary zinc for about 25% (Fig. 4, page 184). The rubber industry in 1966 consumed some 265,000 long tons of reclaimed rubber, or about 12% of total consumption of new rubber of all types. Paper and textiles are among other materials that are recycled in large volume.

Urban renewal, beautification programs, and other factors have been troubling the secondary materials industry in recent years (43), and one of the most difficult problems to be faced is air pollution: from smelters, from the burning of polyethylene and polyvinyl chloride insulation on copper wire, from incineration of auto hulks, and from a range of other sources. The equipment that is available to control such emissions is the same as that used elsewhere in industry. Technical problems exist in applying such equipment to some types of secondary operations, but the major difficulty is often cost. Members of the secondary materials industry have been estimated to have an average plant investment of only $1 million, and for units of that order of size the cost of air pollution control equipment can be burdensome or even prohibitive.

Solid waste disposal by industry

Most industrial solid waste is hauled to private dumps, usually by outside contractors, although some is disposed of by landfilling on the company site and some is burned in the plant and the residue hauled away. But cartage costs are rising, reflecting a growing scarcity of dumping sites and growing regulation of dumping practices, and the time may be coming when companies will find it more economical to burn more of their own solid wastes.

Preparation: dealer yards and plants

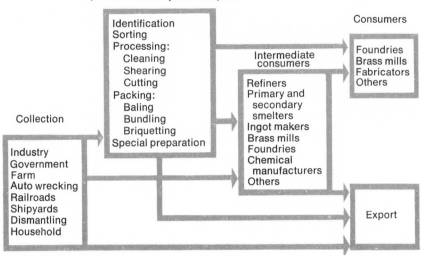

Figure 4

Flow chart of recycled nonferrous scrap metals

Large amounts of the materials of production are recycled via the secondary materials industries. In 1966, secondary aluminum accounted for about 20% of total U.S. consumption, secondary copper for about 42%, and secondary zinc for about 25%. Air pollution is one of the most difficult problems facing the secondary materials industries, partly because of technical problems, partly because of the cost of control equipment.

SOURCE: "A Study of Dislocation Factors: The Secondary Material Industries in a Changing Urban Society," National Association of Secondary Material Industries, New York, N.Y., 1965.

Until the past few years in this country, facilities for burning solid wastes were designed largely to accommodate municipal wastes of relatively low heating value. Design data are thus not extensive for equipment to burn the more refractory, high-heating-value industrial wastes. Designers have had to work with incorrect basic data on the wastes to be burned and have had to design units to operate properly over a wide range of wastes, heating values, degrees of impurity, and rates of disposal. The result sometimes has been equipment that operates at too high a temperature, costs more than it should to maintain, and causes additional pollution problems. More attention is being focused on such difficulties, and data and computational methods are available that can be used to make many of the required combustion calculations. When used with the computer these data and methods have proved to be a very useful design tool (27). Wider use of the computational facilities and thermodynamic data that are already at hand would be a step toward better incineration. A national survey has been proposed to determine the chemical and physical analyses of industrial wastes in order to provide further data to support the conception and design of devices, including incinerators, for processing them.

Among the novel industrial incinerators that have been developed recently is the open-pit incinerator (30). Since the device has no top, heat can radiate to the sky, and the effect is to limit the temperature inside the unit to a level that causes negligible damage to the refractory lining. All of the air is supplied from above the combustion area through high-velocity nozzles, causing maximum turbulence and recirculation of the gases produced by combustion. The open-pit design has worked well on solids of high heating value and those that tend to melt, such as waxes, nylon, and polyethylene. Emission of particles can be a problem with some wastes, but a steel mesh screen placed on top of the incinerator can be used to reduce such emissions. The open-pit design has been investigated on a pilot-scale for use with municipal refuse. It was found to be inferior to the standard multiple-chamber design in emission of both particles and gaseous pollutants (6).

Heat recovery, central facilities

Industry recovers waste heat from the combustion of some solid wastes, such as bark, bagasse, corn cobs, and spent coffee grounds, but the total represents only a fraction of the energy available in solid industrial wastes. The desirability of recovering such energy, if feasible, and the apparent need for industry to burn more of its own wastes, suggest the use of a central facility to burn all combustible wastes, both solid and otherwise, on a given plant site (20). Air pollution control equipment should be less costly for a single large facility than for several small ones, and labor and other costs might also be lower. Such units would have to burn and recover heat from a variety of wastes: paper, wood, solid and liquid production wastes, waste treatment and production sludges. Automatic conveying, preparation, feeding, firing, and ash removal would be required. Facilities of this kind would often present severe engineering problems and might be difficult to justify economically even for a very large plant. At least one such unit is being designed, however, for a plant in the Northeast, and is scheduled to go into operation in 1970. The steam produced by heat from the combustion of the wastes will be fed into the plant's main steam system.

Recommendations: industrial solid wastes

Recommendation S6: *Efforts to improve the economics of recycle of solid materials by the secondary materials industry should be encouraged. A distinction should be maintained between solid materials that are recycled and those that are true solid wastes.*

Recommendation S7: *Studies should be made of the chemical and physical nature and the volume of industrial solid wastes, insofar as proprie-*

tary problems allow, in order to support the conception and design of equipment, including incinerators, for disposing of them economically.

MINING AND PROCESSING WASTES

Solid wastes from mining and processing are recycled to a degree, but the accumulated national total of such wastes has been estimated at around 21 billion tons, about 2 billion tons higher than in 1965 (47). Annual output by 1980 is expected to reach about 2 billion tons of mine waste, mill tailings, washing plant rejects, processing plant wastes, and smelter slags and rejects. About 60% of these wastes have economic value either for their mineral content or for use as aggregate and for similar structural purposes. About 37% of mining and processing wastes have no known economic value, but are public health and safety hazards, prevent the use of land they occupy for other purposes, or are an esthetic problem. The remaining 3% of mineral wastes are of small volume, have no value, and are remotely located and thus currently constitute no real problem.

Copper mining wastes

The copper mining industry in the western U.S. recovers several hundred tons of copper daily from mining wastes that are produced in volumes of several hundred thousand tons daily (18). In the process, the industry uses about 250,000 tons per year of incinerated or burned auto hulks and about 50,000 tons of detinned tin plate scrap.

To recover copper, dilute sulfuric acid is percolated through the waste dumps until it has dissolved equilibrium concentrations of copper and other soluble material. The leach liquor is then run through equipment that contains the scrap iron, producing iron (ferrous) sulfate and precipitating the copper, which is recovered by filtration. The volume of leach liquor available from this process at Bingham Canyon, Utah, is approaching 50 million gallons per day, and it has been found to contain 4 to 10 ppm of uranium, a slightly higher level of the metallic element yttrium, and 5000 to 10,000 parts per million of aluminum. Research has found that about 2 tons per day of uranium oxide may be recovered from the liquor by ion exchange, and calculated costs are lower than for any uranium extraction process used today. This work has shown also that the yttrium and aluminum may be recovered, and research on all three recovery processes was moving into the pilot plant stage in mid-1968.

Bauxite processing wastes

More than 5 million tons of red mud are produced annually in this country by plants that convert bauxite into aluminum oxide, from which aluminum is made electrolytically. The composition of red mud varies with the source of the bauxite and the processing method, but a typical analysis shows it to include about 20% aluminum oxide, 49% iron (ferric) oxide, and lesser amounts of oxides of silicon, calcium, sodium, titanium, phosphorus, and sulfur. Red mud also contains traces of a number of other elements.

Red muds have been investigated for use as thermal insulation, as an additive to concrete, and in such products as Portland cement and slag wool. Some such products have reached the commercial stage, but no consistent outlet has attained the scale at which it could consume the amount of red mud that is produced. One new approach that shows promise is to convert red mud slurries into porous structural blocks by a foaming process (46). Economic studies suggest a potential market of more than 1 million tons per year, enough to consume the annual red mud output of a large bauxite refining plant. The process is being pursued further with an aluminum company.

Phosphate mining wastes

A mineral waste problem that awaits improved solutions is the disposal and utilization of the colloidal clay wastes or slimes produced in phosphate mining operations in Florida (8). The slimes leave the processing plant containing 4 or 5% solids in water and about one third of the total phosphate mined (measured as bone phosphate of lime equivalent). Currently the slimes are pumped to huge settling ponds and, as the solids settle, clear water is drawn from the top of the ponds and returned to the process. The solids settle very slowly, and after years of settling the slimes may still have been concentrated to no more than 30% solids. The settling properties of the slimes thus impede the reclamation of land occupied by the ponds, and there is furthermore no economical means of recovering the phosphate in the slimes. The phosphate industry and others have expended considerable effort seeking means of improving the settling of slimes and of using them in some way or recovering the phosphate they contain. These efforts to date have not achieved significant success.

Recommendations: mining and processing wastes

Recommendation S8: *Research and development on processes for recovering various minerals from mining and processing wastes should be maintained at an adequate level against the day when changing economics warrant the recovery of such minerals. Work on other means of utilizing or disposing of these wastes should also be maintained at a steady level.*

EFFECTS OF SOLID WASTES

Among the obvious effects of solid wastes are the esthetics problem and the air and water pollution caused by unsatisfactory means of disposal. Solid wastes can prevent or control the use of the land they occupy and diminish the value of nearby land. They contain useful materials and energy, although in a form that makes their recovery by the available technology uneconomic in most cases today.

The scientific literature does not contain the data required to support quantitative estimates of direct relationships between solid wastes and disease. A thorough study of the literature (39) concluded among other things that "It should not be surprising that so much opinion and so little data were discovered. . . ." The relationships are complex, disease pathways are obscure, reliable methods of study are scarce. The study concluded also that the circumstantial and epidemiological data support the conclusion that a relationship exists, although it is not well defined.

Flies are known carriers of disease, and they breed in large numbers in many types of solid wastes. A direct relationship between solid wastes and fly-borne disease in the U.S. has not been established, although the available knowledge of the dynamics of disease transmission, and related factors, can allow the conclusion to be reached that control of solid wastes can contribute to the prevention of fly-borne disease. Solid wastes appear not to be important in the transmission of disease by mosquitoes in the U.S. Very few cases of rodent-borne human diseases are being reported in this country, and the relationship of such diseases to solid wastes and their rodent population cannot be estimated. Evidence does exist that workers engaged in solid waste handling experience relatively high accident frequency rates, although definitive data are scarce. The occupation may be intrinsically hazardous, and there is in addition good reason to believe that some of the high accident rates that have been reported are due largely to poor or nonexistent safety programs.

Recommendations: effects of solid wastes

Recommendation S9: *The effort to upgrade solid wastes management, utilization, and disposal should be justified on the basis of esthetic values and control of air and water pollution.*

LITERATURE CITED

1. "An Abandoned Strip Mine Is to Fill," *Environ. Sci. Technol.,* **2,** 402 (1968).

2. "Automobile Disposal—A National Problem," U.S. Bureau of Mines, Department of the Interior, Government Printing Office, Washington, D.C., 1967.

3. Black, R. J., Muhich, A. J., Klee, A. J., Hickman, H. L., Jr., Vaughan, R. D., "An Interim Report. 1968 National Survey of Community Solid Waste Practices," presented at 1968 annual meeting, Institute for Solid Wastes, American Public Works Association, Miami Beach, Fla., October 1968, Bureau of Solid Waste Management, U.S. Department of Health, Education, and Welfare, Washington, D.C.

4. Bowerman, F. R., testimony before Subcommittees on Business and Commerce and on Public Health, Education, Welfare, and Safety, of the Committee on the District of Columbia, U.S. Senate, 90th Congress, 1st Session, Government Printing Office, Washington, D.C., 1967.

5. Burchinal, J. C., Wilson, H. A., Dobson, A. L., Cromwell, D. L., Cook, H. A., Qasim, S. R., Lin, Y. H., "Sanitary Landfill Investigations," in "Solid Waste Research and Development," Engineering Research Foundation Conference, Milwaukee, Wis., July 1967, preprint B-3, Engineering Foundation, New York, N.Y.

6. Burckle, J. O., Dorsey, J. A., Riley, B. T., "The Effects of the Operating Variables and Refuse Types on the Emissions from a Pilot-Scale Trench Incinera-

tor," in "Proceedings, 1968 National Incinerator Conference," American Society of Mechanical Engineers, New York, N. Y., May 1968, p. 34.

7. "Copper Control in Vehicular Scrap," Ralph Stone and Co., Inc., Contract No. 14-09-0070-382 with the U.S. Bureau of Mines, March 1968.

8. Cox, J. L., "Phosphate Wastes," in "Proceedings of the Symposium: Mineral Waste Utilization," IIT Research Institute, Chicago, Ill., March 1968, p. 50.

9. Criss, G. H., Olsen, A. R., "The Chemistry of Incinerator Slags and Their Compatibility with Fireclay and High Alumina Refractories," in "Proceedings, 1968 National Incinerator Conference," American Society of Mechanical Engineers, New York, N.Y., May 1968, p. 53.

10. Dean, K. C., "Bureau of Mines Research for Utilizing Automobile Scrap," paper presented at annual convention of the Institute of Scrap Iron & Steel, Inc., Los Angeles, Calif., January 1967, Institute of Scrap Iron & Steel, Washington, D.C.

11. Eberhardt, H., Mayer, W., "Experiences with Refuse Incinerators in Europe: Prevention of Air and Water Pollution, Operation of Refuse Incineration Plants Combined with Steam Boilers, Design and Planning," in "Proceedings, 1968 National Incinerator Conference," American Society of Mechanical Engineers, New York, N.Y., May 1968, p. 73.

12. Essenhigh, R. H., "Incineration — A Practical and Scientific Approach," *Environ. Sci. Technol.,* **2,** 524 (1968).

13. Essenhigh, R. H., "Burning Rates in Incinerators. Part I: A Simple Relation between Total, Volumetric, and Area Firing Rates. Part II: The Influence of Moisture on the Combustion Intensity," in "Proceedings, 1968 National Incinerator Conference," American Society of Mechanical Engineers, New York, N.Y., May 1968, p. 87.

14. Fernandes, J. H., "Incinerator Air Pollution Control," in "Proceedings, 1968 National Incinerator Conference," American Society of Mechanical Engineers, New York, N.Y., May 1968, p. 101.

15. "Fluid Bed Incinerators Studied for Solid Waste Disposal," *Environ. Sci. Technol.,* **2,** 495 (1968).

16. Golueke, C. G., McGauhey, P. H., "Comprehensive Studies of Solid Wastes Management; First Annual Report," 67-7, Sanitary Engineering Research Laboratory, University of California, Berkeley, Calif., May 1967.

17. Harding, C. I., "Recycling and Utilization," in "Proceedings, The Surgeon General's Conference on Solid Waste Management for Metropolitan Washington," U.S. Public Health Service Publication No. 1729, Government Printing Office, Washington, D.C., July 1967, p. 105.

18. Hayes, E. T., "Man-Made Ores," in "Proceedings of the Symposium: Mineral Waste Utilization," IIT Research Institute, Chicago, Ill., March 1968, p. 3.

19. Heaney, F. L., "Regional Districts for Incineration," *Civil Eng.,* **38** (8), 69 (1968).

20. Hescheles, C. A., "Burning All Industrial Wastes in a Central Facility," paper 68-PEM-10, American Society of Mechanical Engineers Plant Engineering and Maintenance Division Conference, Kansas City, Mo., April 29-May 1, 1968, American Society of Mechanical Engineers, New York, N.Y.

21. "Iron and Steel Scrap Consumption Problems," Business and Defense Services Administration, U.S. Department of Commerce, Government Printing Office, Washington, D.C., 1966.

22. Kaiser, E. R., "Combustion and Heat Calculations for Incinerators," in "Proceedings, 1964 National Incinerator Conference," American Society of Mechanical Engineers, New York, N.Y., May 1964, p. 81.

23. Kaiser, E. R., Friedman, S. B., "The Pyrolysis of Refuse Components," paper presented at 60th annual meeting, American Institute of Chemical Engineers, New York, N.Y., November 1967.

24. Kaiser, E. R., Tolciss, J., "Smokeless Burning of Automobile Bodies," Technical Report 764.2, College of Engineering, New York University, New York, N.Y., June 1961.

25. Kenahan, C. B., Sullivan, P. M., "Let's Not Overlook Salvage," APWA Rep., 34 (3), 5 (1967).

26. Melcher, N. B., "Utilization of Ferrous Scrap," in "Proceedings of the Symposium: Mineral Waste Utilization," IIT Research Institute, Chicago, Ill., March 1968, p. 132.

27. Monroe, E. S., Jr., "New Developments in Industrial Incineration," in "Proceedings, 1966 National Incinerator Conference," American Society of Mechanical Engineers, New York, N.Y., May 1966, p. 226.

28. Moore, H. C., in "Incineration of Solid Wastes," Metropolitan Engineers Council on Air Resources, New York, N.Y., March 1967, p. 10.

29. "Municipal Refuse Disposal," American Public Works Association, Public Administration Service, Chicago, Ill., 1966.

30. Peskin, L. C., "The Development of Open Pit Incinerators for Solid Waste Disposal," J. Air Pollut. Contr. Ass., 16, 550 (1966).

31. "Preliminary Survey on Development of an Incinerator for Removal of Combustibles from Scrapped Automobile Bodies. Final Report," prepared by Battelle Memorial Institute for Institute of Scrap Iron & Steel, Inc., Washington, D.C., August 1957.

32. Prescott, J. H., "Composting Plant Converts Refuse Into Organic Soil Conditioner," Chem. Eng., 74 (23), 232 (1967).

33. Rampacek, C., "Reclaiming and Recycling Metals and Minerals Found in Municipal Incinerator Residues," in "Proceedings of the Symposium: Mineral Waste Utilization," IIT Research Institute, Chicago, Ill., March 1968, p. 124.

34. "Report on the Role of Plastics in Solid Waste," prepared by Battelle Memorial Institute, for The Society of the Plastics Industry, New York, N.Y., 1967.

35. "The Role of Packaging in Solid Waste Management 1966 to 1976," U.S. Public Health Service Publication No. 1855, Bureau of Solid Waste Management, U.S. Department of Health, Education, and Welfare, Government Printing Office, Washington, D.C., 1969.

36. Schoenberger, R. J., Trieff, N. M., Purdom, P. W., "Special Techniques for Analyzing Solid Waste or Incinerated Residue," in "Proceedings, 1968 National Incinerator Conference," American Society of Mechanical Engineers, New York, N.Y., May 1968, p. 242.

37. Sebastian, F. P., Ariey, A. F., Garretson, B. B., "Modern Refuse Incineration in Dusseldorf—A Composite of the Best European Practices," paper 68-PWR-3, Institute of Electrical and Electronic Engineers—American Society of Mechanical Engineers Joint Power Generation Conference, San Francisco, Calif., September 1968, American Society of Mechanical Engineers, New York, N.Y.

38. "Sewage Sludge and Refuse Composting Test Begins," Environ. Sci. Technol., 2, 589 (1968).

39. "Solid Waste/Disease Relationships," U.S. Public Health Service Publication No. 999-UIH-6, Washington, D.C., 1967.

40. "Solid Wastes," Environ, Sci. Technol., 1, 199 (1967).

41. "Solid Wastes Management in Germany, Report of the U.S. Solid Wastes Study Team Visit, June 25-July 8, 1967," U.S. Public Health Service Publication No. 1812, Government Printing Office, Washington, D.C., 1968.

42. Stone, R., Conrad, E. T., "Land Reclamation by Accelerated Stabilization," in "Solid Waste Research and Development," Engineering Research Foundation Conference, Milwaukee, Wis., July 1967, preprint B-5, Engineering Foundation, New York, N.Y.

43. "A Study of Dislocation Factors: The Secondary Material Industries in a Changing Urban Society," National Association of Secondary Material Industries, New York, N.Y., 1965.

44. "Summer Study on the Management of Solid Wastes. Final Report, Vol. 1," Urban Systems Laboratory, Massachusetts Institute of Technology, Cambridge, Mass., September 1968.

45. "The Use of Rubber in Roads," Rubber Trends, No. 37, 3, (March 1968).

46. "Utilization of Red Mud Wastes for Lightweight Structural Building Products," IIT Research Institute Contract No. 14-09-0070-386, with the U.S. Bureau of Mines, August 1968.

47. Vogely, W. A., "The Economic Factors of Mineral Waste Utilization," in "Proceedings of the Symposium: Mineral Waste Utilization," IIT Research Institute, Chicago, Ill., March 1968, p. 7.

48. Walker, A. B., "Air Pollution Control Equipment for Incinerators," in "Incineration of Solid Wastes," Metropolitan Engineers Council on Air Resources, New York., N.Y., March 1967, p. 75.

Pesticides in the Environment

Contents

Pesticides in the Environment
INTRODUCTION

Great concern has arisen in recent years over the effects of pesticides in the environment. The principal interest has centered around the widespread presence of residues of the chlorinated hydrocarbon insecticides, such as DDT. Concern over the amounts and possible effects of pesticide residues has produced rigid legal controls on the composition and use of pesticides and on the amounts of residues permitted on raw agricultural commodities. If this concern is to continue to produce positive effects, it must be accompanied by full realization of the nature, uses, and value of pesticides.

Within the framework of current practice and knowledge, certain basic questions must be answered if the position of pesticides as environmental contaminants is to be seen clearly:

- What is known about pesticide residues in the environment?
- Are the existing data adequate to support a valid conclusion on the extent of contamination by such residues?
- How can contamination of the environment by pesticide residues be reduced?
- What is the effect of pesticide residues on fish and wildlife?
- What is the effect of pesticide residues on human health?
- What additional research should be undertaken to clarify areas that are not adequately understood today?

BACKGROUND

The word "pesticide" is a general term that covers fungicides, herbicides, insecticides, fumigants, and rodenticides. The sharply rising production of these materials is one measure of their value in agriculture, in controlling disease-bearing pests, and in other uses. U.S. production of pesticidal chemicals was more than 1 billion pounds in 1967, 18% higher than in 1965 (Table 1, page 196).

The synthetic organic chemicals are the most important of these compounds, in terms of both rate of growth and potential for contaminating the environment. Annual consumption of synthetic organic pesticides in this country is now around 800 million pounds per year. More than 300 organic pesticidal chemicals are in use in the U.S., in more than 10,000 formulations, but relatively few of them are used in large enough amounts and are sufficiently long-lived to offer potential environmental hazard. The names and chemical structures of some important synthetic organic pesticides, independent of their potential for contamination, appear in Table 2, page 197.

Both among chemical classes and within classes, the properties of these and other pesticides can differ widely. Their potential as environmental contaminants can vary accordingly. Among the properties that

Table 1

Approximate production of pesticidal chemicals, United States: 1965, 1967 [a]

Chemical	1965	1967
	1000 pounds	1000 pounds
Fungicides:		
Copper naphthenate	3,268	3,473
Copper sulfate	47,272	33,992
Ferbam	2,384	2,331
Mercury fungicides	1,602	912
Nabam	2,489	1,361
Pentachlorophenol (PCP)	39,965	44,239
2,4,5-Trichlorophenol and salts	4,003	14,008
Zineb	5,075	3,055
Other organic fungicides	44,969	63,269
Total	151,027	166,640
Herbicides:		
2,4-D acid	63,320 [b]	77,139 [b]
2,4-D acid esters and salts	63,360	83,750
DNBP	4,619	N.A.
DNBP, ammonium salt	59	58
Phenyl mercuric acetate (PMA)	588	518
Sodium chlorate	32,000	30,000
2,4,5-T acid	11,601 [b]	14,552 [b]
2,4,5-T acid esters and salts	13,516	27,189
Other organic herbicides	105,861	206,759
Total	220,003	348,274
Insecticides, fumigants, rodenticides:		
Aldrin-toxaphene group	118,832	120,183
Calcium arsenate	4,192	2,500
DDT	140,785	103,411
Dibromochloropropane	3,433	5,240
Lead arsenate	7,098	6,000
Methyl bromide	14,303	19,665
Methyl parathion	29,111	33,344
Parathion	16,607	11,361
Other organics	167,368	202,600
Total	501,729	504,304
Grand Total	**872,759**	**1,019,218**

[a] Includes material produced for export. [b] Not included in totals because of duplication.
SOURCE: "The Pesticide Review—1968," U.S. Department of Agriculture, Agricultural Stabilization and Conservation Service, Washington, D.C., December 1968.

Table 2

Nomenclature and structure of pesticides referred to in text

Common Name   Chemical Name   Structural Formula

CHLORINATED HYDROCARBON INSECTICIDES

aldrin
    1,2,3,4,10,10-hexachloro-1,4-
    4a,5,8,8a-hexahydro-1,4-*endo*-
    exo-5,8-dimethanonaphthalene

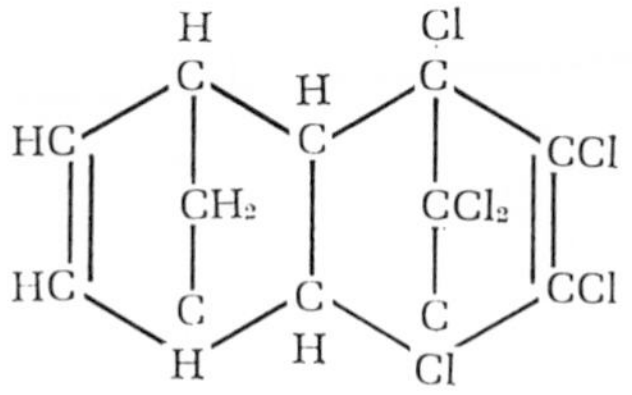

dieldrin
    1,2,3,4,10,10-hexachloro-6,7-
    epoxy-1,4,4a,5,6,7,8,8a-octa-
    hydro-1,4-*endo*-*exo*-5,8-dimeth-
    anonaphthalene

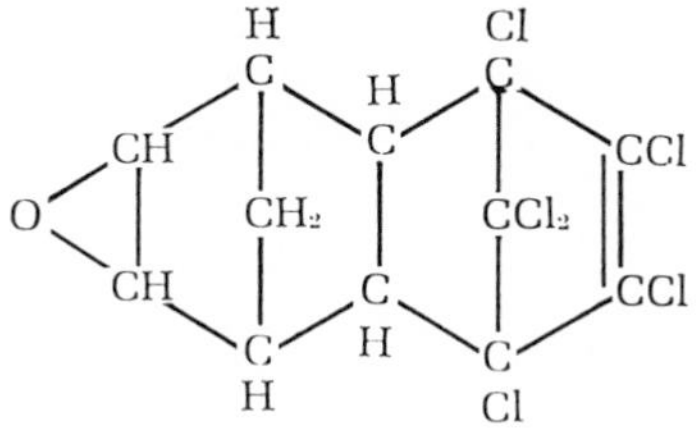

endrin
    1,2,3,4,10,10-hexachloro-6,7-
    epoxy-1,4,4a,5,6,7,8,8a-octa-
    hydro-1,4-*endo*-*endo*-5,8-di-
    methanonaphthalene

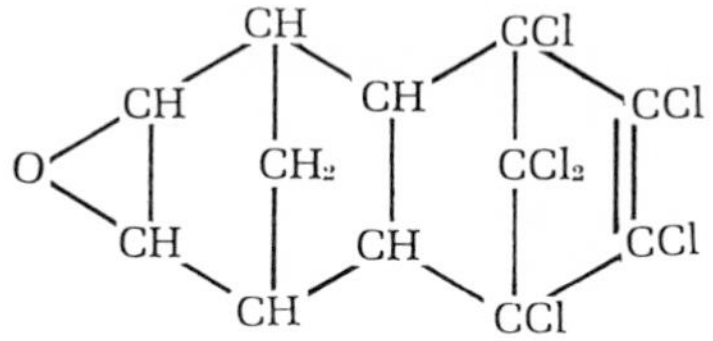

heptachlor
    1,4,5,6,7,8,8-heptachloro-3a,4,7,
    7a-tetrahydro-4,7-endometh-
    anoindene

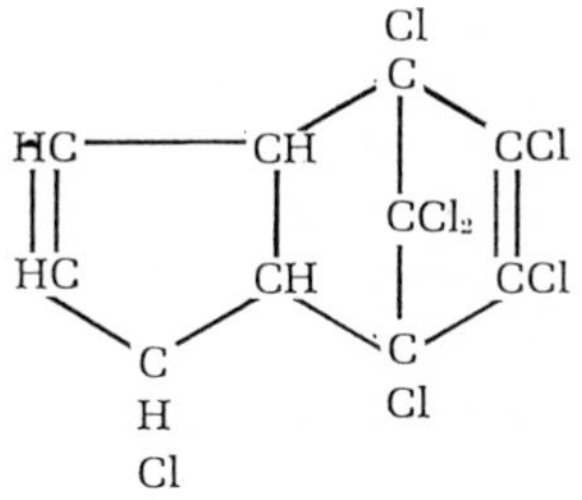

DDT
    2,2-bis (*p*-chlorophenyl)-1,1,1-
    trichloroethane

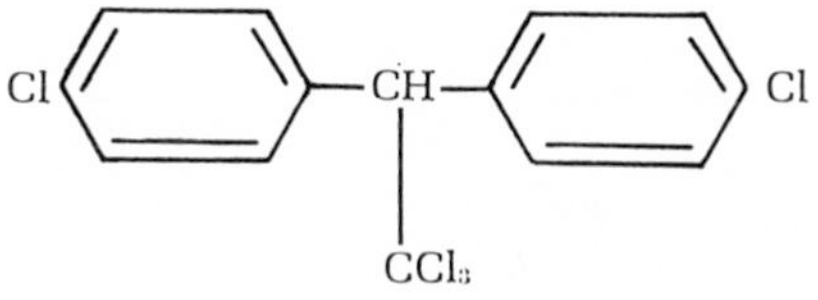

Table 2—(continued)

Nomenclature and structure of pesticides referred to in text

Common Name	Chemical Name	Structural Formula

CHLORINATED HYDROCARBON INSECTICIDES

DDD, TDE
2,2-bis (p-chlorophenyl)-1,1-
dichloroethane

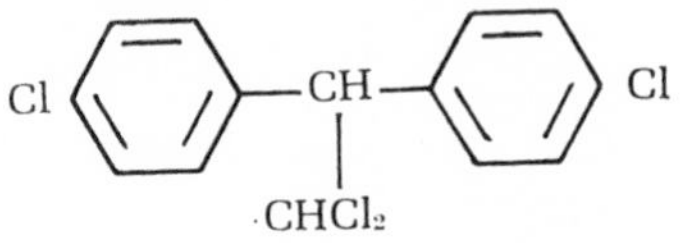

DDE
Dichlorodiphenyl
dichloroethylene

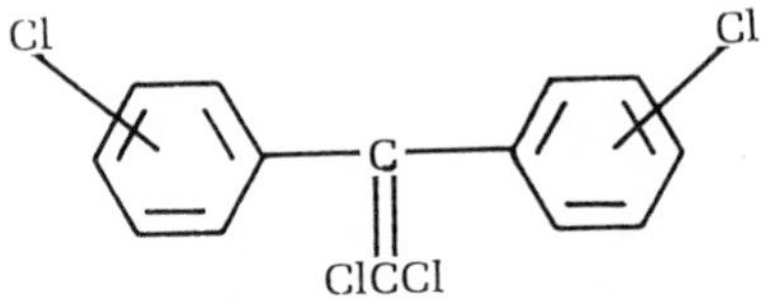

methoxychlor
2,2-bis (p-methoxyphenyl)-1,
1,1-trichloroethane

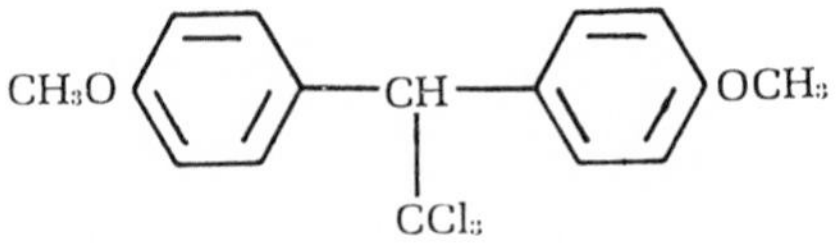

BHC
lindane
(gamma isomer)
1,2,3,4,5,6-Hexachloro-
cyclohexane

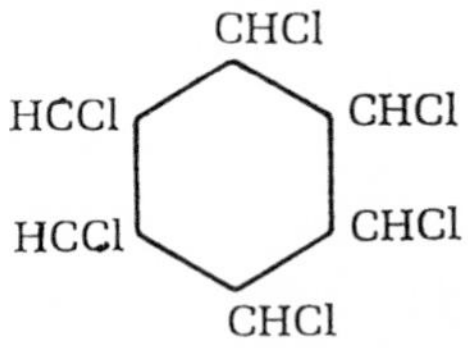

toxaphene
Synthesized by chlorination of
camphene to chlorine content
of 67-69%.

tetradifon
2,4,5,4'-tetrachlorodiphenyl
sulfone

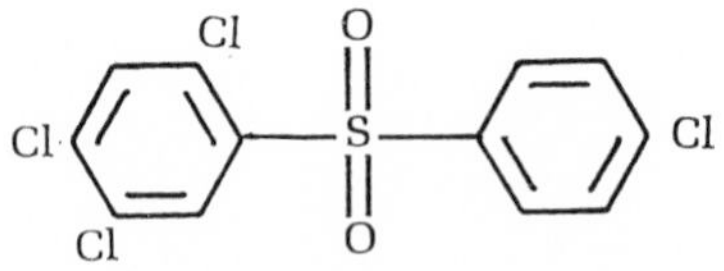

198

Table 2—(continued)

Nomenclature and structure of pesticides referred to in text

Common Name	Chemical Name	Structural Formula

CHLORINATED HYDROCARBON INSECTICIDES

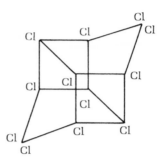

mirex

    Dodecachlorooctahydro-1,3,
4-metheno-2H-cyclobuta [cd]
pentalene

ORGANOPHOSPHORUS INSECTICIDES

fenthion

    O,O-Dimethyl O-[4-(methyl-
thio)-m-tolyl] phosphoro-
thioate

diazinon

    O,O-Diethyl O-(2-isopropyl
-4-methyl-6-pyrimidyl)
phosphorothioate

azinphosmethyl

    O,O-Dimethyl S-[4-oxo-1,2,3-
benzotriazin-3(4H)-ylmethyl]
phosphorodithioate

malathion

    O,O-dimethyl S-(1,2-di-
carbethoxyethyl) phosphorodithioate

methyl parathion

    O,O-Dimethyl-O-p-nitrophenyl
phosphorothioate

199

Table 2—(continued)

Nomenclature and structure of pesticides referred to in text

Common Name	Chemical Name	Structural Formula
ORGANOPHOSPHORUS INSECTICIDES		
parathion	*O,O*-Diethyl-*O*-*p*-nitrophenyl phosphorothioate	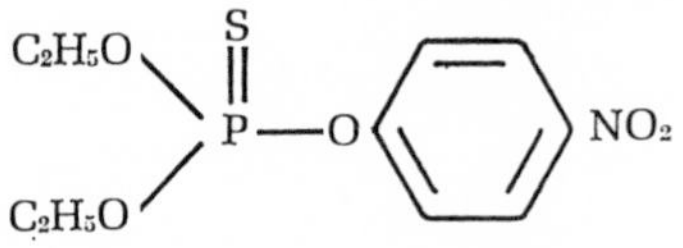
phorate	*O,O*-Diethyl *S*-(ethylthio) methyl phosphorodithioate	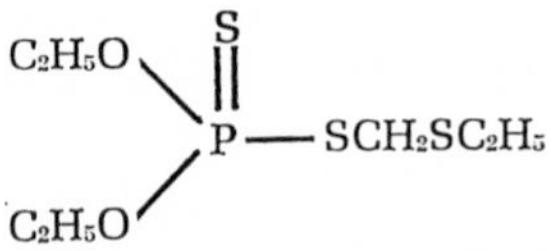
mevinphos	2-carbomethoxy-1-propen -2yl dimethyl phosphate	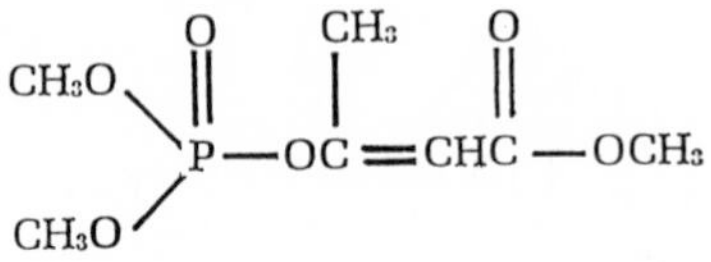
CARBAMATE INSECTICIDES		
carbaryl	N-Methyl-1-naphthyl-carbamate	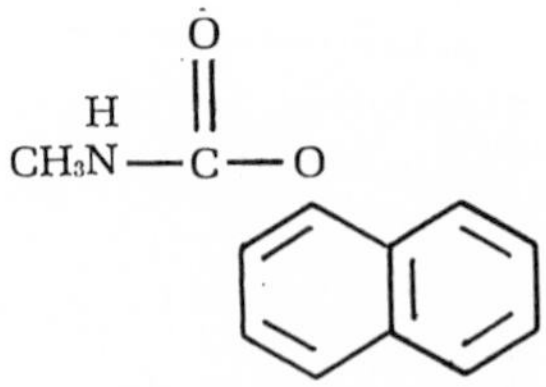
	4-dimethylamino-3,5-xylyl N-methylcarbamate	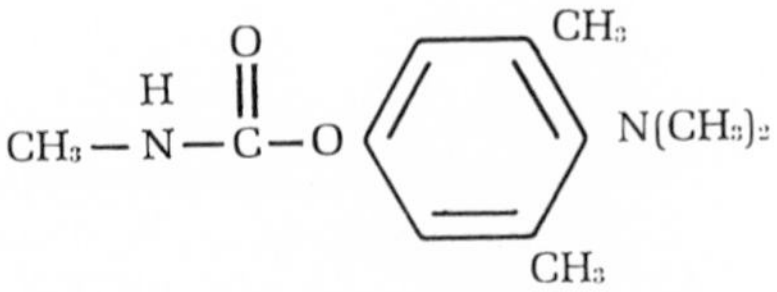

Table 2—(continued)

Nomenclature and structure of pesticides referred to in text

Common Name   Chemical Name   Structural Formula

HERBICIDES

2,4-D
     2,4-dichlorophenoxyacetic acid

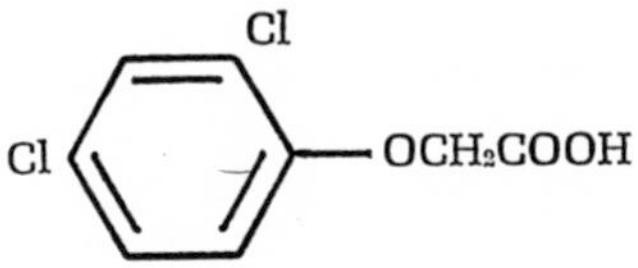

2,4,5-T
     2,4,5-trichlorophenoxyacetic
               acid

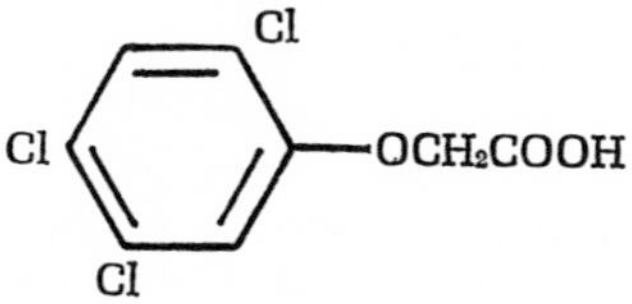

fenoprop
     2-(2,4,5-Trichlorophenoxy)
               propionic acid

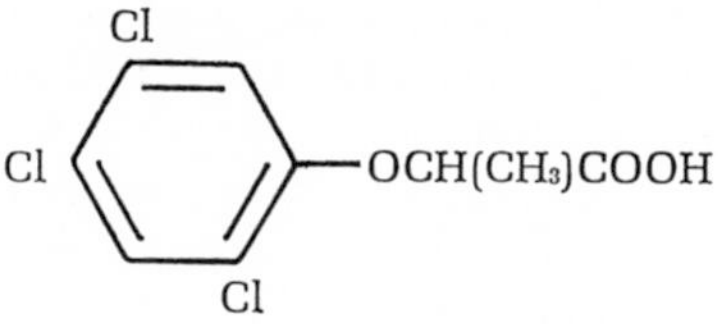

2,3,6-TBA
     2,3,6-trichlorobenzoic acid

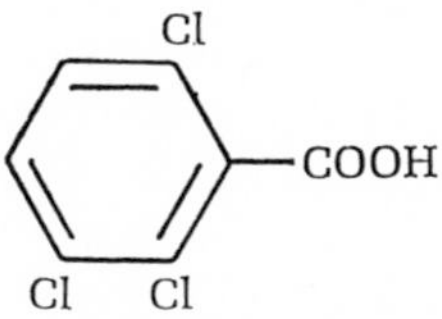

fenac
     2,3,6-trichlorophenylacetate

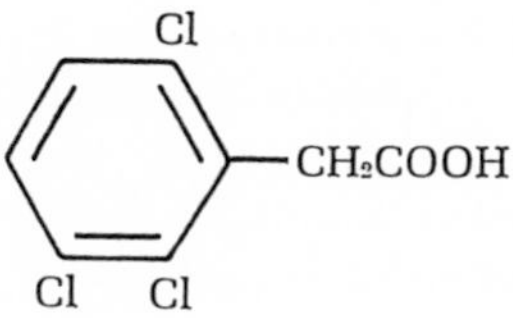

are important in the latter respect are the pesticide's tendency to vaporize, its tendency to dissolve in water and other solvents, and its degree of resistance to various degradation processes.

Synthetic organic pesticides normally are produced as concentrated (technical) materials that later are formulated before application. Organic pesticides can often be applied at rates of well below 1 pound of the active chemical per acre. The primary aim of formulating pesticides is to put them into a form that assures even distribution of a small amount of the active chemical over a large area at the desired rate per unit of area. Formulated materials include dusts, impregnated granules, solutions, emulsions, and suspensions of wettable powders. They are based on diluents such as clays, talc, and water and nonaqueous solvents. The formulated pesticide may contain as little as 0.1% or as much as 95% by weight of the active chemical. In some cases the unformulated technical material is applied directly. Pesticidal dusts, sprays, or granules are applied by aircraft or ground equipment. Depending on the purpose, the materials may be worked into the soil.

The marketing and use of pesticides are subject to a number of state laws and regulations and to two basic and interrelated federal statutes: the Federal Insecticide, Fungicide, and Rodenticide Act; and the Federal Food, Drug, and Cosmetic Act. Under federal law, any pesticide to be shipped in interstate commerce must be registered with the U.S. Department of Agriculture. To register a product the maker must disclose its chemical composition, the crops on which it is to be used, and the specific conditions of use. He must show that the product is useful for its intended purposes, that it is not a hazard to public health or wildlife, and that its uses are in accord with good agricultural practice.

If food or feed uses are involved, the Department of Health, Education, and Welfare must establish a tolerance for the pesticide. Any raw agricultural commodity may be condemned as adulterated if it contains any pesticide whose safety has not been cleared or which is present in amounts that exceed the tolerance. To have a tolerance established, the maker must disclose the chemical identity of the compound; its toxicity to laboratory animals; the amount, frequency, and time of application to the specific crops covered; data that show the amount of residue that will remain after the pesticide has been applied in the proposed manner; and the tolerance requested, with supporting data. The established tolerances normally are stated in parts per million by weight. The tolerance for DDT on potatoes, for example, is 1 part per million (ppm); on dried hops it is 80 ppm.

Pesticides furthermore are affected indirectly by the Food Additive Regulations, under the Food, Drug, and Cosmetic Act, which regulate materials added intentionally or incidentally to processed foods. One clause in the regulations states that no additive that can cause cancer under any conditions may be permitted in a food.

Intensive research has accompanied and supported the development of current practices and controls in the use of pesticides. It is safe to say that the means of examining pesticide residues in the environment are more sensitive and specific than for any other major contaminant group. Existing analytical chemical methods can often determine such residues in the range of parts per billion (one thousand million) or parts per trillion (one million million). Consequently, the role of pesticides as environmental contaminants is better understood than that of any other major class of contaminants. A particularly large body of data exists for residues in foods (69, 150), which generally are far below the legal tolerances. This report accordingly does not deal with that aspect of the subject. For residues in soil and water the data are extensive, though less so than for residues in foods. Very little data exist for pesticide residues in air. Gaps remain also in our knowledge of how to reduce pesticidal contamination and of the effects of residues on man and other forms of life.

PESTICIDE RESIDUES IN SOIL

Pesticide residues in soils may pose several problems to agriculture. Conceivable effects of pesticide residues in soil are injury to crops grown in later years, production of illegal residues in crops that absorb them, or harmful effects on living organisms in the soil. The largest amounts of residues usually result from contamination after crops are sprayed or from applying pesticides directly to the soil. Smaller amounts may reach the soil in contaminated plant or animal material (2, 8, 99, 129).

Residues in soils are not limited to the modern organic pesticides. In several areas in the U.S., arsenic residues have increased significantly as a result of continued use of arsenical insecticides. More than 3500 pounds of lead arsenate per acre were applied to one commercial apple orchard over a 25-year period. Residual arsenic usually was confined to the top 6 to 8 inches of soil and did not harm established trees, whose roots extend below that level (90). The roots of young trees may not reach so deeply, however, and arsenic residues have injured young peach or apricot trees severely, and even killed them, when they were planted in old apple orchards (16, 173).

The most common pesticide residues in soils are those of the chlorinated hydrocarbon insecticides. Most other pesticides, such as the organophosphorus and carbamate types, decompose in the soil rapidly enough so that their residues disappear between crop seasons. However, even certain of the organophosphorus compounds, which normally break down rapidly, may persist for several years under some conditions (115), such as relatively dry soil.

Most herbicides decompose rapidly in soils, chiefly through the action of microorganisms (63, 159, 160). Even after heavy applications, it is unusual to find phytotoxic residues (those that can harm plants) after one year, and in most cases the chemicals dissipate much sooner. On the other hand, some herbicides are very persistent, one of them being 2,3,6-TBA, a chlorinated benzoic acid (47, 141). Also, very high concentrations of herbicides are sometimes used to control deep-rooted perennial weeds such as Canada thistle, and in such cases phytotoxic residues may persist for several years. Land that is badly infested with deep-rooted perennial weeds is not available for cropping, however, so that such residues are not a serious problem provided that they decompose eventually in the soil and do not enter water supplies.

Factors affecting accumulation of residues in soil

The persistence of pesticides in soil depends on many factors (53). The major factors, not necessarily in order of importance, are the pesticide itself, soil type, soil moisture, soil temperature, wind or air movement, cover crops, soil cultivation, method of application to the soil, formulation, and soil microorganisms.

The pesticide itself

The chlorinated hydrocarbon insecticides, such as DDT, are more persistent than many other commonly used pesticides. Large differences exist also within each group of chemicals. The time required for half of the pesticide to disappear from the soil (half life) can range from a few days to several months. In experiments in Wisconsin, seven insecticides were applied at a rate of 5 pounds per acre and worked into the soil to a depth of 5 inches. Six-inch soil samples were then collected (and analyzed) at regular intervals over a five-month period. The results (103, 107) are shown in Table 3.

The problems of evaluating pesticide residues in soil are sometimes made more complex by toxic compounds formed through the action of microorganisms on the parent pesticide. The organophosphorus insecticide, phorate, for example, is oxidized in soil to the sulfoxide and the sulfone, each of which is also toxic (99). Thus the analytical method that is used to evaluate a residue must determine not only the parent pesticide but all of its toxic conversion products. The method that is used most widely, and that is the most specific, is based on gas-liquid chromatography.

Soil type

Available data suggest that pesticides persist longer in soils that are higher in organic matter than in mineral (sand or clay) soils. High-organic soils tend to assume a colloidal form which binds the residues tightly to the soil particles. In a muck soil, which is about 50% organic matter, insecticide residues are bound to the soil particles to such an extent that they are less effective against insects than in a sandy soil (106). Crops, moreover, absorb pesticides most readily from sandy soils and least readily from muck soils (98).

Soil moisture

The moisture content of soil can also influence the persistence of pesticides. Water apparently causes aldrin to be displaced from soil particles, and much of the insecticide then vaporizes and escapes from

Table 3

Persistence of some common pesticides in soil[a]

Insecticide	Type	Time for 50% of applied dose to disappear	Time to reach residue level of 0.1 ppm. (3% of applied dose)
aldrin	chlorinated hydrocarbon	2 months	—
carbaryl (Sevin)	carbamate	1 month	—
phorate (Thimet)	organophosphorus	1 month	—
azinphosmethyl (Guthion)	organophosphorus	20 days	—
parathion	organophosphorus	20 days	90 days
methyl parathion	organophosphorus	—	30 days
malathion	organophosphorus	—	8 days

[a] Not all of the pesticides shown in this table are necessarily labeled for use in soil at 5 pounds per acre.

> *Figures show that rate of disappearance of various pesticides from soil can vary widely. In these experiments, close to 40% of the aldrin applied was recovered as aldrin and dieldrin five months after the soil was treated. Dieldrin is a breakdown product of aldrin and is itself a commercial pesticide. The above table shows that the organophosphorus compounds studied disappear rapidly from soil.*

the soil. One of the main escape routes for both aldrin and heptachlor is vaporization, which for both occurs more readily from moist than from dry soil. Parathion is decomposed and disappears through reaction with water (hydrolysis), or by being converted to its amino form by microorganisms, whose action is enhanced by water (103, 104, 105).

Soil temperature

Available data suggest that rising soil temperature increases the rate at which pesticides in the soil vaporize and escape, and the rate at which they decompose. In one laboratory experiment, the rate of decomposition of aldrin was measured at three temperatures in a Miami silt loam. Residues were determined for both aldrin and dieldrin, the breakdown product of aldrin. This work showed clearly that rising temperature increased both the rate of conversion of aldrin to dieldrin and the rate of subsequent decomposition of dieldrin (106). The results are shown in Table 4, page 206.

Table 4
Effect of soil temperature on disappearance of aldrin from soil

Temperature	Amount of aldrin plus dieldrin remaining in soil after four weeks
7°C.	92%
26°C.	82%
46°C.	40%

Figures show that rising temperature increases rate at which aldrin and dieldrin, its breakdown product, disappear from soil.

Cover crops

Cover crops such as alfalfa increase the persistence of volatile pesticides (those that vaporize readily) in soils. The cover crop probably reduces the rate of vaporization at the soil-air interface (100). In one instance, two to three times more residue was recovered from plots covered with alfalfa than from plots on which no crop was growing.

Soil cultivation

Cultivation of soils increases the rate at which pesticides disappear. The amount of applied DDT lost from a field plot in four months was measured in one study in which part of the plot was cultivated regularly and part was left uncultivated. A similar experiment was made with aldrin (104). The results appear in Table 5.

Mode of application and formulation

The formulation of a pesticide and the method used to apply it are decisive factors in the persistence of residues in soil. In a study with aldrin, an emulsifiable concentrate and a granular formulation were applied directly to the surface of test plots. In part of each plot, the material was worked into the soil, and the amounts of pesticide remaining were measured after one year (102). The results appear in Table 6.

Microbial degradation

The persistence of residues in soil is affected by the population and activity of microorganisms, which attack various pesticides. Aldrin, for example, is oxidized to dieldrin by microbiological action. It persists longer in dry soils, in which microorganisms are relatively inactive and oxidize little of it to dieldrin. It also persists longer in sandy soils, which contain few microorganisms, or in soils in which the population of microorganisms has been reduced by autoclaving (heating) (105).

Table 5

Effect of cultivation on disappearance of DDT and aldrin from soil

Insecticide	Amount remaining after four months	
	Cultivated	Uncultivated
DDT	55.9%	74.2%
aldrin	29.3%	46.9%

Figures show how cultivation increases disappearance of DDT and aldrin from soil.

Parathion, when tested in the laboratory at 30°C., persisted longest in dry soil, which inhibited its two modes of decomposition: conversion to the amino form by microorganisms, and hydrolysis (which also depends in part on the population of microorganisms). No aminoparathion was formed in autoclaved soils because of the low population of microorganisms. In soils in which aminoparathion did form, yeasts were the microorganisms primarily responsible, bacteria apparently having no effect (103).

Pesticide residue levels in soils

A number of surveys have been made of the amounts of pesticide residues that actually are present in soils, and data are also available on the relationship of the amounts found to the amounts that were applied. In a study of the latter point (107), a loam soil was treated

Table 6

Effect of incorporation on disappearance of aldrin from soil

Formulation	% of applied dose recovered after one year	
	Applied to surface	Worked into soil
Emulsifiable concentrate	6.5%	44%
Granular	13%	62%

Figures show how formulation of aldrin and method used to apply it affect its persistence in soil.

with aldrin and heptachlor in abnormally high doses: 5 pounds of active ingredient per acre per year for five years. Other plots received a single application of 25 pounds per acre. Still other plots were treated at the normal rate: 1, 2, or 3 pounds per acre per year for three years. The results of residue analyses of these plots indicate that in this type of soil, a Carrington silt loam, the same percentage of the applied dose of aldrin or heptachlor remains whether the dose is 1 pound per acre or 5 pounds per acre. The data appear in part in Table 7.

Field surveys of residues

Residues of chlorinated hydrocarbon pesticides were surveyed in a large number of agricultural soils in southern Ontario (72). The most widespread residues were those of DDT and its conversion products (Table 8). The highest concentration of these residues (in the range of 120 ppm) was in soils in an orchard in which DDT had been used extensively from 1950 to 1961. Other orchard soils also contained high residue levels. The highest concentration of cyclodiene residues (aldrin, dieldrin, endrin) was found in soil from a farm where four crops of radishes were grown each year and the cyclodienes were used on each new crop to control cabbage maggot. The sample was a muck soil, from which residues do not escape as readily as from mineral soils; it contained 2.1 ppm of aldrin, 1.6 ppm of dieldrin, and 3.8 ppm of endrin. In all other cases where cyclodiene residues in soil exceeded 1.0 ppm, the major crops were vegetable root crops. These normally receive relatively heavy applications of pesticides, and the materials are worked into the soil.

Since 1964, the U.S. Department of Agriculture has been monitoring pesticide residues in soil extensively, especially in the cotton-growing areas of the Mississippi Delta (64). About 3200 samples were analyzed

Table 7

Effect of application rate on disappearance of aldrin from soil

Rate of application	Amount of residue	
	In 1963	In 1962
5 pounds per acre per year for five years (1958-1963)	2.9 ppm (19% of total applied dose)	
1 pound per acre[a] per year for three years (1960-1962)		0.41 ppm (22% of total applied dose)
Single dose of 25 pounds per acre (1958)	1.7 ppm (11% of total applied dose)	

[a] Heptachlor gave an almost identical result to that shown for aldrin.

Figures show relationship between amounts of pesticides applied to soil and amount remaining as residue. The data presented are residues of aldrin and dieldrin.

in the first season. The cotton insecticides used chiefly in the two years before the program began were methyl parathion, endrin, and DDT. Lesser amounts of toxaphene and Guthion were also used. In 1965 the analytical work was expanded to include fungicides, herbicides, and defoliants.

The most important finding in the first report on this work was that these organic pesticides did not appear to have built up progressively in soil, sediment, or water in the areas monitored. In one area, a total of 30 pounds of DDT per acre had been applied to cotton fields in the nine years 1955-63. In the spring of 1964, 1.3 ppm was found in this soil. This is roughly equivalent to 1.3 pounds per acre in the top 3 inches of soil, or one third to one half of the amount applied per acre in a single year. Thirteen applications of endrin to cotton since 1956 at 0.21 pound per acre per application resulted in an average soil residue of 0.05 ppm in 1964. In August 1964, 0.12 part per billion (ppb) of endrin was found in water in this area, and quick runoff water contained 6.7 ppb the following January.

Residues of aldrin in these soils ranged up to 0.20 ppm and of dieldrin up to 0.11 ppm. These levels are lower than the amount of material used in one application. The average level of BHC found was 0.02 ppm or less. DDT and its conversion products were the residues found most often. From 16% to 100% of cropland soils, depending on the

Table 8

Frequency of occurrence of chlorinated hydrocarbon insecticide residues in southern Ontario soils

(Figures show number of soil samples examined and frequency of occurrence of residues)

Pesticide	Non-detectable	Less than 0.1 ppm	0.1-1.0 ppm	1.0-5.0 ppm	5.0-50 ppm	More than 50 ppm
Heptachlor	31	6	1	—	—	—
Heptachlor epoxide	31	5	2	—	—	—
Gamma chlordane	30	3	5	—	—	—
Aldrin	19	12	6	1	—	—
Dieldrin	18	5	11	4	—	—
Endrin	35	2	0	1	—	—
Endosulfan	34	1	2	1	—	—
DDT	7	2	4	14	7	4
DDE	7	6	15	5	5	—
DDD	18	7	9	4	—	—
Kelthane	32	0	0	4	2	—

SOURCE: Harris, C. R., Sans, W. W., Miles, J. R. W., "Exploratory Studies on Occurrence of Organochlorine Insecticide Residues in Agricultural Soils in Southwestern Ontario," *J. Agr. Food Chem.*, **14**, 398 (1966).

area, contained such residues. The average residue levels varied from 0.08 to 2.17 ppm.

There was some evidence that arsenic had built up in the past, owing presumably to the use of calcium arsenate before it was succeeded by the organic pesticides. Arsenic residues averaged 2.8 to 12.8 ppm in cultivated fields and 1.2 to 5.9 ppm in uncultivated areas.

Absorption of pesticide residues by crops

Concern over possible absorption of pesticide residues by crops grown in contaminated soil has led to extensive research. In a program in Wisconsin, a number of crops were grown on soil treated with aldrin and heptachlor, whose residues are relatively long-lived in soil. Some crops did not absorb measurable amounts of these pesticides, while others absorbed significant amounts. In general, on the basis of the Wisconsin work, it seems safe to conclude that residues of aldrin and heptachlor absorbed by crops will be only a small fraction of the concentration in the soil.

Potatoes, radishes, and carrots were grown on soil treated with 1 pound of aldrin per acre. The potatoes contained no measurable residue, the radishes contained 0.03 ppm, and the carrots contained 0.05 ppm (107). Of all the crops studied in the Wisconsin work, carrots contained the highest concentrations of residues absorbed from the soil.

Studies of five varieties of carrots showed that the rate of absorption of aldrin and heptachlor residues differed markedly among the five. Residue levels in the carrots varied from 22 to 80% of the concentrations in the soils (98, 101), which were treated at various rates with aldrin and heptachlor.

Cucumbers were grown on soils that contained 2 to 4 ppm of aldrin plus dieldrin, or 1.60 to 3.80 ppm of heptachlor plus heptachlor epoxide, a conversion product of heptachlor. The concentrations of residues in the cucumbers ranged, in general, from 2 to 6% of the concentrations in the soil. The experiment was arranged so that some of the growing cucumbers were lying on the ground, while others did not touch the soil. Both contained the same levels of residues, which apparently were absorbed by the root system and translocated into the cucumbers (108).

Tests were made on third cuttings of fresh alfalfa grown on soil that contained 0.2 to 0.7 pound per acre of aldrin plus dieldrin, or heptachlor plus heptachlor epoxide, in the top 6 inches of soil. Purified extracts of this alfalfa were not toxic to fruit flies exposed for 48 hours in a bioassay. Extracts from alfalfa from soils that contained higher levels of residues were toxic to the flies and also contained measurable amounts of the residues, which were analyzed by gas-liquid chromatography.

Residue levels in or on alfalfa grown on soil treated with aldrin were 0.88% $\pm$ 0.23 of the residue level in the soil at harvest time. For soil treated with heptachlor, the levels in or on the alfalfa were 3.01% $\pm$ 0.85 of the level in the soil (108). These data might be used to approximate the amount of residues in or on alfalfa, once the concentration in the soil is known. Previous data (107) indicate that residues in a loamy soil in Wisconsin amount to about 20% of the total applied dose. On this basis, a yearly application of aldrin or heptachlor worked into the soil at a rate of 1 pound per acre would result in residues of 1 pound in the top 6 inches of soil after five years. This would be a concentration of about 0.5 ppm of aldrin or heptachlor residues in the top 6 inches of soil. Alfalfa grown on this soil might then contain about 0.005 ppm of aldrin plus dieldrin, or 0.015 ppm of heptachlor plus heptachlor epoxide.

Effects of residues on crop growth and soil microorganisms

Work has been done also on the effects of pesticide residues on the growth of crops and on soil microorganisms (116). In general, it appears that rates of application of 100 pounds per acre of DDT, far above the usual application rates, are required to reduce the yield of crops such as rye, beans, and strawberries (34). In New Jersey, application of 15 pounds of lindane per acre, also far above the usual application rate, reduced the yield of beets, lettuce, and spinach (18).

Residues of chlorinated hydrocarbon pesticides in soils, in the amounts usually found, appear to have little effect on soil microorganisms (116). Soil fumigants and fungicides are the most lethal of any pesticides to these microorganisms (117).

PESTICIDE RESIDUES IN WATER

Pesticides may contaminate surface and ground water because of aerial spraying, runoff from treated areas, percolation through soil to ground waters, waste discharge by pesticide producers, misuse, and other means. Determining the precise amounts present is difficult, but the large volume of available data indicates that they are in the range of parts per billion or parts per trillion (ppt) by weight. (One part per billion is equivalent to 1 milligram of pesticide per 1000 liters of fresh water. One part per trillion is one-thousandth part of this).

Analytical problems

It might be simple to calculate the maximum possible concentrations of dissolved pesticides in surface waters by using data on the solubility of the compounds and the temperature of the water. However, water normally contains living organisms, suspended solids, and dissolved minerals and organic matter, and these materials affect drastically the state in which pesticides exist in water. They are adsorbed on solid particles, they are dissolved in fatty substances, and they form complexes and otherwise associate with organic materials. Nor do pesticides exist in simple solution in rainwater. Raindrops form when water condenses on dust particles and thus will contain solids from soil and smoke, salts from the ocean, pollen, spores, bacteria, and other substances that affect the form in which the pesticides exist.

One normal method of removing and concentrating a pesticide from a sample of water for analysis is to extract it with an organic solvent which can later be evaporated. Because pesticides are retained in water in so many different states, however, this method can be expected to remove only part of the toxicant present. When the pesticide is sufficiently stable, the degree of extraction can be improved by hydrolyzing the sample with acid or alkali, or by oxidizing the organic matter, before extracting the pesticide with the organic solvent. One of the most common methods of removing and concentrating pesticides for analysis is to adsorb them on charcoal. However, charcoal will not remove pesticides completely from water, and there is as yet no method for completely desorbing the pesticide from the charcoal (61). It is difficult to devise adequate experiments for determining the per cent recovery of pesticides from water using the charcoal method.

It is also difficult to get samples that are adequate for determining background values for substances in the water that might cause the chosen analytical methods to give incorrect results. Background values are especially important when determining the extremely low concentrations of pesticides that are found in water. The usual analytical methods, based on gas-liquid chromatography, are not specific enough to rule out interference by other organic compounds.

Thus the analyst has two problems: His extraction methods may not remove all of the pesticide from the water sample, and his results therefore may be low; interfering substances may cause his analytical methods to produce results that are too high or that indicate that residues are present when they are not. In spite of these two difficulties, a great deal of useful data have been obtained on pesticide residues in water. Most of this work has involved the extremely stable chlorinated hydrocarbon insecticides. Herbicides and organophosphorus insecticides may persist to a significant degree in soil (3), however, and the possibility that they may enter surface or ground waters must be considered. A reliable and sensitive method for monitoring water for organophosphorus insecticides has been developed (188).

Pesticide residue levels in water

The first published results (20) from the pesticide monitoring program that is by far the most comprehensive to date showed that DDT and dieldrin were present in 38 samples of water from 10 rivers. DDT was identified in the Susquehanna River, the Delaware, the Chattahoochee, the Tennessee, the Rio Grande, the San Joaquin, the Sacramento, the Yakima, and the Columbia. Dieldrin was identified in the Savannah River. The analytical methods used included charcoal adsorption, infrared analysis, and flame ionization gas chromatography. Their sensitivity was about 1 ppb.

A second study (178) in this series identified dieldrin, endrin, DDT, and DDE, in that order of frequency of occurrence, in all major river basins in the U.S. Concentrations ranged from 4 to 118 ppt. Aldrin and heptachlor were less common, and heptachlor epoxide was not identified in any sample. DDD was detected in one sample, and presumptive evidence of BHC was found at one sampling station. The analytical methods used were liquid-liquid extraction (167), thin layer chromatography (163), and microcoulometry. A third study in this series (19) involved analyses of 6000 samples collected annually from more than 100 stations from 1958 through 1965. These were the results:

- Dieldrin has been the dominant pesticide residue in all river basins since 1958, at levels of 1 to 22 ppt.
- In the lower Mississippi, in the fall of 1963, endrin residues reached a maximum of 214 ppt. Since then the levels have decreased, ranging from 15 to 116 ppt in the Mississippi in 1965.
- DDT and related compounds have been fairly common in surface waters since 1958.

Aldrin, BHC, heptachlor, and heptachlor epoxide were detected in certain samples in this study, usually in the range of parts per trillion, but no pattern of contamination emerged. The analytical methods used were thin layer chromatography, electron capture gas chromatography, and microcoulometry. Electron capture detection gave sensitivities in the range of 1 to 2 ppt. Most samples contained residues in the parts-per-trillion range.

The literature contains many other reports of pesticide residues in water.* The data show that most surface waters of the U.S. contain chlorinated hydrocarbon insecticides, particularly DDT and dieldrin, and certain herbicides, such as 2,4-D. Many of these compounds are quite stable in soil and may find their way eventually into surface and ground water. They have been used in recent years in amounts that would assure the presence of traces of them in water for several years in the future, even if all use of them were to stop now.

Effects of pesticide residues in water

Pesticide residues in water may reach humans through drinking water, but the concentrations in most cases are far below the level at which the residues would be toxic. There is no evidence to suggest that long-term consumption of such water would produce harmful effects.

The chief known hazard of residues of chlorinated hydrocarbon pesticides is due to their concentration in the food chain. DDD in a lake, for example, may be taken up selectively by plankton, which may be eaten by small fish, which may be eaten in turn by lake trout. The concentration of the residue is magnified at each stage. This biological magnification does not occur in most human food, with the possible exception of some fish and wildfowl. It can, however, produce harmful effects on fish and wildlife.†

It is difficult to draw useful conclusions from the available data on fluctuations in the concentrations of pesticide residues in water. The

---

* See references 17, 21, 35, 36, 39, 40, 41, 51, 62, 64, 68, 84, 88, 91, 96, 97, 113, 114, 123, 130, 131, 132, 133, 134, 168, 169, 177, 179, 181.
† See references 6, 24, 48, 55, 60, 87, 114.

problem may be partially due to errors in chemical analysis. It is also due to the ubiquitous presence and unpredictable movements of pesticides in all areas surrounding water, including air.

PESTICIDE RESIDUES IN AIR

Very little data exist on pesticides in air, largely because there is no adequate sampling equipment that can be used to obtain the data. Part of the sampling problem is that pesticides may be present in air simultaneously as both particles and vapor. The concentration of most of the newer organic pesticides in air at some distance from the point of application is usually very low, and very large volumes of air must be sampled to accumulate enough of the pesticide to be detectable. DDT co-distills with water at 25° to 35° C. (7). Thus it seems possible to lose a significant amount of the pesticide during the sampling process if the sampling medium is a liquid. Other chlorinated hydrocarbons also can reasonably be expected to co-distill with liquids.

Until more reliable sampling techniques are developed, therefore, little reliable data on pesticides in air can be expected. It seems justifiable to develop certain principles on a purely rational basis, however, and some qualitative data are available from observation.

Sources of residues in air

Pesticides become airborne at least briefly when they are applied by spraying. Droplets from coarse spray jets are apt to be quite large, ranging in diameter from 25 to 100 microns (a micron is 1000th of a millimeter). They travel through the air at high speed and either hit the target or fall to the ground or floor quite rapidly. Droplets from finer spray jets, with diameters of 20 to 50 microns, remain airborne for a longer time. The liquid carrier may evaporate, at least in part, leaving even smaller particles of pesticide that remain airborne still longer. Pesticide dusts and aerosols may contain still smaller particles, those in aerosols being as small as 2 microns in diameter. Some pesticides, particularly fumigants, may be applied as a true vapor and remain airborne indefinitely or until they either decompose or are adsorbed on some other material.

Pesticides may also enter the air by vaporization of residues, stock materials, or wastes. They may enter the air in smokes or other clouds produced in manufacturing or processing, from burning "empty" containers, or from fires in warehouses. Such sources doubtless are most significant in industrial situations, where workmen may be exposed to relatively high concentrations. Finally, winds that are strong enough to produce dust storms will also pick up pesticide residues that are adsorbed on the dust particles or that are in the same range of particle size.

Distribution and dispersion of residues in air

The distribution of airborne pesticides depends heavily on the local meteorological conditions and on particle size. The meteorological aspects have been well studied in connection with other problems and are beyond the scope of this report. Such principles, however, may be useful in timing aerial applications of pesticide sprays so as to minimize drift, and a good deal of this type of data has been gathered (1). Most of these data tend to be more sophisticated on particle size than on meteorology. The aim of such studies, moreover, usually is to determine the point of deposit of airborne particles. Thus the work deals largely with particles more than 10 microns in diameter, which settle relatively rapidly.

Smaller particles drift farther with the wind and become more dilute in numbers of particles per unit volume of air. Also, their mass is so slight that much larger numbers of them per unit volume of air are required to create a contamination problem comparable to that created by larger particles. The distance traveled by such particles depends on the height above the ground at which they enter the air, and most studies of them, therefore, have dealt specifically with pesticides applied by aircraft.

Reactions of residues in air

It seems safe to assume that pesticides are oxidized more rapidly in air than in water or soil, because, in relation to their mass, more of their surface is exposed to oxygen. It also seems reasonable to assume that decomposition by radiant energy (photolysis) is important in the breakdown of organic pesticides in air, at least when the particle is of a size that remains airborne for several hours. For example, methoxychlor in hexane solution disappears very rapidly when exposed to ultraviolet light (124). The nature of such reactions and their speed under practical conditions can be determined only after adequate air sampling methods are developed.

Significance of residues in air

Pesticides by definition are toxic to the target organisms, and usually they are toxic in some degree to nontarget organisms as well. The hazard to nontarget organisms depends partly on the nature of the exposure, such as inhalation, ingestion, or contact with the skin. The hazard to mammals generally is greater if the pesticide is inhaled, presumably because the body absorbs it from the lungs more quickly and completely than from the digestive tract or through intact skin. Thus pesticides that are apt to be encountered in air at significant distances from the point of application are primarily a potential respiratory hazard. Vapors will be too dilute, and the particles that remain airborne too small, to present a hazard by ingestion or contact with the skin.

The degree of this respiratory hazard cannot be evaluated until more is known of the concentrations of pesticides and their breakdown products in air at various times and places. Certainly it would be dangerous to generalize on the presence or absence of hazard without such information. Methods have been developed for estimating respiratory exposure (50), but they work best where the potential exposure is heavy, such as near the point of use of the pesticide.

Since the highest concentrations of airborne pesticides can be expected near the point of application, the people who are most likely to be exposed are equally likely to be aware of the hazard because they are working near that point. They can use respirators or take other protective measures when they feel it necessary to do so. Less well informed applicators, such as housewives, are protected by marketing regulations. In general such regulations have worked well.

It is much more difficult to evaluate the hazard at a distance from the point of use, because of the lower concentrations of pesticides involved. Some data are available, however, dealing primarily with concentrations in orchards and forests at or near the time of application (125). Concentrations at from several feet to several miles downwind of the point of application have been surmised largely from deposits of pesticides on the ground and on crops in neighboring fields.

Measurements of parathion at various distances from a treated orchard showed not more than 0.02 milligram per cubic meter (mg/m^3) at a nearby residence and only traces, at most, at greater distances (13). In a study in 10 communities (166), some air samples were taken near heavy agricultural use of pesticides and some before, during, and after local pest control programs in which the community itself was fogged. Up to 8.5 mg/m^3 of DDT was found during spraying or dusting operations. In agricultural communities, near the center of town and generally at least a mile from any point of application, the maximum concentrations found were 0.022 mg/m^3 of DDT, 0.0006 mg/m^3 of chlordane, 0.004 mg/m^3 of aldrin, and 0.015 mg/m^3 of toxaphene. In a community that was being fogged, up to 8 mg/m^3 of DDT were found and up to 0.130 mg/m^3 of malathion. In all 10 communities, most samples showed much lower concentrations than these, and many showed no detectable amount. However, the data are too sparse, and the variability among samples too great, to permit generalization.

It is doubtful if any of the concentrations actually reported for pesticides in air, except in the immediate vicinity of the point of application, are high enough to present an acute hazard to humans in a short period of exposure. Significant effects from long-term exposure have not been detected, in spite of some community studies of the question, chiefly involving parathion (79). In these studies, made near Wenatchee, Wash., people who were definitely exposed to organophosphorus insecticides showed significant symptoms consistent with poisoning during the time of their exposure. Illness resembling mild poisoning was not significantly more common among persons living in an agricultural community during the spraying season who had no occupational or gross accidental exposure than among people living in a nonagricultural area where pesticides were not used.

With highly toxic fumigants, such as hydrogen cyanide and methyl bromide, ventilation of the building has been assumed adequately to protect people outside nearby buildings.

Very few cases of harm to animals have been documented for airborne pesticides. However, cattle have been killed by TEPP (tetraethyl pyrophosphate) when an inversion held a cloud of dust in a restricted area for nearly two hours (147).

Crops can be harmed by airborne weed killers, particularly of the phenoxy (2,4-D) type, that may drift a long way from the point of application. The ester types, some of which are relatively volatile, may drift for miles and still damage sensitive crops. The distance at which harm can occur can be greatly reduced by using less volatile esters or salts, by using sprays instead of dusts, and by limiting aerial application to low altitudes and low wind conditions.

Research needed on pesticides in air

The most urgent need in evaluating airborne pesticides is better air sampling procedures. Highly mobile equipment that can concentrate pesticides from large volumes of air with reasonably high efficiency is essential to work on most other research problems in this area. Development of such equipment must be accompanied by development of methods for separating the pesticides from their breakdown products and from other air contaminants that interfere with analysis.

Such equipment and methods would permit high-priority research on the effects of air, humidity, and light on the chemical reactions of pesticides in air and the identification of the products of such reactions. The toxicology of the end products could then also be determined.

Research is also needed on the concentrations and dispersal of airborne pesticides and their noxious breakdown products in various air sheds under a variety of conditions. Several research groups are already gathering similar information on other air pollutants, and it might reasonably be anticipated that they will undertake such studies.

More research would be desirable on the toxicity of pesticides when they are inhaled, as opposed to dermal or oral exposure. Such studies would be simplified by more accurate methods of determining the concentrations and time periods involved in respiratory exposure. The results would be useful in selecting justifiable and effective protective measures. They would also be useful in evaluating the hazard from smoke that results from burning materials that are contaminated by pesticides. In one such case, up to 7.9 mg/m^3 of parathion was found in smoke (182). Much more data of this kind would help to determine what steps should be taken to protect fire-fighters and others during warehouse fires.

As soon as sound sampling methods are available, a nationwide monitoring program could be started. It would determine the levels of pesticides in air and how those levels change from year to year. Such a program would also permit the start of epidemiological studies designed to evaluate the effects of long-term exposure on urban and other populations.

Recommendations: pesticide residues in soil, water, and air

Recommendation P1: *Pesticide monitoring programs on all phases of*

217

the environment should be continued. In the case of air (and wildlife) the present programs should be extended.

Recommendation P2: *For purposes of chemical analysis, research should be pursued on the development of more adequate methods for the separation of minute amounts of pesticides from water and air.*

Recommendation P3: *Research should be expanded on the toxicity of pesticides when they are inhaled as opposed to dermal exposure or oral intake.*

MINIMIZING CONTAMINATION OF THE ENVIRONMENT
WITH PESTICIDES

Clearly it is desirable to minimize contamination of the environment by pesticides, and the problem is amenable to attack from several directions:

- Use of the minimum amount of pesticide.
- Modification of application equipment.
- Modification of formulation.
- Eradication of pests.
- Use of more effective pesticides.
- Nonchemical methods of pest control.

Use of minimum amount of pesticide

More than the minimum required amount of pesticide is sometimes used because the threat of invasion by pests causes farmers to spray at regular intervals whether pests are present or not. Cotton, for example, is often sprayed every five, seven, or 10 days. Continuous careful professional monitoring of developing insect populations should make it possible to reduce the number of such scheduled treatments to the minimum actually required. Unnecessary applications can also be reduced by determining the critical period for treatment, which may depend on the life cycle and behavior of both crop and pest. One instance is treatment for sugarcane borer in Louisiana, which was found to be largely wasted after August (112).

Another way to decrease the amount of pesticide used is to apply only the amount required to effect economic control. In some cases, only 75% control of a pest may prevent a decrease in crop yield.

A third approach is to treat only those areas that are heavily infested by the pest. When the entire watershed of an oak-hickory forest in the Nantahala Mountains in North Carolina was treated for elm spanworm, 0.346 ppb of DDT was found in the mountain water. When DDT was applied only to the 49% of the forest that was infested, its residues could not be detected in the water (68). A study of treatment of 525,000 acres in Salmon National Forest for spruce budworm showed that the target insects were effectively controlled by treating less than 10% of the entire area (30).

Modification of application equipment

Marked reduction in the amount of pesticide used could be achieved in many cases by using improved application equipment. The importance of the quality of application is evident in the results of a study of swath patterns after an aerial application of granules (109). The study was made under conditions as nearly ideal as possible, but still only about 17% of the material was applied at the proper rate (Fig. 1).

The application of dust formulations of pesticides presents several

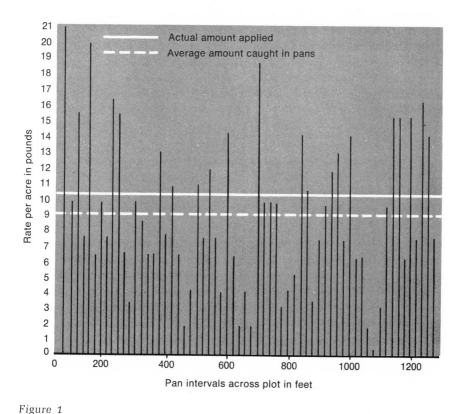

Figure 1

Inefficiency of standard aerial applicator as shown by swath pattern study

Pans spread across test plot at 20-foot intervals collected granules spread by standard airborne application equipment. Amounts caught in pans show variability of distribution pattern. Only about 17% of material was applied at proper rate.

SOURCE: Lofgren, C. S., "Large Scale Tests to Evaluate Multiple Low Dosages of Heptachlor," Report of Methods Improvement Section, Plant Pest Control Division, ARS, U.S. Dept. of Agr., Gulfport, Miss., 1959.

problems. A study of commercial dusting equipment showed that in many cases the pesticide and clay separate from each other during application, resulting in uneven deposits of the toxicant (26).

More uniform application would reduce the total amount of pesticide required. Another study showed that only 10 to 20% of the dust discharged from a conventional duster was deposited on the plant surface at which it was aimed (22).

Improved application of dusts may be possible with electrostatic equipment, which produces charged particles. In two tests on sweet corn, an electrostatic duster deposited a 57% higher concentration of DDT with positively charged particles than with uncharged particles, and a 36% higher concentration with negatively charged particles (71). Similar results were obtained in applications to cowpeas.

Equipment that can be used to apply low volumes of highly concentrated insecticide formulations, or even the technical material, by air promises to be of great help in reducing the amount of pesticide needed to control some pests (121). This low volume technique has been used to treat the boll weevil with malathion (25).

Overall, the development of better application equipment requires coordinated effort among biologists, agricultural engineers, and applicators. Unfortunately, such coordination is often minimal (29).

Modification of formulation

Improved formulations of pesticides could reduce the amount of chemical required to control pests. A small amount of Piccopale resin used as an additive in a granular formulation of heptachlor increased the persistence of the insecticide in soil to 250% of its persistence when applied in a standard liquid formulation (Table 9). The additive apparently prevented heptachlor from vaporizing and leaving the soil (11). Less total insecticide would thus have to be applied in such a formulation to achieve the same degree of control as with the liquid formulation. A similar effect was found in laboratory work in which two cellulose ether polymers were used as additives with Phosdrin. They more than doubled the residual effectiveness of Phosdrin against Mexican bean beetles (4). Research on additives for liquid formulations that would help to "fix" the pesticide to the plant might be fruitful. Losses caused by washing off by rain could be reduced by such means, allowing use of less chemical and reducing contamination of runoff water.

Additives in the formulation might also improve the performance of systemic insecticides, which are taken up by the plant and then act against pests who feed on it. Three quaternary ammonium salts added to Zectran formulations increased the uptake of the insecticide by cotton plants, thus increasing its effectiveness and reducing the dose required to control the pest (118).

In the use of granular heptachlor against the imported fire ant (89), it was possible to reduce the dosage from 2 pounds per acre to 1.25 pounds by removing 80% by weight of the fine particles from the formu-

Table 9
The effect of additives on persistence of heptachlor in soil

Additive [a]	Heptachlor applied [b]	Residue found [b] As Heptachlor	As Heptachlor epoxide	Total	Per cent insecticide remaining
lube oil	0.71 ppm	.09 ppm	.04 ppm	.13 ppm	18%
Piccopale resin	0.87	.39	.06	.45	52
alkylated polystyrene	0.83	.21	.04	.25	30
aromatic plasticizer	0.80	.19	.04	.23	29
heavy aromatic naphtha	0.81	.11	.06	.17	21

[a] Used at twice the level of heptachlor.
[b] Calculated on basis that all insecticide is in top inch of soil.

Addition of Piccopale resin to granular heptachlor formulation increased persistence of insecticide in soil more than did other additives. Increased persistence would allow less pesticide to be used to achieve same effect on pests over same period of time.

SOURCE: Annual Report, Methods Improvement Laboratory, Plant Pest Control Division, Agricultural Research Service, U.S. Department of Agriculture, 1959-1960, p. 13. Plots treated Oct. 1, 1959 and sampled Nov. 12, 1959.

lation. The lower dose rate was permitted by the elimination of the loss of active ingredient due to drift of the finer particles away from the target area.

Application of insecticides as liquefied gas aerosols can also reduce the dosage required. Extensive studies with pea aphid showed that only half as much DDT was required per acre with an aerosol formulation as with a dust (46). Furthermore, heavy rain occurring immediately after application did not reduce the effectiveness of control by the aerosol formulation (12, 45). Aerosol application has also been used against Japanese beetle on sweet corn and Mexican bean beetle on stringbeans (12). The aerosol method apparently produces particles of concentrated insecticide that stick tenaciously to the plant surfaces and are not removed by rainfall. However, little recent work has been reported on the use of the technique.

Eradication of pests

A revolutionary and most important means of minimizing environmental contamination by pesticides is to eradicate the pest, thus eliminating the need for the pesticide (146). In recent years, the Mediterranean fruit fly has been eradicated in Florida (37) and the screw worm fly in the southeastern U.S. and almost throughout the country (95). Other examples include the Khapra beetle (95), the melon fly (119), the Parlatoria date scale (32), and the citrus black fly (142). Eradication is being tried with the imported fire ant and the cereal leaf beetle. The Mediterranean fruit fly was eradicated from Texas in its most recent incursion into this country (59). Eradication of just three pests—the boll weevil, the bollworm, and the codling moth—could reduce the amount of insecticide applied annually in the U.S. by an estimated 40% (70).

The cost of eradicating a pest may not be excessive in view of the damage the pest does and the cost of successive years of controlling it. The screw worm fly was eradicated from the Southeast at a cost estimated to be equivalent to less than half the damage that the pest could do in a single year if it were uncontrolled. More recently (1968), several new screw worm infestations have occurred. The cost of eliminating the Mediterranean fruit fly from Florida was less than the cost of the annual quarantine and regulatory measures involved in living with the pest (145).

Both biological and chemical methods have been used to eradicate pests. With the screw worm, millions of the maggots were raised artificially, the pupae were treated with gamma radiation from cobalt-60, and the resulting sterile male flies were released to compete with native flies. The fly was eradicated from the Southeast in a year and a half.

With the Mediterranean fruit fly in Florida, the infested area was bounded by traps baited with a potent synthetic sex attractant (15), a protein hydrolyzate, and malathion. Only 4 fluid ounces of technical malathion per acre were required in this bait. Since the flies are attracted to the bait, it is effective even on those flies that normally would be protected from direct spray by foliage or other cover. The bait has injured no wildlife or humans and has not harmed the aquatic environment.

Use of more effective pesticides

The ideal pesticide should be as effective as possible against one or several pests and as safe as possible to all other forms of life, including beneficial insects and predators, fish and other wildlife, domestic animals, and man. Only compounds that degrade rapidly in the environment should be used. These objectives are extremely difficult to achieve, but progress has been made in many instances.

One example is Mirex bait (110, 111), which was developed in the fire ant control program. Mirex, a chlorinated hydrocarbon related to chlordane, exhibits extremely low toxicity to mammals. It is possible with 2 to 4 grams of this active ingredient to eradicate the imported fire ant on 1 acre of land. Use of the bait has caused no residue problems. No harm to wildlife has been reported, and no harm to the aquatic environment has been observed.

The biological efficacy of pesticides might also be increased by synergists. Much laboratory effort has been spent on developing synergists for organophosphorus and carbamate insecticides,* but little of this work has been reduced to practice. One group, for example, was able to show that certain synergists increased the insecticidal action of organophosphorus compounds applied directly to boll weevils, but they were not able to extend the treatment successfully to on-plant control of the insect

---

* See references 56, 57, 58, 66, 85, 143, 165.

(23). However, the development of better synergists and methods of application may yet make it practical to increase the activity of systemic insecticides in plants. Many of the studies of synergism have been made to solve problems caused by insects' having become resistant to pesticides, but the same principle could be applied to increase the efficacy of the materials before their use is developed extensively.

The need for more effective pesticides will generate a growing need for chemical tools such as selective lethal agents, chemosterilants, synthetic attractants, and systemic repellents (52). An equally important problem, however, is to insure that these superior molecules replace the less desirable compounds in practical pest control (122).

Nonchemical methods of pest control

Among nonchemical methods of pest control the most sensational examples are the use of the sterile male technique to eradicate the screw worm fly, first from the Island of Curacao, then from the southeastern U.S., and then in Texas. (The tremendous effort in Texas, though successful, requires a wide buffer zone in Mexico to keep Texas and the Plains States free of the screw worm.) There are, however, many other nonchemical means of pest control, and a number of them have been in use for years (31).

Quarantine, preventing the spread of pests, is perhaps the most effective nonchemical way to combat them. In recent years, the U.S. has been unusually successful at quarantine. Notable exceptions are the infestation of the central U.S. by the cereal leaf beetle, the infestation of Hawaii by the African snail, and repeated invasions by the Khapra beetle. In fiscal 1966, plant quarantine inspectors made 34,641 interceptions of diseases, insects, and other plant pests that otherwise might have invaded the U.S. (172). One effective way to prevent invasion of pests from other countries is to assist those countries in fighting and, possibly, eradicating the pests. This is being done in Mexico with the screw worm fly and the citrus black fly, and in Costa Rica with the Mediterranean fruit fly.

Biological control, the introduction of predators or pathogens to fight a specific pest, has been used for a long time. The Vedalia beetle, a very early example, was introduced in California more than 75 years ago to fight cottony cushion scale in citrus orchards.

One simple nonchemical control method is to destroy the stalks after harvesting cotton and corn. The method is still very effective in preventing over-wintering of several insect pests.

In controlling mosquitoes in marshes, draining was considered the best approach at one time. More recently, permanent impoundment of marshes has shown promise as a means of decreasing mosquito breeding areas without removing the habitat of water birds and other marsh life. Studies in Florida have shown that the number of birds that use impounded marshes is 10 times the number that use the unimpounded ones (170). The impoundments provide more accessible open water and more of the fish and submerged aquatic plants that birds feed on.

If control programs are arranged so that parasites and predators of pests suffer minimum damage, much of the chemical control that otherwise would be required can be avoided. On a broader basis, control practices of the future will consider all aspects of the given situation: the pest and its biology, the available control methods, and the consequences of using them singly or in combination. Chemicals will remain a major weapon against pests for the foreseeable future, but the trend is toward integrated pest control: the application of appropriate combinations of chemicals, biological control, cultivation practices, and a range of other methods to achieve economic control with minimum adverse effect.

Recommendations: minimizing contamination of the environment with pesticides

Recommendation P4: *An extensive educational program at all government levels is required to teach all pesticide users the optimum methods of pest control.*

Recommendation P5: *Research on biological and cultural methods of pest control should be continued.*

Recommendation P6: *Persistent pesticides should only be used in minimal amounts and under conditions where they have been shown not to cause widespread contamination of the environment. Where possible, highly-persistent materials should be replaced by rapidly degradable materials.*

PESTICIDES AND WILDLIFE

Although pesticides have been used commonly and increasingly for the better part of a century, only in the 1960's have scientists begun seriously to study their effects on wildlife and other nonpest organisms and their environment. The data required to support judgments of the hazard to wildlife thus have been meager until very recent years. In the past decade, however, research has expanded remarkably on the infinitely varied problems of pesticide-wildlife relationships.*

Occurrence of residues

The occurrence of pesticide residues in wildlife can be illustrated by contrasting two areas: California, where pesticides are used heavily, and where residues in wildlife have been studied intensively for years; and Antarctica, where neither condition holds. Such a contrast highlights the frequency, types, and amounts of residues. In addition, an area more distant than Antarctica from the points of use of pesticides could not be found; contrasting that continent with California suggests differences in the two ecologies that can become the meat of significant judgments.

Between 1963 and 1965, the California Department of Fish and Game and the federal Bureau of Sports Fisheries and Wildlife collected 2100 samples from 86 species of California wildlife and their immediate en-

---

* See references 54, 67, 128, 144, 151, 153, 156, 171.

vironments (92). More than half of these samples were analyzed individually for residues, and many of the rest were included in analyses of composite residues. The animals came from throughout California and undoubtedly differed in the degree to which they had been exposed to pesticides.

The study showed that residues of chlorinated hydrocarbon pesticides were present almost universally. The general conclusions were these:

• Residues were common both in wildlife and in their environment.

• Species which depend on aquatic or wetland habitats appear to be exposed more heavily to insecticide residues than are species who depend on dry habitats.

• The exceptions among the dry-land species are carnivorous forms, such as predatory birds, which depend on contaminated foods.

• The moderate to high levels of residues found in the tissues of some species probably result less from direct exposure than from the biological concentration associated with the food chain.

Most samples of water in the California study contained residues. Particulate matter suspended in water, which tends to adsorb residues, often contained higher levels than unfiltered water or bottom sediments. Suspended material filtered from water contained from 10,000 to 100,000 times the level of residue remaining in the water after filtration. Soils from both arid and marsh lands contained low levels of residues.

Residues in the tissues of animals ranging from insects through birds varied according to the likely exposure. However, animals from untreated areas usually contained residues in their fatty tissue. Tule elk, for example, averaged about 14 ppm of DDT and its metabolic breakdown products in their fat (92), roughly the same level as in humans.

Some species contained very high residues, either because they were intensely exposed on agricultural land or because of peculiarities in their feeding habits. Ring-necked pheasants from the rice-growing areas of the Sacramento Valley, for example, showed residues of several pesticides. They averaged about 58 ppm of DDT alone, with an upper limit of about 2770 ppm.

Waterfowl and all carnivorous birds showed moderate to high values. Residues of DDT, toxaphene, and dieldrin were common in birds that eat fish. Species of birds that had high residue levels in their fat normally had higher concentrations in their ovaries and eggs. Fish, as expected, contained residues, and they were present in all species who swim up rivers from the sea to breed. Predatory fish contained the highest levels.

Wildlife in Antarctica differed from that in California in three major ways (65, 162): Residues, where present, were very low; only certain groups of animals contained them; and no residues could be found in the physical environment, including samples of snow and water from widely separated points.

Extensive sampling of invertebrate wildlife detected no measurable residues of DDT and DDE (a conversion product of DDT in the body).

About one quarter of the Adelie penguin and Weddell seal samples contained small amounts of residues of DDT and DDE. All samples of adult Skua (a wide-ranging bird of the gull family) contained residues. Overall, the highest residues found were 2.8 ppm of DDE in Skuas, 0.44 ppm of DDT in fish, 0.18 ppm of DDT in penguins, and 0.12 ppm of DDT in seals. All of these species but the Skuas are limited to the edge of the Antarctic continent.

These residues in Antarctic wildlife have raised some interesting questions. The important points are that the residues are present, and that they occur in a pattern that suggests that transferral via the food chain is involved. There is no evidence that the residues found are harming the wildlife.

Residue transfer and response of species

Pesticide residues in animal tissue originate in an environment that normally contains traces of residue, which normally enter the animal food chain in contaminated foods. Contaminated food must be essentially the only way in which land-dwelling animals acquire residues in their tissues. These residues are confined to the few pesticides that are magnified in the food chain. Primarily these are the chlorinated hydrocarbons; the residues of most other pesticides are metabolized.

Contaminated feeds are important sources of residues in aquatic animals, too, but they are particularly important in secondary links in the food chain. Residues may first enter the aquatic food chain because of the tendency of some pesticides to be adsorbed on particles suspended in the water. Suspended particles, and the adsorbed residues, then are concentrated by organisms that obtain food by filtering it from the water. The particles are only incidentally associated with food.

Also, there is increasing evidence that aquatic organisms in water that contains sublethal amounts of pesticides will acquire residues directly through the gills and skin [5]. In one experiment [38], 20 micrograms (20 millionths of a gram) per liter of DDT was added to an experimental aquatic environment. The DDT was labeled with radioactive carbon-14, which allows the material to be traced by measuring the radioactivity it emits. After 14 days, the water contained 0.42 microgram per liter of DDT, the bottom soil 0.006 ppm, and the vegetation 15.6 ppm. Snails in the system contained 0.16 ppm, and bluegill sunfish 1.0 ppm. The habits of these animals make it clear that they did not acquire all of these residues by feeding. Another study suggests that a planktonic invertebrate can pick up residues of herbicides directly [42].

The fact that pesticide residues can be degraded to compounds that also are significantly toxic poses two problems in evaluating biological effects: selection of analytical methods that will detect both the parent residue and its significant conversion products; and assessment of the significance of the residues found. The conditioning influences and interactions in an ecological system, moreover, are much more complex than in the laboratory. Many scientists have been aware of these difficulties, but only recently have data begun to come from an approach to toxicology that is based on chemistry and oriented toward ecology. Such an approach involves three steps:

- Study of persistent residues in soils, plants, and water.
- Study of the influences of life forms on the rate and character of the degradation of the residues.
- Study of the effect of the residues on the biological systems in which they are present.

The first of these steps is exemplified by research that showed the persistence and initial movements of DDT and its conversion products in a farm pond (21). The second is illustrated by research that showed that DDT conversion rates vary with the quality of the water (126). In particular, DDT was converted more quickly to DDD where plants and animals were abundant in water. There is also evidence that DDT degrades more slowly in the tissue of an animal from a cold mountain lake than in the tissue of one from a warm lowland lake (157). Intestinal action can also contribute to biological degradation of pesticide residues (120, 126, 140). Intense research at these two levels of examination is badly needed.

At the third level of examination, the effects of residues on biological systems, it is clear that different species respond in different ways to the same level of residue. Thus chemical analysis of residues and their conversion products produces only part of the required information. Other kinds of information are needed to assess the biological importance of residues.

The differing response of different species to residues is exemplified among birds, although a definite cause-and-effect relationship between pesticide residues and the decline of some species of birds has yet to be established. In Great Britain, as in the U.S., most birds contain pesticide residues. Herons seem to carry the heaviest residue loads of all birds, yet their numbers are not declining, nor do they seem to be suffering other physiological impairment. On the other hand, several species of carnivorous birds that, like herons, are at the end of the food chain, also carry heavy loads, and their numbers are declining. Among them are the kingfishers, the golden eagle, the peregrine falcon, the sparrow hawk, and the Bermuda petrel (128, 185).

Other work on correlations between residues and declining species shows that ring-necked pheasants in California carry almost twice the average load of Western grebes (87, 92, 157). In both cases, high residue loads seem to inhibit reproduction, but the effect is scarcely noticeable in the pheasants, while reproduction among Western grebes is virtually at a standstill at some locations. In contrast, fish taken from Clear Lake, Calif., where Western grebes are noticeably affected by residue loads, carry even higher loads without any seeming ill effects.

The physiological bases of the differing response of different species to pesticide residues are essentially unknown. The differences appear to be innate in the species. It is known, however, that relative immunity

to residues can be acquired by vertebrates that live in heavily contaminated environments and reproduce selectively for resistance. The
only such species in nature known to date to have acquired relative immunity to residues are fish and frogs in the Mississippi Delta region
(174). The biological processes involved seem not to differ from those
by which insects acquire resistance to insecticides. Resistance to DDT
has been produced experimentally in other fish and in mice (38, 93, 135,
136). Indeed, the U.S. Fish and Wildlife Service is currently experimenting
with selective breeding as a means of producing rainbow trout resistant
to DDT.

Yet producing insecticide-resistant vertebrates, whether or not intentionally, does not necessarily safeguard wildlife. The "protection" acquired by one species may well pose a hazard to others. In one study
(155), 95% of the vertebrate predators (11 species) offered endrin-resistant
mosquito fish died after consuming only one fish. Ecologic effects may
be profound from acquired resistance.

Consequences of residues: measurement and judgment

The biggest single problem with pesticide residues in natural environments is the movement of persistent residues along food chains, coupled
with the biological concentration of the residues at each step in the
chain. The movement of residues along food chains can be traced in two
general ways: by inference or by direct measurement.

The inferential method depends on chemical analyses of residues, the
biology of the species involved, and the linkage of residue levels with
biological events. The biological events include individual death rates,
abrupt decline in numbers of species, and inhibition of reproduction in
species, population-wide. In the three best documented examples of the
inferential method, pronounced mortality or inhibition of reproduction
occurred among the species at the end of the food chain: the robin (9),
the grebe (81, 87), and the lake trout (24). The three sequences are these:

- DDT—leaf—litter—earthworm—robin
- DDT—lake—plankton—fish—grebe
- DDT—lake—plankton—small fish—lake trout

Similar sequences have been inferred since, but the one of greatest
current concern is the linkage of residues in birds' eggs, inhibition of
reproduction, and decline of the species. The best examples are the
eagles, falcons, and hawks. These species are difficult to study, at best,
and experiments are generally impossible. However, the bald eagle and
peregrine falcon have both declined rapidly in numbers in recent years
(82). Residue analysis of their eggs, counts of birds, and direct observation of nests in Great Britain, the U.S., and Canada suggest that the
phenomenon may be real (54, 92, 128, 185). Until recently the linkage
was entirely inferential.

It has now been suggested, however, that population declines in some
birds may be linked to aberrant calcium metabolism correlated with
known pesticide residues in bird tissues. Derangement of calcium metab-

olism could result from the breakdown of steroids by microsomal enzymes in the liver induced by low dietary levels of the chlorinated hydrocarbons (137, 161, 180). There is currently some evidence to show declines in egg weight and eggshell thickness and increases in the egg-breaking habit among birds who prey on animals and fish (83, 149, 157).

Direct measurement of the movement of residues along food chains has begun with the labeling of pesticides with radioactive isotopes in the field (139). The labeled residues can be traced by measuring their radioactive emissions. Such methods allow the pathways taken by residues to be described much more precisely than by the inferential method, and allow much more data to be gathered as well. One major handicap in direct measurement is that the degradation products for some pesticides are not known.

In general, direct measurement of residues along food chains has confirmed conclusions reached earlier by inference. Where a large body of data have already been built up by experiment and observation, residue levels and biological events, whether analyzed chemically or radioactively, can be correlated directly. This situation exists now for many game birds and fish.

Further work required

Serious appraisal of the continued presence of pesticide residues in wildlife requires study in several areas:

- When does a given residue load kill individual organisms or inhibit them physiologically?
- When is a species declining in numbers because of residues?
- When are the levels of residues in the environment increasing?

The first of these questions involves close study of the toxicology of a variety of species of wildlife. A notable effort of this kind is under way at the Patuxent Research Refuge of the U.S. Fish and Wildlife Service (54). The second and third questions involve monitoring schemes. Various state and federal agencies collect residue data on wildlife, but as yet there is no overall environmental monitoring program that applies strictly to wildlife. Current efforts depend heavily on the established monitoring activities of the U.S. Department of Agriculture, the Department of Health, Education, and Welfare, and other agencies.

Attempts to correlate residue levels with biological response have led to the suggestion that only certain organs be collected from wildlife for analysis. Residues vary greatly in concentration in some organs, are often stored passively, and may bear no relationship to observed responses. Residues in brain tissue seem to correlate most closely with death and behavioral response (14, 164, 186). As yet, however, there is no concerted attempt to coordinate the collection of indicator organs even under a loose monitoring program.

Attempts to monitor declines in species or broader involvement of life forms with pesticides are even less well advanced. Indicator species that can be used for monitoring should be abundant, widely distributed, and easy to collect. Workers in Great Britain have suggested that the eggs of seabirds should be used to measure changes in general contamination, and that the Northern Pike and Eel should be suitable for studying local conditions (127). No formal suggestions have been made toward establishing indicator species in North America.

International monitoring requires cosmopolitan species whose feeding habits do not vary over their ranges. The single organization that could coordinate an international monitoring program is the International Union for the Conservation of Nature. That body is currently considering the question of indicator species. One expected consequence of the selection of such species is that tolerances will be established for the permissible levels of pesticide residues in the various phases of the environment.

Our ultimate concern must lie with inhibition by pesticide residues of productivity in entire ecosystems. No one yet has been able to conclude that such inhibition is taking place, but presumptive evidence is strong. DDT strongly reduces photosynthetic rates in marine phytoplankton (184). Estuarine and marine organisms are commonly contaminated, and there seems to be evidence of community-wide reproductive inhibition (27, 152, 154, 183). Broader research support is required before a final judgment can be made on changes in basal productivity induced by the continuing presence of pesticide residues in the environment.

Recommendations: pesticides and wildlife

Recommendation P7: *More research should be conducted on the relationship between environmental pesticide contaminants and wildlife. This research, though based on chemistry and biology, should be done in an ecological context.*

PESTICIDES AND HUMAN HEALTH

Humans have been poisoned fatally by most of the major pesticides, and there is little doubt that under proper conditions almost all pesticides can cause acute illness. Whether caused by overexposure at work, accidental ingestion, or attempts at suicide, acute illness is well documented for many pesticides, though not for all (74, 76, 94). The problem of acute intoxication has been approached by many means, including warning labels on the product and education of users and physicians. The success of current control efforts can best be gauged by the fact that despite the vast increase in the availability and use of pesticides, the incidence of fatal poisoning in the U.S. has held virtually constant at 1 per 1 million population per year over a 25-year period (75).

Although it is actually outside the province of this review, an analysis of pesticide deaths in the U.S. is of interest. In 1956, 152 deaths in the U.S. were caused by all pesticides. Of these, 104 were caused by compounds older than DDT. Thirty-five deaths were associated definitely with new synthetic pesticides, and some of the 12 deaths caused by unidentified pesticides may also have been associated with these materials. During 1956, 94 of the 152 deaths were of children through age 9, and 78 were of children 3 years old or younger. These data illustrate dramatically the necessity for great care in handling not only pesticides, but all toxic materials, where children may have access to them (77).

Pesticidal compounds should all be handled with caution, regardless of the degree of toxicity indicated by experiments on animals. It is difficult to evaluate the hazard to humans on the basis of animal data (78), and the possibility always exists that the toxicity of a compound will vary markedly with the species. An excellent manual has been published on the safe use of pesticides (158).

Reported episodes of illness caused by ingestion of food contaminated by a pesticide have been more common in foreign countries than in the U.S. In some instances the contamination has been accidental (44); in others people have eaten foodstuffs, such as seed grain, that had been deliberately treated with a pesticide. In one episode in Turkey, seed grain treated with hexachlorobenzene, an insecticide, was eaten, instead of being planted. The result was more than 3000 cases of illness and 330 deaths (28). In the U.S., there is no record of major food poisoning episodes caused by contamination by pesticides. In two cases in this country people applied the insecticides toxaphene and nicotine to their gardens, ate the crops within the next few days, and became seriously ill. The toxaphene residue found on the crop was 3000 ppm, and the nicotine residue was similar. These levels are in marked contrast with the established tolerances, which were zero in both cases (76).

Long-term, low-level exposure

These acute or subacute episodes are relatively clear-cut, but next must be faced the need to evaluate the effects of long-term exposure of humans to comparatively low levels of many pesticides in the environment and in the body itself. Results of studies in the U.S. and elsewhere generally agree that humans now carry a body burden of 10 to 20 ppm of chlorinated hydrocarbon insecticides and their conversion products in fatty tissue (Tables 10, 11, page 232). Much of the total consists of DDT and related materials, but it also includes dieldrin, BHC, and heptachlor epoxide (43, 86, 148, 187). Only DDT has been measured for a significant length of time in people, and it appears to have reached a constant level of concentration in the body fat of the population of the U.S. (80). The levels found for the other compounds, which have not been in use as long as DDT, are extremely low. It is not yet possible to state conclusively whether they have reached a constant concentration in the body. There is no evidence at present that any other group of pesticides is stored in the body or that the body contains any metabolites resulting from the degradation of pesticides to which the population is regularly exposed.

The chlorinated hydrocarbon insecticides, particularly DDT, have been in the human environment for more than 20 years. The older pesticides—lead arsenate, mercurials, copper compounds, and other inorganic materials—have been in the environment throughout this century and to a considerable extent in the last. What effect have they had? Simply put,

Table 10

Concentration of DDT-derived material in body fat

Country	Year	No. of samples	Analysis method	DDT[a] (ppm)	DDE as DDT (ppm)	Total[b] as DDT (ppm)	DDE as DDT (% of total)
United States	1961-62	28	Colorimetric	3.7	6.9	10.6	65
			GLC[c]	2.4	4.3	6.7	64
France	1962-63	5	Colorimetric	3.1	6.5	9.6	68
			GLC[c]	3.5	5.3	8.8	60
India (Delhi area, civilian)	1964	24	Colorimetric	18	12	30	40
			GLC[c]	14.3	12.9	27.2	47
India (other cities, military)	1964	11	Colorimetric	7	4	11	36
			GLC[c]	4.7	7.1	11.8	60

[a] Includes p,p'- and o,p'-DDT.
[b] Includes all detected isomers of DDT and DDE, but not DDD.
[c] Gas-liquid chromatography.

SOURCE: Hayes, W. J., "Monitoring Food and People for Pesticide Content," in "Scientific Aspects of Pest Control," Publication 1402, National Academy of Sciences—National Research Council, Washington, D.C., 1966.

Table 11

Average concentration of chlorinated hydrocarbon pesticides (other than those derived from DDT) in body fat of the general population of various countries[a]

Country	Year	No. of samples	Storage Level in Body Fat (ppm) BHC isomers	dieldrin	endrin	Heptachlor epoxide
United States	1961-62	28	0.20	0.15	[b]	[b]
United States	1962-63	282	0.57	0.11[c]	nd	[b]
United States	1964	64	[b]	0.31	<0.02	0.10
United States	1964	25	0.60	0.29	<0.03	0.24
England	1961-62	131	[b]	0.21	[b]	[b]
England	1963-64	65	0.42	0.26	[b]	<0.1
England	1964	100	0.02[d]	0.21	<0.02	<0.01
France	1961	10	1.19	[b]	[b]	[b]
India	1964	35	1.43	0.04	nd	nd

[a] All analyses were carried out by gas-liquid chromatography.
[b] The specific pesticide was not tested for, or at least such testing was not mentioned in the published paper. If the pesticide was looked for but not detected, the result is shown as less than the sensitivity of the method used when this value is known; or, if the limit of sensitivity is not known, the result is simply shown as not detectable (nd).
[c] Only 64 samples were tested for dieldrin content.
[d] Only 20 samples were tested for BHC content.

SOURCE: Hayes, W. J., "Monitoring Food and People for Pesticide Content," in "Scientific Aspects of Pest Control," Publication 1402, National Academy of Sciences—National Research Council, Washington, D.C., 1966.

they have had no detectable effect on the population. It is not possible to prove a negative, to prove that no effects are occurring. It is possible, however, to examine the basis for the inability to detect any such effects.

Volunteers have tolerated 35 milligrams of DDT per man per day for periods of 21 months with no detectable effect except that they stored and excreted more of the pesticide's breakdown products than they would have normally. This dosage rate is about 200 times the rate found in restaurant meals in the U.S. in 1953 and 1954 (176) and close to 1000 times the average in 1962 (49) (Table 12, page 234). The results of a 21-month study cannot be extrapolated to a lifetime, but the absence of detectable effects is reassuring. Data on the rates of death and illness in the U.S. for the period 1945-65, when DDT came into wide use, show no sharp deviation from the trends in 1925-45, the period immediately preceding the introduction of DDT (175).

It has been suggested that some pesticides may cause leukemia. However, the trend in the occurrence of leukemia has not changed since DDT and the other new organic pesticides were introduced (Fig. 2, page 235). Nor has there been a sharp change in the incidence of aplastic anemia, agranulocytosis, or other diseases of the blood that have sometimes been attributed to pesticides. If individual cases of these diseases are due to pesticides, the evidence is not available.

Suggestions that pesticides cause illness not known to be related to the type of illness caused by acute poisoning have usually stressed diseases whose causes are unknown. Infectious hepatitis has been mentioned as a disease that may be related to exposure to pesticides, but this disease, the camp jaundice of the Civil War, was present long before the modern pesticides. Some have claimed that certain people are hypersensitive or allergic to pesticides (76), but the evidence for such claims is too sparse to allow them to be discussed objectively and in detail. In the past few years it has been found that chlordane, DDT, and some other pesticides accelerate their own breakdown in the body by causing the enzymes in the liver that control the metabolic process to proliferate. This effect may or may not prove to be beneficial (73).

Some have suggested that long-term exposure to low levels of pesticides in the environment may cause cancer (33). Accurate evaluation of this hazard must await a detailed analysis of how chemical carcinogens act to cause cancer. If a significant fraction of human cancer of unknown origin is caused by chemicals, they are likely to be chemicals of natural origin (10). Pesticides display no carcinogenic activity even faintly comparable to that of some compounds that are widespread in nature. Examples include aflatoxin, cycasin, and the pymolozidine alkaloids.

Work is needed on the evaluation of the effects of known chemical carcinogens in relation to the size of the dose. The results of such work should allow more reasonable assessment of the carcinogenic activity of all new compounds (including pesticides) to which man is exposed.

The number of illnesses and deaths known to have been caused by ac-

Table 12

Estimated daily content of DDT and DDE in complete meals in the United States

Year / Location	Source	Number	DDT[a]	DDE as[a] DDT	Total[a] as DDT	DDE as DDT (% of total)
1953-1954						
Wenatchee, Wash.	Restaurant	18	0.178	0.102	0.280	37
Tacoma, Wash.	Prison	7	0.116	0.063	0.179	35
1954-1955						
Tallahassee, Fla.	Prison	12	0.202	0.056	0.258	21
1956-1957						
Walla Walla, Wash.	College dining room for meat abstainers	11	0.041	0.027	0.068	39
1959-1960						
Anchorage, Alaska	Hospital	3	0.184	0.029	0.213	14
1961-1962 Washington, D. C. Baltimore, Md. Atlanta, Ga. Minneapolis, Minn. San Francisco, Cal.	Market Basket survey	36[b]	0.026[c]	0.017[c]	0.043[c]	40[c]
1962-1964						
Wenatchee, Wash.	Restaurant	12	0.038	0.049	0.087	56
Wenatchee, Wash.	Household	17	0.314	0.193	0.507	40
1962-1964 Atlanta, Ga. Baltimore, Md. Minneapolis, Minn. St. Louis, Mo. San Francisco, Cal.	Market Basket survey	23[b]	0.023[c]	0.013[c]	0.036[c]	36[c]
1964 Baltimore, Md.	Market Basket survey	1[b]	0.023[c]	0.017[c]	0.040[c]	43[c]

[a] Total daily content in milligrams.

[b] This figure refers to the number of diet samples, each consisting of the total normal 14-day food intake for males 16 to 19 years old, which were tested. In some instances, additional diet samples were taken and aliquots were analyzed for pesticide content of various classes of foodstuffs, but no composite value was given.

[c] The author did not calculate the daily DDT or DDE intake. However, using the author's mean dietary concentrations of DDT and DDE and the mean daily food intake of 3.78 kg from the Market Basket survey, the reviewer has calculated the values shown.

SOURCE: Hayes, W. J., "Monitoring Food and People for Pesticide Content," in "Scientific Aspects of Pest Control," Publication 1402, National Academy of Sciences—National Research Council, Washington, D.C., 1966.

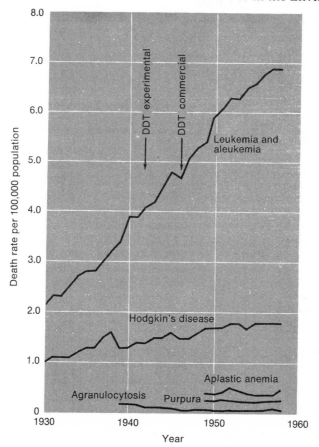

Figure 2

Lack of effect of advent of DDT on death-rate trends for five diseases

Curves show no marked changes in trends in death rates from leukemia and certain diseases of the blood following the introduction of DDT, which has sometimes been suggested as a cause of all of the diseases shown.

SOURCE: Hayes, W. J., "Proceedings of the Short Course on the Occupational Health Aspects of Pesticides," University of Oklahoma, Norman, Okla., 1964.

cidental or deliberate misuse of pesticides is far outweighed by the benefits these chemicals have brought in controlling disease-bearing pests and in increased production of food (138). There is no evidence at present that long-term low-level exposure to pesticides at concentrations approximating those found in the diet or the environment in the U.S. has any deleterious effect on man. At this time, therefore, the net effect of pesticides on human health in the broad sense is positive.

235

Recommendation P8: *Additional research is required on the impact of long-term, low-level exposure to pesticides on humans and other forms of life. In this connection, study is also required of the dose-response relationship of pesticide chemicals suspected of being carcinogens.*

LITERATURE CITED

1. Akesson, N. B., Yates, W. E., "Problems Relating to Application of Agricultural Chemicals and Resulting Drift Residues," *Ann. Rev. Entomol.*, **9**, 285 (1964).

2. Aldrich, R. J., "Residues in Soil," *J. Agr. Food Chem.*, **1**, 257 (1953).

3. Alexander, M., "Biodegradation: Problems of Molecular Recalcitrance and Microbial Fallibility," *Advan. Appl. Microbiol.*, **7**, 35 (1965).

4. Aller, H. E., Dewey, J. E., "Adjuvants Increasing the Residual Activity of Phosdrin," *J. Econ. Entomol.*, **54**, 508 (1961).

5. Allison, D., Kallman, B. J., Cope, O. B., Van Valin, C., "Some Chronic Effects of DDT on Cutthroat Trout," *U.S. Fish Wildlife Serv. Res. Rept.*, **64**, (1964).

6. Anderson, R. B., Everhart, W. H., "Concentrations of DDT in Landlocked Salmon *(Salmo salar)* at Sebago Lake, Maine," *Trans. Am. Fish. Soc.*, **95**, 160 (1966).

7. Antommaria, P., Corn, M., De Maio, L., "Airborne Particulates in Pittsburgh: Association with p,p'-DDT," *Science*, **150**, 1476 (1965).

8. Bailey, G. W., White, J. L., "Review of Adsorption and Desorption of Organic Pesticides by Soil Colloids, with Implications Concerning Pesticide Bioactivity," *J. Agr. Food Chem.*, **12**, 324 (1964).

9. Barker, R. J., "Notes on Some Ecological Effects of DDT Sprayed on Elms," *J. Wildlife Management*, **22**, 269 (1958).

10. Barnes, J. M., "Carcinogenic Hazards from Pesticide Residues," *Residue Rev.*, **13**, 69 (1966).

11. Barthel, W. F., Annual Report, Methods Improvement Laboratory, Plant Pest Control Division, U.S. Dept. Agr., ARS, 1959-1960, p. 13.

12. Barthel, W. F., Unreported Observations from York and Adams County, Pennsylvania Treatments, 1947, unpublished.

13. Batchelor, G. S., Walker, K. C., "Health Hazards Involved in Use of Parathion in Fruit Orchards of North Central Washington," *A.M.A. Arch. Ind. Hygiene Occupational Med.*, **10**, 522 (1954).

14. Bernard, R. F., "DDT Residues in Avian Tissue," *J. Appl. Ecol.*, **3** (Suppl.), 193 (1966).

15. Beroza, M., Green, N., Gertler, S. I., "New Attractants for the Mediterranean Fruit Fly," *J. Agr. Food Chem.*, **9**, 361 (1961).

16. Blodgett, E. C., "A Systemic Arsenic Toxicity of Peach and Apricot on Old Apple Land," *Plant Disease Reptr.*, **25**, 549 (1941).

17. Bodhaine, G. L., "Pesticides in the Boise River Basin," U.S. Geol. Surv., Open-File Rept., Portland, Ore., 1966.

18. Boswell, V. R., Clore, W. J., Pepper, B. B., Taylor, C. B., Gilmer, P. M., Carter, R. L., "Effects of Certain Insecticides in Soil on Crop Plants," *U.S. Dept. Agr. Tech. Bull.* 1121, 1955.

19. Breidenbach, A. W., Gunnerson, C. G., Kawahara, F. K., Lichtenberg, J. J.,

Green, R. S., "Chlorinated Hydrocarbon Pesticides in Major River Basins, 1957-1965," *Publ. Health Repts.* (U.S.) **82**, 139 (1967).

20. Breidenbach, A. W., Lichtenberg, J. J., "DDT and Dieldrin in Rivers: A Report of the National Water Quality Network," *Science,* **141**, 899 (1963).

21. Bridges, W. R., Kallman, B. J., Andrews, A. K., "Persistence of DDT and Its Metabolites in a Farm Pond," *Trans. Am. Fisheries Soc.,* **92**, 421 (1963).

22. Brittain, R. W., Carleton, W. M., "How Surfaces Affect Pesticidal Dust Deposition," *Agr. Eng.,* **38**, 22 (1957).

23. Bull, D. L., Lindquist, D. A., House, V. S., "Synergism of Organophosphorus Systemic Insecticides," *J. Econ. Entomol.,* **58**, 1157 (1965).

24. Burdick, G. E., Harris, E. J., Dean, H. J., Walker, T. M., Skea, J., Colby, D., "Accumulation of DDT In Lake Trout and the Effect on Reproduction," *Trans. Am. Fisheries Soc.,* **93**, 127 (1964).

25. Burges, E. D., "Control of the Boll Weevil with Technical Malathion Applied by Aircraft," *J. Econ. Entomol.,* **58**, 414 (1965).

26. Burkhardt, G., Unpublished Observations on Study of Commercial Dusting Equipment by Agricultural Engineering Department of the University of Maryland, 1946.

27. Butler, P. A., "The Significance of DDT Residues in Estuarine Fauna," in Chemical Fallout, Proc. 1st Rochester Conf. on Environmental Toxicity, Univ. Rochester, 1969.

28. Cam., C., Nigogosyan, G., "Acquired Toxic Porphyria Cutanea Tarda Due to Hexachlorobenzene," *J. Am. Med. Assoc.,* **183**, 88 (1963).

29. Carleton, W. M., Liljedahl, L. A., Irons, F., Hedden, O. K., Brazee, R. D., "Development of Equipment in the Application of Agricultural Chemicals," U.S. Dept. Agr., ARS 20-9 (1960).

30. Casebeer, R. L., "Monitoring the 1964 Spruce Budworm Aerial Spray Project," U.S. Dept. Agr. Forest Serv. (1964).

31. Christenson, L. D., "Application of Sterilization Techniques for Controlling and Eradicating Insect Pests," U.S. Dept. Agr. *ARS 33-110,* 95 (July 1966).

32. Clarkson, M. R., "Exclusion and Eradication *vs.* Reduction of Plant and Animal Pests," Symposium Address, Am. Assoc. Advancement of Science, Dec. 30, 1957, *Publ. Am. Assoc. Advanc. Sci.,* No. 61, 3 (1960).

33. Clayson, D. B., "Chemical Carcinogenesis," Little, Brown and Co., Boston, 1962.

34. Clore, W. J., Westlake, W. E., Walker, K., Boswell, V. R., "Residual Effects of Soil Insecticides on Crop Plants," Wash. State Univ., Wash. Agr. Expt. Stas. 627 (1961).

35. Cohen, J. M., Pinkerton, C., "Widespread Translocation of Pesticides by Air Transport and Rain-out," *Advan. Chem. Ser.* No. 60, American Chemical Society, Washington, D.C., 1966, p. 163.

36. Compton, B., Nair, J. H., III, "Chlorinated Pesticides in Surface and Ground Waters of New York State," Rept. to N.Y. State Dept. Health from Syracuse Univ. Research Corp., April 1966.

37. Cooperative Plant Pest Control Programs, FY 1964, U.S. Dept. Agr., ARS, December 1964.

38. Cope, O. B., "Contamination of the Freshwater Ecosystem by Pesticides," *J. Appl. Ecol.,* **3** (Suppl.), 33 (1966).

39. Cope, O. B., "Effects of DDT Spraying for Spruce Budworm on Fish in the Yellowstone River System," *Trans. Am. Fisheries Soc.,* **90**, 239 (1961).

40. Cottam, C., "Pesticides and Water Pollution," *Proc. Natl. Conf. Water Pollution,* U.S. Dept. HEW, 222 (1960).

41. Croker, R. A., Wilson, A. J., "Kinetics and Effects of DDT in a Tidal Marsh Ditch," *Trans. Am. Fisheries Soc.,* **94,** 152 (1965).

42. Crosby, D. G., Tucker, R. K., "Toxicity of Aquatic Herbicides to *Daphnia magna,*" *Science,* **154,** 289 (1966).

43. Dale, W. E., Quinby, G. E., "Chlorinated Insecticides in the Body Fat of People in the United States," *Science,* **142,** 593 (1963).

44. Davies, G. M., Lewis, I., "Outbreak of Food-Poisoning from Bread Made of Chemically Contaminated Flour," *Brit. Med. J.,* 393 (Aug. 18, 1956).

45. Ditman, L. P., Goodhue, L. D., Personal communication, 1946.

46. Ditman, L. P., Goodhue, L. D., Smith, F. F., Burkhardt, G., "Insecticidal Aerosols for Pea-Aphid Control. II," *J. Econ. Entomol.,* **39,** 199 (1946).

47. Dowler, C. C., Sand, P. F., Robinson, E. L., "Effect of Soil Type on Preplant-ing Soil-Incorporated Herbicides for Witchweed Control," *Weeds,* **11,** 276 (1963).

48. Dugan, P. K., "Influence of Chronic Exposure to Anionic Detergents on Toxicity of Pesticides to Goldfish," *J. Water Pollut. Contr. Fed.,* **39,** 63 (1967).

49. Durham, W. F., Armstrong, J. F., Quinby, G. E., "DDT and DDE Content of Complete Prepared Meals," *Arch. Environmental Health,* **11,** 641 (1965).

50. Durham, W. F., Wolfe, H. R., "Measurement of the Exposure of Workers to Pesticides," *Bull. World Health Organ.,* **26,** 75 (1962).

51. Durum, W. H., "Programs and Plans for Pesticide Monitoring," U.S. Geol. Surv., unpublished report (1965).

52. Dykstra, W. W., Lennon, R. E., "The Role of Chemicals for the Control of Vertebrate Pests," U.S. Dept. Agr. *ARS 33-110,* 29 (1966).

53. Edwards, C. A., "Insecticide Residues in Soils," *Residue Rev.,* **13,** 83 (1966).

54. "Effects of Pesticides on Fish and Wildlife," U.S. Fish Wildlife Serv. Circ., 226, 1965, p. 77.

55. Eisler, R., Edmunds, P. H., "Effects of Endrin on Blood and Tissue Chemis-try of a Marine Fish," *Trans. Am. Fisheries Soc.,* **95,** 153 (1966).

56. Eldefrawi, M. E., Hoskins, W. M., "Relation of the Rate of Penetration and Metabolism to the Toxicity of Sevin to Three Insect Species," *J. Econ. Entomol.,* **54,** 401 (1961).

57. Eldefrawi, M. E., Miskus, R., Sutcher, V., "Methylenedioxyphenyl Deriva-tives as Synergists for Carbamate Insecticides on Susceptible, DDT and Parathion-Resistant Houseflies," *J. Econ. Entomol.,* **53,** 231 (1960).

58. Fahmy, M. A., Gordon, H. T., "Selective Synergism of Carbamate Insecti-cides on Houseflies by Aryloxyalkylamines," *J. Econ. Entomol.,* **58,** 451 (1965).

59. Fancher, C. C., Mediterranean Fruit Fly, Monthly Report, U.S. Dept. Agr., ARS, Plant Pest Control, September 1966.

60. Faust, S. D., "Pollution of the Water Environment by Organic Pesticides," *Clin. Pharmacol. Therap.,* **5,** 677 (1964).

61. Faust, S. D., Suffet, I. H., "Recovery, Separation, and Identification of Or-ganic Pesticides from Natural and Potable Waters," *Residue Rev.,* **15,** 44 (1966).

62. Fish-Pesticide Research Laboratory, Denver, Colo., Unpublished data.

63. Freed, V. H., Vernetti, J., Montgomery, M., "The Soil Behavior of Herbicides as Influenced by Their Physical Properties," *Proc. Western Weed Control Conf.,* **19,** 21 (1962).

64. Gentry, J. W., "Monitoring the Agricultural Use of Pesticides," Natl. Acad. Sci.-Natl. Res. Council Publ. No. 1402, 303 (1966).

65. George, J. L., Frear, D. E. H., "Pesticides in the Antarctic," *J. Appl. Ecol.,* **3** (Suppl.), 155 (1966).

66. Georghiou, G. P., Metcalf, R. L., "Synergism of Carbamate Insecticides with Octachlorodipropyl Ether," *J. Econ. Entomol.,* **54,** 150 (1961).

67. Goodman, G. T., Edwards, R. W., Lambert, J. M., eds., "Ecology and the Industrial Society," John Wiley & Sons, New York, 1965.

68. Grzenda, A. R., Nicholson, H. P., Teasley, J. I., Patric, J. H., "DDT Residues in Mountain Stream Water as Influenced by Treatment Practices," *J. Econ. Entomol.,* **57,** 615 (1964).

69. Gunther, F. A., "Advances in Analytical Detection of Pesticides," Natl. Acad. Sci.—Natl. Res. Council Publ. No. 1402, 276 (1966).

70. Hall, D. G., "Use of Insecticides in the United States," *Bull. Entomol. Soc. Amer.,* **8,** 90 (1962).

71. Harrell, E. A., Bowman, M. C., Hare, W. W., "Field Evaluation of an Electrostatic Duster," *J. Econ. Entomol.,* **58,** 71 (1965).

72. Harris, C. R., Sans, W. W., Miles, J. R. W., "Exploratory Studies on Occurrence of Organochlorine Insecticide Residues in Agricultural Soils in Southwestern Ontario," *J. Agr. Food Chem.,* **14,** 398 (1966).

73. Hart, L. G., Fouts, J. R., "Further Studies on the Stimulation of Hepatic Microsomal Drug Metabolizing Enzymes by DDT and Its Analogs," *Naunyn-Schmiedebergs Arch. Exptl. Pathol. Parmakol.,* **249,** 486 (1965).

74. Hayes, W. J., Jr., "Clinical Handbook on Economic Poisons," Public Health Service, U.S. Dept. Health, Education, and Welfare Publication No. 476, Revised 1963.

75. Hayes, W. J., Jr., "Occurrence of Poisoning by Pesticides," *Arch. Environ. Health,* **9,** 621 (1964).

76. Hayes, W. J., Jr., "Proceedings of the Short Course on the Occupational Health Aspects of Pesticides," University of Oklahoma, Norman, Oklahoma (1964).

77. Hayes, W. J., "Pesticides in Relation to Human Health," *An. Rev. of Entomology,* **5,** 379-404 (1960).

78. Hayes, W. J., "Toxicity of Pesticides to Man: Risks of Present Levels," Proc. Royal Soc. B., **167,** 101-127 (1967).

79. Hayes, W. J., Jr., Dixon, E. M., Batchelor, G. S., Upholt, W. M., "Exposure to Organic Phosphorus Sprays and Occurrence of Selected Symptoms," *Public Health Repts.* (U.S.), **72,** 787 (1957).

80. Hayes, W. J., Jr., Durham, W. F., Cueto, C., Jr., "Effect of Known Repeated Oral Doses of Chlorophenothane (DDT) in Man," *J. Am. Med. Assoc.,* **162,** 890 (1956).

81. Herman, S. G., Garrett, R. L., Rudd, R. L., "Pesticides in the Western Grebe," in Chemical Fallout, Proc. 1st Rochester Conf. on Environmental Toxicity, Univ. Rochester, 1969.

82. Hickey, J. J., "The Population Biology of the Peregrine Falcon," Univ. Wisconsin Press. In press, 1969.

83. Hickey, J. J., Anderson, D. W., "Chlorinated Hydrocarbons and Eggshell Changes in Raptorial and Fish-Eating Birds," *Science,* **162:** 271-273 (1968).

84. Hindin, E., May, D. S., Dunstan, G. H., "Collection and Analysis of Synthetic Organic Pesticides from Surface and Ground Water," *Residue Rev.,* **7,** 130 (1964).

85. Hoffman, R. A., Hopkins, T. L., Lindquist, A. W., "Tests with Pyrethrum

Synergists Combined with Some Organic Phosphorus Compounds Against DDT-Resistant Flies," *J. Econ. Entomol., 47,* 72 (1954).

86. Hoffman, W. S., Fishbein, W. I., Andelman, M. B., "The Pesticide Content of Human Fat Tissue," *Arch. Environmental Health,* **9,** 387 (1964).

87. Hunt, E. G., Bischoff, A. I., "Inimical Effects on Wildlife of Periodic DDD Applications to Clear Lake," *Calif. Fish Game,* **46,** 91 (1960).

88. Ingraham, H. S., "Periodic Report of the Water Quality Surveillance Network 1960 Through 1964," New York State Dept. of Health, Albany, N.Y., 1966.

89. "Interim Federal Specification. Insecticide, heptachlor, granulated," U.S. Dept. Agr., AGR-ARS O-I-00528, March 7, 1961.

90. Jones, J. S., Hatch, M. B., "The Significance of Inorganic Spray Residue Accumulations in Orchard Soils," *Soil Sci.,* **44,** 37 (1937).

91. Kallman, B. J., Cope, O. B., Navarre, R. J., "Distribution and Detoxification of Toxaphene in Clayton Lake, New Mexico," *Trans. Am. Fisheries Soc.,* **91,** 14 (1962).

92. Keith, J. O., Hunt, E. G., "Levels of Insecticide Residues in Fish and Wildlife in California," Trans. 31st N. Amer. Wildlife and Natural Resources Conference, 150 (1966).

93. King, S. F., "Some Effects of DDT on the Guppy and the Brown Trout," U.S. Fish Wildlife Service., Spec. Sci. Rept. (Fisheries), No. 399 (1962).

94. Kleinman, G. D., "Occupational Disease in California Attributed to Pesticides and Other Agricultural Chemicals," Calif. Dept. of Public Health, Bureau of Occupational Health, 1964, 28 pp.

95. Knipling, E. F., "Some Basic Principles in Insect Population Suppression," *Bul. Ent. Soc. of America,* **12** (1), 7 (1966).

96. LeGrand, H. E., "Environmental Framework of Ground-Water Contamination," *Ground Water,* **3,** No. 2 (April 1965).

97. LeGrand, H. E., "Patterns of Contaminated Zones of Water in the Ground," *Water Resources Res.,* **1,** 83 (1965).

98. Lichtenstein, E. P., "Absorption of Some Chlorinated Hydrocarbon Insecticides from Soils into Various Crops," *J. Agr. Food Chem.,* **7,** 430 (1959).

99. Lichtenstein, E. P., "Persistence and Degradation of Pesticides in the Environment," Natl. Acad. Sci.—Natl. Res. Council Publ. No. 1402, 221 (1966).

100. Lichtenstein, E. P., Mueller, C. H., Myrdal, G. R., Schulz, K. R., "Vertical Distribution and Persistence of Insecticidal Residues in Soils as Influenced by Mode of Application and a Cover Crop," *J. Econ. Entomol.,* **55,** 215 (1962).

101. Lichtenstein, E. P., Myrdal, G. R., Schulz, K. R., "Absorption of Insecticidal Residues from Contaminated Soils into Five Carrot Varieties," *J. Agr. Food Chem.,* **13,** 126 (1965).

102. Lichtenstein, E. P., Myrdal, G. R., Schulz, K. R., "Effect of Formulation and Mode of Application of Aldrin on the Loss of Aldrin and Its Epoxide from Soils and Their Translocation into Carrots," *J. Econ. Entomol.,* **57,** 133 (1964).

103. Lichtenstein, E. P., Schulz, K. R., "Effects of Moisture and Microorganisms on the Persistence and Metabolism of Some Organophosphorus Insecticides in Soils, with Special Emphasis on Parathion," *J. Econ. Entomol.,* **57,** 618 (1964).

104. Lichtenstein, E. P., Schulz, K. R., "Effect of Soil Cultivation, Soil Surface and Water on the Persistence of Insecticidal Residues in Soils," *J. Econ. Entomol.,* **54,** 517 (1961).

105. Lichtenstein, E. P., Schulz, K. R., "Epoxidation of Aldrin and Heptachlor in Soils as Influenced by Autoclaving, Moisture, and Soil Types," *J. Econ. Entomol.,* **53,** 192 (1960).

106. Lichtenstein, E. P., Schulz, K. R., "Persistence of Some Chlorinated Hydrocarbon Insecticides as Influenced by Soil Types, Rate of Application and Temperature," *J. Econ. Entomol.,* **52,** 124 (1959).

107. Lichtenstein, E. P., Schulz, K. R., "Residues of Aldrin and Heptachlor in Soils and Their Translocation into Various Crops," *J. Agr. Food Chem.,* **13,** 57 (1965).

108. Lichtenstein, E. P., Schulz, K. R., Skrentny, R. F., Stitt, P. A., "Insecticidal Residues in Cucumbers and Alfalfa Grown on Aldrin- or Heptachlor-Treated Soils," *J. Econ. Entomol.,* **58,** 742 (1965).

109. Lofgren, C. S., "Large Scale Tests to Evaluate Multiple Low Dosages of Heptachlor," Report of Methods Improvement Section, Plant Pest Control Division, ARS, U.S. Dept. of Agr., Gulfport, Miss., 1959.

110. Lofgren, C. S., Bartlett, F. J., Stringer, C. E., "Imported Fire Ant Toxic Bait Studies: Evaluation of Carriers for Oil Baits," *J. Econ. Entomol.,* **56,** 62 (1963).

111. Lofgren, C. S., Stringer, C. E., Bartlett, F. J., "Imported Fire Ant Toxic Bait Studies: GC-1283, a Promising Toxicant," *J. Econ. Entomol.,* **55,** 405 (1962).

112. Long, W. H., Concienne, E. J., "Critical Period for Controlling the Sugarcane Borer in Sugarcane in Louisiana," *J. Econ. Entomol.,* **57,** 350 (1964).

113. Mack, G. L., Unpublished data, Food Sci. Dept., N.Y. Agr. Expt. Sta., Geneva, N.Y.

114. Mack, G. L., Corcoran, S. M., Gibbs, S. D., Gutenmann, W. H., Reckahn, J. A., Lisk, D. J., "The DDT Content of Some Fishes and Surface Waters of New York State," *N.Y. Fish and Game J.,* **11,** 148 (1964).

115. MacPhee, A. W., Chisholm, D., MacEachern, C. R., "Persistence of Certain Pesticides in the Soil and Their Effect on Crop Yields," *Can. J. Soil Sci.,* **40,** 59 (1960).

116. Marth, E. H., "Residues and Some Effects of Chlorinated Hydrocarbon Insecticides in Biological Material," *Residue Rev.,* **9,** 1 (1965).

117. Martin, J. P., "Influence of Pesticide Residues on Soil Microbiological and Chemical Properties," *Residue Rev.,* **4,** 96 (1963).

118. Matteson, J. W., Taft, H. M., "The Effect of Various Adjuvants on the Systemic Insecticidal Activity of Phorate and Zectran," *J. Econ. Entomol.,* **57,** 325 (1964).

119. The Melon Fly, PA-581, U.S. Dept. Agr., ARS, August 1963.

120. Mendel, J. L., Walton, M. S., "Conversion of *p,p'*-DDT to *p,p'*-DDD by Intestinal Flora of the Rat," *Science,* **151,** 1527 (1966).

121. Messenger, K., "Low Volume Aerial Spraying Will Be Boon to Applicators," *Agr. Chem.,* **18,** December, 63 (1963).

122. Metcalf, R. L., "Requirements for Pesticides of the Future," U.S. Dept. Agr., *ARS 33-110,* 9 (1966).

123. Middleton, F. M., Lichtenberg, J. J., "Measurements of Organic Contaminants in the Nation's Rivers," *Ind. Eng. Chem.,* **52,** 6, 99A (1960).

124. Middleton, J. T., Participant in open discussion, in "Research in Pesticides," C. O. Chichester, ed., Academic Press, New York, 1965, p. 228.

125. Middleton, J. T., "Research in Pesticides," C. O. Chichester, ed., Academic Press, New York, 1965, p. 191.

126. Miskus, R. P., Blair, D. P., Casida, J. E., "Conversion of DDT to DDD by

Bovine Rumen Fluid, Lake Water, and Reduced Porphyrins," *J. Agr. Food Chem.,* **13,** 481 (1965).

127. Moore, N. A., ed., "Pesticides in the Environment and Their Effects on Wildlife," *J. Appl. Ecol.,* **3** (Suppl.), 311 pp. (1966).

128. Moore, N. W., "Pesticides and Birds—a Review of the Situation in Great Britain in 1965," *Bird Study,* **12,** 222 (1965).

129. Newman, A. S., Downing, C. R., "Herbicides and the Soil," *J. Agr. Food Chem.,* **6,** 352 (1958).

130. Nicholson, H. P., Grzenda, A. R., Lauer, G. J., Cox, W. S., Teasley, J. I., "Water Pollution by Insecticides in an Agricultural River Basin. I. Occurrence of Insecticides in River and Treated Municipal Water," *Limnol. Oceanog.,* **9,** 310 (1964).

131. Nicholson, H. P., Thoman, J. R., in "Research in Pesticides," C. O. Chichester, ed., Academic Press, New York, 1965, p. 182.

132. Nicholson, H. P., Webb, H. J., Lauer, G. J., O'Brien, R. E., Grzenda, A. R., Shanklin, D. W., "Insecticide Contamination in a Farm Pond. Part I—Origin and Duration." Grzenda, A. R., Lauer, G. J., Nicholson, H. P., "Part II—Biological Effects," *Trans. Am. Fisheries Soc.,* **91,** 213 (1962).

133. Novak, A. F., Rao, M. R. R., "Food Safety Program: Endrin Monitoring in the Mississippi River," *Science,* **150,** 1732 (1965).

134. O'Neill, R. D., Dugan, P. R., Pfister, R. M., Sprague, M. L., "Evaluation of the Extent and Nature of Pesticide and Detergent Involvement in Surface Waters of a Selected Watershed," N.Y. State Dept. Health Res. Rept. No. 10, Part 1 (1963).

135. Ozburn, G. W., Morrison, F. O., "Development of a DDT-Tolerant Strain of Laboratory Mice," *Nature,* **196,** 1009 (1962).

136. Ozburn, G. W., Morrison, F. O., "The Effect of DDT on Respiratory Metabolism of DDT-Tolerant Mice *(Mus musculus),"* *Can. J. Zool.,* **43,** 709 (1965).

137. Peakall, D. B., "Pesticide-Induced Enzyme Breakdown of Steroids in Birds," *Nature,* **216,** 505 (1967).

138. "Pesticides and Public Policy," U.S. Congress (Senate), Committee on Government Operations, July 1966.

139. Peterle, T. J., "The Use of Isotopes to Study Pesticide Translocation in Natural Environments," *J. Appl. Ecol.,* **3** (Suppl.), 181 (1966).

140. Peterson, J. E., Robison, W. H., "Metabolic Products of *p,p'*-DDT in the Rat," *Toxicol. Appl. Pharmacol.,* **6,** 321 (1964).

141. Phillips, W. M., "Residual Herbicidal Activity of Some Chloro-Substituted Benzoic Acids in Soil," *Weeds,* **7,** 284 (1959).

142. Plant Pest Control Programs of the Southern Region, Annual Report, U.S. Dept. Agr., ARS, 1964.

143. Plapp, F. W., Jr., Bigley, W. S., Chapman, G. A., Eddy, G. W., "Synergism of Malathion Against Resistant Houseflies and Mosquitoes," *J. Econ. Entomol.,* **56,** 643 (1963).

144. "Pollution-Caused Fish Kills in 1965," U.S. Dept. Interior, Federal Water Pollution Control Adminis., Publ. WP-12, Government Printing Office, Washington, D.C., 1966, p. 28.

145. Popham, W. L., "Recent Trends in Regulatory and Control Programs," Address before Nat. Assoc. of Commissioners, Secretaries and Directors of Agriculture, San Francisco, Calif., Sept. 20, 1956.

146. Popham, W. L., "Regulatory and Control Programs on Use of Chemicals," U.S. Dept. Agr., ARS 20-29 (1960).

147. Quinby, G. E., Doornink, G. M., "Tetraethyl Pyrophosphate Poisoning Following Airplane Dusting," *J. Am. Med Assoc.,* **191,** 1 (1965).

148. Quinby, G. E., Hayes, W. J., Jr., Armstrong, J. F., Durham, W. F., "DDT Storage in the U.S. Population," *J. Am. Med. Assoc.,* **191,** 175 (1965).

149. Ratcliffe, D. A., "Decrease in Eggshell Weight in Certain Birds of Prey," *Nature,* **215,** 208 (1967).

150. "The Regulation of Pesticides in the U.S.," U.S. Dept. Agr., U.S. Dept. HEW, Food & Drug Admin., Publ. 305-329 (ARS-240), March 1968, Government Printing Office, Washington, D.C.

151. "Research in Pesticides," Chichester, C. O., ed., Academic Press, New York, 1965.

152. Risebrough, R. W., "Chlorinated Hydrocarbons in Marine Ecosystems," in *Chemical Fallout,* Proc. 1st Rochester Conf. on Environmental Toxicity, Univ. Rochester, 1969.

153. Risebrough, R. W., "Pesticides: Transatlantic Movements in the Northeast Trades," *Science,* **159,** 1233-1236 (1968).

154. Risebrough, R. W., Peakall, D. B., Herman, S. G., Kirven, M. N., Reiche, P., "Polychlorinated Biphenyls in the Global Ecosystem," *Nature,* **220,** 1098 (1968).

155. Rosato, P., Ferguson, D. H., "The Toxicity of Endrin-Resistant Mosquito Fish to Eleven Species of Vertebrates," *Bioscience,* **18:** 783 (1968).

156. Rudd, R. L., "Pesticides and the Living Landscape," University of Wisconsin Press, Madison, Wisc., 1964, p. 320.

157. Rudd, R. L., et al., Unpublished data.

158. "Safe Use of Pesticides," American Public Health Association, New York, N.Y., 1967.

159. Sheets, T. J., "Review of Disappearance of Substituted Urea Herbicides from Soil," *J. Agr. Food Chem.,* **12,** 30 (1964).

160. Sheets, T. J., Harris, C. I., "Herbicide Residues in Soils and Their Phytotoxicities to Crops Grown in Rotation," *Residue Rev.,* **11,** 119 (1965).

161. Simkiss, K., "Calcium in Reproductive Physiology," Reinhold Publishing Co., New York, 1967.

162. Sladen, W. J. L., Menzie, C. M., Reichel, W. L., "DDT Residues in Adelie Penguins and a Crabeater Seal from Antarctica, *Nature,* **210,** 670 (1966).

163. Smith, D., Eichelberger, J., "Thin-Layer Chromatography of Carbon Adsorption Extracts Prior to Gas Chromatographic Analysis for Pesticides," *J. Water Pollut. Contr. Fed.,* **37,** 77 (1965).

164. Stickel, L. F., Stickel, W. H., Christensen, R., "Residues of DDT in Brains and Bodies of Birds That Died on Dosage and in Survivors," *Science,* **151,** 1549 (1966).

165. Sun, Y. P., Johnson, E. R., "Synergistic and Antagonistic Actions of Insecticide-Synergist Combinations and Their Mode of Action," *J. Agr. Food Chem.,* **8,** 261 (1960).

166. Tabor, E. G., "Contamination of Urban Air Through the Use of Insecticides," *Trans. N.Y. Acad. Sci.,* **28,** 569 (1966).

167. Teasley, J. I., Cox, W. S., "Determination of Pesticides in Water by Microcoulometric Gas Chromatography After Liquid-Liquid Extraction," *J. Am. Water Works Assoc.,* **55,** 1093 (1963).

168. Terriere, L. C., Kiigemagi, U., Gerlach, A. R., Borovicka, R. L., "The Persistence of Toxaphene in Lake Water and Its Uptake by Aquatic Plants and Animals," *J. Agr. Food Chem.,* **14,** 66 (1966).

169. Thoman, J. R., Nicholson, H. P., "Pesticides: A Hazard to Water Quality," Proc. Western Resources Conf., 1963, University of Colorado Press, Boulder, Colo., 1963.

170. Trost, C. H., "Florida Impoundments for Mosquito Control," Pesticide Wildlife Studies, U.S. Dept. of Interior Circular 199, 1963.

171. Tukey, J. W. (chairman, Environmental Pollution Panel, President's Science Advisory Committee), "Restoring the Quality of Our Environment," Rept. of the Environmental Pollution Panel, President's Science Advisory Committee, The White House, 1965, 317 pp.

172. "USDA Quarantine Inspectors Score Well in Fiscal 1966," *U.S. Dept. Agr. Newsletter,* **25** (20), 3 (1966).

173. Vandecaveye, S. C., Horner, G. M., Keaton, C. M., "Unproductiveness of Certain Orchard Soils as Related to Lead Arsenate-Spray Accumulations," *Soil Sci.,* **42,** 203 (1936).

174. Vinson, S. B., Boyd, C. E., Ferguson, D. E., "Resistance to DDT in the Mosquito Fish, *Gambusia affinis,*" **139,** 217 (1963).

175. Vital Statistics of the United States, U.S. Public Health Service, 1925-65, Government Printing Office, Washington, D.C.

176. Walker, K. C., Goette, M. B., Batchelor, G. S., "Dichlorodiphenyltrichloroethane and Dichlorodiphenyldichloroethylene Content of Prepared Meals," *J. Agr. Food Chem.,* **2,** 1034 (1954).

177. Warnick, S. L., Gaufin, R. F., Gaufin, A. R., "Concentrations and Effects of Pesticides in Aquatic Environments," *J. Am. Water Works Assoc.,* **58,** 601 (1966).

178. Weaver, L., Gunnerson, C. G., Breidenbach, A. W., Lichtenberg, J. J., "Chlorinated Hydrocarbon Pesticides in Major U.S. River Basins," *Public Health Repts.* (U.S.), **80,** 481 (1965).

179. Weibel, S. R., Weidner, R. B., Cohen, J. M., Christianson, A. G., "Pesticides and Other Contaminants from Rainfall and Runoff," *J. Am. Water Works Assoc.,* **58,** 1075 (1966).

180. Welch, R. M., Levin, M., Conney, A. H., "Effect of Chlorinated Insecticides on Steroid Metabolism," in Chemical Fallout, Proc. 1st Rochester Conf. on Environmental Toxicity, Univ. of Rochester, 1969.

181. Wheatley, G. A., Hardman, J. A., "Indications of the Presence of Organochlorine Insecticides in Rainwater in Central England," *Nature,* **207,** 486 (1965).

182. Wolfe, H. R., Durham, W. F., Walker, K. C., Armstrong, J. F., "Health Hazards of Discarded Pesticide Containers," *Arch. Environmental Health,* **3,** 531 (1961).

183. Woodwell, G. M., Wurster, C. F., Isaacson, P. A., "DDT Residues in an East Coast Estuary: A Case of Biological Concentration of a Persistent Pesticide," *Science,* **156,** 821 (1967).

184. Wurster, C. F., "DDT Reduces Photosynthesis by Marine Phytoplankton," *Science,* **159,** 1474 (1968).

185. Wurster, C. F., Wingate, D. B., "DDT Residues and Declining Population in the Bermuda Petrel," *Science,* **159,** 979 (1968).

186. Wurster, C. F., Jr., Wurster, D. H., Strickland, W. N., "Bird Mortality After Spraying for Dutch Elm Disease with DDT," *Science,* **148,** 90 (1965).

187. Zavon, M. R., Hine, C. H., Parker, K. D., "Chlorinated Hydrocarbon Insecticides in Human Body Fat in the United States," *J. Am. Med. Assoc.,* **193,** 837 (1965).

188. Zweig, G., Hitt, J., "Rapid Screening for the Detection of Organophosphate Pesticides for Water Quality Surveillance," 1966, unpublished work.

INDEX

A

Absorption,
    pesticides by crops, 210
Acid mine drainage, 144
Activated carbon,
    waste water treatment, 126
Additives,
    pesticide formulations, 220
Advanced waste treatment,
    recommendations, 14, 138
    research, 123
Agriculture,
    water pollution, 142
Agriculture Department,
    pesticides monitoring, 208
Air,
    composition, 24
Air environment, 21-92
    recommendations, 7, 45, 58, 63, 73, 74,
      81, 85
Air pollutants,
    effects, 75
    major sources, 25
    movements, 27, 44
    pesticides, 19, 214
Air pollution,
    municipal incinerators, 172
    secondary materials
      industry, 183
Air quality control regions,
    U.S., 27, 30
Aldrin,
    persistence in soil, 206
Alkalized alumina sorption process, 68
Aluminum oxide,
    processing wastes, 186
Analytical chemistry,
    air pollution, 82
    air pollution recommendations, 12, 85
    need for research, 3, 6
    pesticide residues in water, 211
    water pollution, 152
    water pollution recommendations, 16,
      155
Analytical Methods Evaluation Service, 82
Animals,
    effects of air pollutants, 78
    effects of pesticides, 224
Antarctica,
    pesticides in wildlife, 224
Apartments,
    incinerators, 176
Application techniques,
    pesticides, 206, 219
Arsenic,
    soil residues, 203, 210
Ash
    See Fly ash
Atmosphere,
    temperature, 41
Atmospheric areas,
    U.S., 27, 30
Automobiles
    See Motor vehicles

B

BOD
    See Biochemical oxygen demand
Bacteria,
    water, 134, 147
Bauxite,
    processing wastes, 186
Biochemical oxygen demand, 96, 101
Biodegradation,
    animal wastes, 143
    pesticides, 206
Biological aspects,
    water pollutants, 100
Biological control,
    pests, 222
Birds,
    effects of pesticides, 225
Blood diseases,
    role of pesticides, 233
Boats,
    wastes, 145
Building blocks,
    production from solid wastes, 179,
      182, 187
Bureau of Mines,
    research on scrap processing, 181
    research on stack-gas cleanup, 68
    solid waste program, 166
Bureau of Solid Waste Management,
    research program, 166

C

CAMP
    See Continuous Air Monitoring
      Program
COD
    See Chemical oxygen demand
California
    See also Names of specific cities
    air quality standards, 76
    motor vehicle standards, 47
    pesticides in wildlife, 224
Cancer,
    role of pesticides, 233
Carbamate insecticides,
    structure, 200
Carbon,
    environmental cycle, 40
    waste water treatment, 126
Carbon dioxide,
    production in landfills, 169
    role in air pollution, 39
Carbon monoxide,
    control in automobile emissions, 50
    role in air pollution, 34
Catalytic conversion,
    sulfur oxides removal from stack gas,
      68
Centrifugation,
    sewage sludges, 116
Charcoal,
    pesticides adsorption, 212

Sampling techniques,
  pesticides in air, 214, 217
Sanitary landfill, 167
Scrap processing,
  auto hulks, 180
  incinerator residues, 177
Screw worm fly,
  eradication, 221
Secondary materials industry, 183
Secondary treatment,
  waste water, 106
Sewage treatment plants,
  U.S. inventory, 108
Sex attractants,
  pest control, 222
Ships,
  wastes, 145
Sinks,
  airborne substances, 27
  definition of term, 6
  waterborne substances, 104
Sludge handling,
  waste water treatment, 111
  water treatment, 121
Smog,
  Los Angeles, 36
Soil,
  persistence of heptachlor, 221
  pesticide residues, 19, 203, 217
  transport of water pollutants, 103
Solid waste disposal,
  air pollutant emissions, 25
  industry practices, 183
  methods, 168
Solid Waste Disposal Act of 1965, 166
Solid wastes, 163-191
  recommendations, 17, **180, 182, 185,**
    187, 188
Solids,
  removal from secondary effluent, 123
Source,
  definition of term, 6
Space heating,
  air pollution, 25, 74
  air pollution recommendations, 11, 74
Stack gas,
  cleanup, 67
Standards,
  automobile emissions, 48
  California air, 76
  diesel engines, 57
  water quality, 98
Storm water,
  urban problems, 119
Structure,
  pesticides, 197
Sulfur,
  content in fuels, 65
  environmental cycle, 30
Sulfur dioxide,
  emissions from stationary sources, 60
  role in air pollution, 27
Sulfur oxides,
  stack-gas cleanup, 67
Suspended solids,
  removal from secondary effluent, 123
Synergism,
  pesticide action, 222
Systems analysis,
  role in environmental control, 5

T

Tall stacks,
  emissions, 64

Taste,
  water, 148
Temperature,
  atmosphere, 41
  filter media operation, 63
  soils, 205
Tennessee Valley Authority,
  composting plant, 178
Tertiary treatment,
  waste water, 123
Tires,
  disposal, 182
Tracers,
  air movement studies, 45
  pesticide movement studies, 226, 229
Transport,
  air pollutants, 7, 27, 45
  pesticides in air, 214, 216
  water pollutants, 12, 98, 103
Transportation,
  solid wastes, 179

U

United States
  See also Federal Government
  air pollutant emissions, 25
  air quality control regions, 27, 30
  atmospheric areas, 27, 30
  municipal sewage treatment inventory, 108
  pesticides production, 196
  solid waste tonnages, 166, 168
  waste production by livestock, 143
  waste water volumes, 96
U.S. Naval Station,
  water-wall incinerator, 174
Utility power plants,
  air pollution, 25, 64, 69, 70
  air pollution recommendations, 10, 73

V

Vacuum filtration,
  sewage sludges, 116
Vegetation,
  effects of air pollutants, 11, 79
Viruses,
  water, 134, 147

W

Washington, D.C.,
  incinerator residues, 177
Waste water,
  advanced treatment, 123
Wastes,
  ultimate disposal, 119, 133
Water,
  pesticide residues, 19, 211, 217
Water analysis,
  typical parameters, 97
Water environment, 93-162
  recommendations, 12, 105, 122, 138,
    141, 146, 151, 155
Water pollutants,
  national sources, 96
Water treatment plant wastes, 121
Watercraft,
  wastes, 145
Wet limestone process, 68
Wet oxidation,
  sewage sludges, 118
Wildlife,
  effects of pesticides, 20, 213, 224